D1441951

GROUND WATER Hydrology

GROUND WATER Hydrology

John Wiley & Sons, Inc.
New York · London · Sydney

David Keith Todd, Ph.D.

Associate Professor of Civil Engineering
University of California, Berkeley

SIXTH PRINTING, JANUARY, 1967

Library of Congress Catalog Card Number: 59-9354
Printed in the United States of America

Preface

Water is an essential commodity to mankind, and the largest available source of fresh water lies underground. Increased demands for water have stimulated development of underground water supplies. Inevitably, when progress magnifies and adds new problems, efforts are increased to solve these problems. This is especially true for ground water. Methods for investigating the occurrence and movement of ground water have been improved, better means for extracting ground water have been developed, principles of conservation have been established, and research of several types has contributed to a better understanding of the subject. As a result, knowledge of ground water hydrology, once veiled in mystery, has expanded rapidly in recent decades. Anticipating the ever-increasing use of ground water, it is reasonable to presume that such knowledge will grow at an even greater rate in the future.

My purpose in writing this book has been to present the fundamentals of ground water hydrology in a manner understandable to those most concerned with such knowledge. Few men specialize in ground water hydrology, yet, because ground water is a major natural resource, it is important to students and professional men in a variety of fields. Chief among these are civil engineers (including specialists in hydraulics, hydrology, sanitary engineering, soil mechanics, and water resources), geologists, and agricultural and irrigation engineers. Personnel in charge of municipal and industrial water supplies often have a vital interest in ground water. Men indirectly concerned can be found in the fields of mining, petroleum engineering, forestry, public health, and law, among others. Although it is impossible to present a subject fitted to the requirements of such a diversity of interests, the common need of all is an understanding of the fundamental principles, methods, and problems encountered in the field as a whole. Thus, this book is an effort to make available a unified presentation of ground water hydrology.

This book presupposes only a background of mathematics through calculus and an elementary knowledge of geology. I believe previous instruction in fluid mechanics and hydrology to be desirable but not essential.

By emphasizing only fundamental considerations of ground water, I have tried to restrict the book to a practical size without impairing its scope. A consistent nomenclature has been adopted with clarity as the criterion, although equivalent well-established expressions are mentioned to avoid confusion. Illustrative examples from field data have been minimized, mainly because of their ready availability elsewhere. Publications of the United States Geological Survey are extensive and contain a wealth of material collected from field investigations. Also, many state water resource agencies have published comprehensive reports of local ground water situations. For instructors using this book as a text, I recommend that data from these sources be presented in the form of illustrations and problems to supplement the text material.

The contents of the book are based on a broad interpretation of ground water hydrology in order to embrace all elements of ground water as a water supply source. The first six chapters cover the basic quantitative aspects of the subject, including use, occurrence, movement, hydraulics, water wells, and ground water levels. Chapter 7 presents ground water quality, a topic as important as ground water quantity, with emphasis on measures of water quality and interpretation of water analyses. Chapter 8 is concerned with the conservation of ground water, expressed by safe yield, and maximum water development by conjunctive use with surface water. Methods for investigating ground water by surface and subsurface procedures are described in Chapters 9 and 10. Two important problems unique to ground water hydrology are artificial recharge and sea water intrusion; these are discussed in Chapters 11 and 12. Economic and legal considerations affect ground water development. Economic aspects are included in Chapter 8, and Chapter 13 provides an introduction to ground water rights, a subject of considerable interest in the last decade in the United States. The final chapter contains a review of the various types of laboratory model and numerical analysis studies that have become valuable ground water research tools. An appendix lists useful conversion factors and constants.

At the end of each chapter appears a list of references pertaining to the specific topic treated. The ground water literature is voluminous, and a comprehensive bibliography not only would be a major undertaking but also would serve little practical purpose except for research workers. Therefore, I have tried to select those references which would be most helpful to the reader desiring more information on a given topic. For many readers the references listed will be sufficient; for others wishing to go further, they will serve only as a beginning. Included in the references at the end of the first chapter are general references and a few foreign books.

Many persons have assisted me, directly and indirectly, in the preparation of this book, including my colleagues at the University of California, members of the California Department of Water Resources, and members of the United States Geological Survey. In Europe, help on special topics was generously given by several engineers and geologists. Questions and reactions of students guided me in the presentation of many topics. Specific chapters were reviewed by F. B. Clendenen, S. T. Harding, and J. F. Poland. To all of these, and to my wife, I should like to acknowledge my indebtedness.

David Keith Todd

Berkeley, California
March 1959

Contents

Introduction

CHAPTER 1

Ground water hydrology may be defined as the science of the occurrence, distribution, and movement of water below the surface of the earth. Geohydrology has an identical connotation, and hydrogeology differs only by its greater emphasis on geology.

Scope

Ground water referred to without further specification is commonly understood to mean water occupying all the voids within a geologic stratum. This saturated zone is to be distinguished from an unsaturated, or aeration, zone where voids are filled with water and air. Water contained in saturated zones is important for engineering works, geologic studies, and water supply developments; consequently, the occurrence of water in these zones will be emphasized here. Unsaturated zones are usually found above saturated zones and extending upward to the ground surface. Because this water includes soil moisture within the root zone, it is a major concern of agriculture, botany, and soil science. No rigid demarcation of waters between the two zones is possible, for they possess an interdependent boundary and water can move from zone to zone in either direction. The interrelationships are described more fully in Chapter 2.

Several of the earth sciences, including geology, hydrology, meteorology, and oceanography, are concerned with the earth's water. But ground water hydrology may be regarded as a specialized science combining elements of geology, hydrology, and fluid mechanics. Geology governs the occurrence and distribution of ground water, hydrology determines the supply of water to the ground, and fluid mechanics explains its movement.

Ground water plays an important part in petroleum engineering. Two-fluid systems, involving oil and water, and three-fluid systems, involving gas, oil, and water, occur frequently in development of petroleum. Although the same hydrodynamic laws govern flows of these systems and ground water, the distinctive nature of water in petroleum reservoirs sets it apart from other ground water. Major differences exist in water quality, depth of occurrence, and methods of development and utilization, all of which contribute to a separation of interests and applications. Therefore, ground water in petroleum reservoirs will not be treated specifically here. It should be noted, however, that ground water hydrology has gained immeasurably from research conducted by the petroleum industry.

Historical Background

Ground water development dates from ancient times. The Old Testament contains numerous references to ground water, springs, and wells; Tolman[36] * described the large underground water tunnels, or kanats, in Persia and Egypt dating from 800 B.C.

Utilization of ground water greatly preceded understanding of its origin, occurrence, and movement. The writings of Greek and Roman philosophers to explain origins of springs and ground water contain theories ranging from fantasy to nearly correct accounts.[7, 24] As late as the seventeenth century it was generally assumed that water emerging from springs could not be derived from rainfall, for it was believed that the quantity was inadequate and the earth too impervious to permit penetration of rain water far below the surface. Thus, early Greek philosophers such as Homer, Thales, and Plato hypothesized that springs were formed by sea water conducted through subterranean channels below the mountains, then purified and raised to the surface. Aristotle suggested that air enters into cold dark caverns under the mountains where it condenses into water and contributes to springs.

The Roman philosophers, including Seneca and Pliny, followed the Greek ideas and contributed little to the subject. An important

* Superscript numbers refer to references at the end of the chapter.

step forward, however, was made by the Roman architect Vitruvius. He explained the now accepted infiltration theory that the mountains receive large amounts of rain which percolate through the rock strata and emerge at their base to form streams.

The Greek theories persisted through the Middle Ages with no advances made until the end of the Renaissance. The French potter and philosopher Bernard Palissy (c. 1510–1589) reiterated the infiltration theory in 1580, but his teachings were generally ignored. The German astronomer Johann Kepler (1571–1630) was a man of strong imagination who likened the earth to a huge animal which takes in the water of the ocean, digests and assimilates it, and discharges the end products of these physiological processes as ground water and springs. The sea water theory of the Greeks, supplemented by vaporization and condensation processes within the earth, was restated by the French philosopher René Descartes (1596–1650).

A clear understanding of the hydrologic cycle was achieved by the latter part of the seventeenth century. For the first time theories were based upon observations and quantitative data. Three Europeans made notable contributions, although others contributed to and supported these advances. Pierre Perrault * (1608–1680) measured rainfall during three years and estimated runoff of the upper Seine River drainage basin. He reported in 1674 that precipitation on the basin was about six times the river discharge, thereby demonstrating as false the early assumption of inadequate rainfall. The French physicist Edmé Mariotté (c. 1620–1684) made measurements of the Seine at Paris and confirmed Perrault's work. His publications appeared in 1686, after his death, and contained factual data strongly supporting the infiltration theory. Meinzer [24] once stated, "Mariotté . . . probably deserves more than any other man the distinction of being regarded as the founder of ground-water hydrology, perhaps I should say of the entire science of hydrology." The third contribution came from the English astronomer Edmund Halley (1656–1742), who reported in 1693 on measurements of evaporation, demonstrating that

* Pierre Perrault was a lawyer by profession and held administrative and financial positions in the French government, hence he is not well known in scientific circles. His interest in ground water, leading to publication of *De l'Origine des Fontaines* in 1674, can be traced to the stimulus of the Dutch mathematician, astronomer, and physicist, Christiaan Huygens, who was then living in Paris and to whom the book is dedicated. Also, Pierre Perrault is often overshadowed by his three distinguished brothers: Nicolas (1611–1661), a noted theologian; Claude (1613–1688), a physician, architect, and scientist, who is regarded as one of the most eminent French scholars of his time; and Charles (1628–1703), author and critic, who is best known for his fairy tales of Mother Goose.

sea evaporation was sufficient to account for all springs and stream flow.

During the eighteenth century, fundamentals in geology were established which provided a basis for understanding the occurrence and movement of ground water. During the first half of the nineteenth century many artesian wells were drilled in France, stimulating interest in ground water. The French hydraulic engineer Henry Darcy (1803–1858) studied the movement of water through sand. His treatise of 1856 defined the relation, now known as Darcy's law, governing ground water flow in most alluvial and sedimentary formations. Later European contributions of the nineteenth century emphasized the hydraulics of ground water development. Significant contributions were made by J. Boussinesq, G. A. Daubrée, J. Dupuit, P. Forchheimer, and A. Thiem. In the twentieth century, increased activity in all phases of ground water hydrology has occurred. Many Europeans have participated with publications of either specialized or comprehensive works. Although too numerous to mention, the names of R. Dachler, E. Imbeaux, K. Keilhack, W. Koehne, J. Kozeny, E. Prinz, and G. Thiem are best known in the United States.

American contributions to ground water hydrology date from near the end of the nineteenth century. In the short interval from then to the present, tremendous advances have been made. Important early theoretical contributions were made by A. Hazen, F. H. King, and C. S. Slichter, and detailed field investigations were begun by men such as T. C. Chamberlin, N. H. Darton, W. T. Lee, and W. C. Mendenhall. Much of the progress in ground water hydrology this century can be attributed to Dr. O. E. Meinzer who, through his consuming interest in ground water and his dynamic leadership of ground water activities of the U. S. Geological Survey, stimulated many individuals in the quest for ground water knowledge.

Utilization of Ground Water

Ground water is an important source of water supply throughout the world. Its use in irrigation, industries, municipalities, and rural homes continues to increase. Cooling and air conditioning in the past twenty years have made heavy demands on ground water because of its characteristic uniformity in temperature. Shortages of ground water in areas of excessive draft emphasize the importance of correct estimates and proper development, regulation, and protection of supplies in order to insure the continued availability of this key natural resource.

Estimates of water use in the United States as of 1955 were prepared by MacKichan [19] of the U. S. Geological Survey. He reported a total usage of 240 billion gallons per day, of which 46.3 billion gallons per day, or 19 per cent, came from ground water. The largest single demand on ground water is irrigation, amounting to 30.0 billion gallons per day, or 65 per cent of all ground water used. According to MacKichan, 91 per cent of this water is pumped in the 17 Western states, where arid conditions fostered extensive irrigation development. Other ground water demands include 9.8 billion gallons per day for industrial requirements, 4.7 billion gallons per day for public water supplies, and 1.8 billion gallons per day for rural water needs other than irrigation. Largest industrial users in order of water requirements are oil refineries, paper manufacturers, metal working plants, chemical manufacturers, air conditioning and refrigerating units, and distilleries.[19] Ground water usage has increased at an accelerating rate in recent years, and indications are that the trend will continue.

Table 1.1 gives a breakdown of ground water use by states and by type of demand as of 1955. States are listed in order of ground water use. Figure 1.1 indicates the proportion of ground water use relative to total water use for each state.

Ground Water in the Hydrologic Cycle

Ground water constitutes one portion of the earth's water circulatory system known as the hydrologic cycle. Figure 1.2 illustrates schematically this cycle. Water-bearing formations of the earth's crust act as conduits for transmission and as reservoirs for storage of water. Water enters these formations from the ground surface or from bodies of surface water, after which it travels slowly for varying distances until it returns to the surface by action of natural flow, plants, or man. The storage capacity of ground water reservoirs combined with small flow rates provide large, extensively distributed sources of water supply.* Ground water emerging into surface stream channels aids in sustaining streamflow when surface runoff is low or non-existent. Similarly, water pumped from wells represents the sole water source in many regions during much of every year.

Practically all ground water originates as surface water. Principal

* The ground water reservoirs of the United States contain far more fresh water than the capacity of all the nation's reservoirs and lakes, including the Great Lakes. It has been estimated that the total usable ground water in storage is of the order of 10 years' annual precipitation or 35 years' runoff.[38]

TABLE 1.1 Use of Ground Water in the United States, 1955

(After MacKichan [19])

Quantities in Million Gallons per Day

State	Public Supplies	Rural	Irrigation	Self-Supplied Industrial	Total Ground Water Use	Ratio of Ground Water Use to Total Water Use, per cent
California	540	89	10,000	460	11,089	36
Texas	550	140	6,500	1,030	8,220	48
Arizona	110	10	4,700	140	4,960	69
New Mexico	85	16	1,400	46	1,547	58
Idaho	56	15	1,100	120	1,291	8
Nebraska	120	60	850	250	1,280	38
Ohio	250	77	1.1	940	1,268	12
Colorado	28	39	1,000	35	1,102	16
Florida	240	27	250	515	1,032	37
Mississippi	95	24	460	430	1,009	69
Kansas	130	46	610	220	1,006	45
Louisiana	83	22	380	480	965	19
Arkansas	28	24	790	121	963	64
Illinois	160	95	3.2	393	651	7
New York	240	110	22	257	629	7
Indiana	140	79	5.1	390	614	9
Oregon	36	18	490	65	609	8
Iowa	100	79	3.4	419	601	33
Washington	150	28	230	180	588	9
Michigan	180	73	5.3	315	573	8
Pennsylvania	120	60	1.6	340	522	5
Utah	110	8	270	130	518	11
New Jersey	160	8	22	296	486	12
Tennessee	100	26	3.6	250	380	9
Wisconsin	140	84	2.6	120	347	7
Georgia	85	23	12	210	330	15
Minnesota	50	72	2.2	190	314	17
Oklahoma	45	15	150	102	312	32
Missouri	41	56	20	190	307	14
Nevada	29	3	210	22	264	13
North Carolina	28	52	1.4	170	251	11
Montana	21	13	150	62	246	2
Alabama	67	28	2.4	142	239	8
Kentucky	45	29	3.9	160	238	7

TABLE 1.1 (*continued*)

Quantities in Million Gallons per Day

State	Public Supplies	Rural	Irrigation	Self-Supplied Industrial	Total Ground Water Use	Ratio of Ground Water Use to Total Water Use, per cent
South Dakota	46	34	6.8	98	185	76
Massachusetts	82	7	0.2	65	154	6
West Virginia	18	17	0	110	145	4
Virginia	10	33	0.4	100	143	7
Maryland	17	36	0.7	79	133	7
South Carolina	27	30	12	50	119	13
North Dakota	10	14	1.4	66	91	22
Connecticut	10	8	1.3	57	76	4
Wyoming	25	9	28	5	67	1
Delaware	11	3	0.4	25	39	11
Vermont	11	8	0	12	31	27
Maine	6	5	0.2	11	22	4
Rhode Island	10	1	0	11	22	6
New Hampshire	9	3	0	4	16	6
District of Columbia	0	0	0	11	11	3
United States	4,700	1,800	30,000	9,850	46,350	19

sources of natural recharge include precipitation, streamflow, lakes, and reservoirs. Other contributions, known as artificial recharge, occur from excess irrigation, seepage from canals, and water purposely applied to augment ground water supplies. Even sea water can enter underground along coasts where hydraulic gradients slope downward in an inland direction. Water within the ground moves downward through the unsaturated zone under the action of gravity, whereas in the saturated zone it moves in a direction determined by the surrounding hydraulic situation.

Discharge of ground water occurs when water emerges from underground. Most natural discharge occurs as flow into surface water bodies, such as streams, lakes, and oceans; flow to the surface appears as a spring. Ground water near the surface may return directly to the atmosphere by evaporation from within the soil and by transpira-

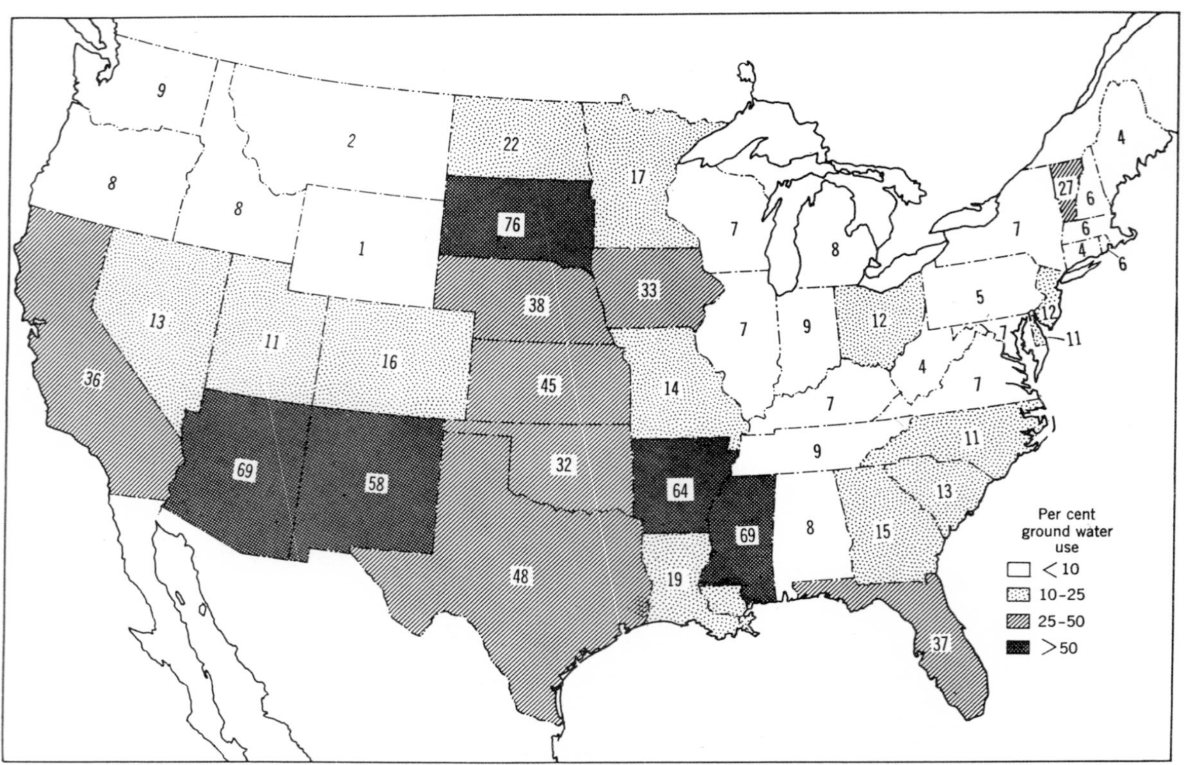

Fig. 1.1. Ground water use relative to total water use in the United States (from MacKichan [19]).

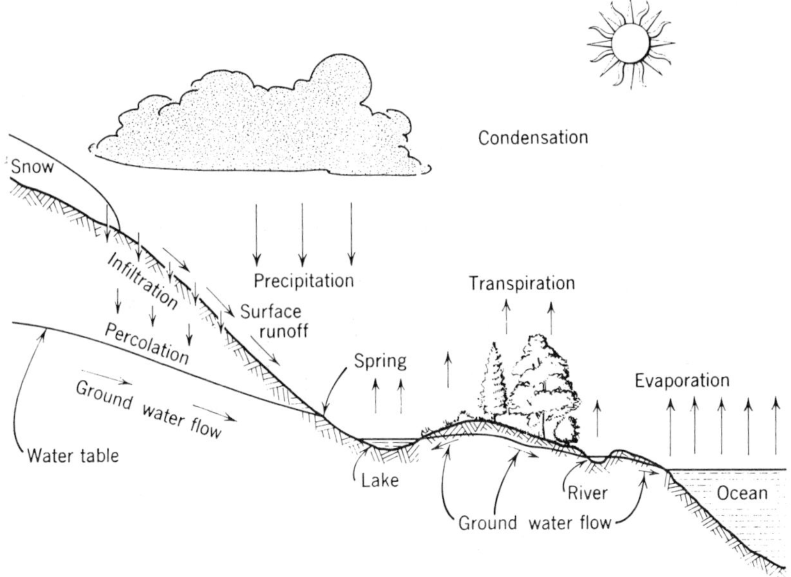

Fig. 1.2. The hydrologic cycle.

tion from vegetation. Pumpage from wells constitutes the major artificial discharge of ground water.

Literature and Data Sources

In the United States a majority of the field measurements and investigations of ground water have been conducted by the Geological Survey. Most work has been on a cooperative basis with individual states. Results are published by the Geological Survey as *Water-Supply Papers* or *Circulars*. Since 1935, records of ground water measurements in key observation wells have been published annually in *Water-Supply Papers* under the title *Water Levels and Artesian Pressures in Observation Wells in the United States*. Prior to 1940, records for each year were published in a single volume, but since then records have been published in six annual volumes covering sections of the country shown in Fig. 1.3. According to A. N. Sayre, Chief, Ground Water Branch, Geological Survey, the objectives of the observation well program are [39]

. . . to provide a day-to-day evaluation of available ground-water supplies, to facilitate the prediction of trends in ground-water levels that will indicate the probable status of important ground-water supplies in the future, to

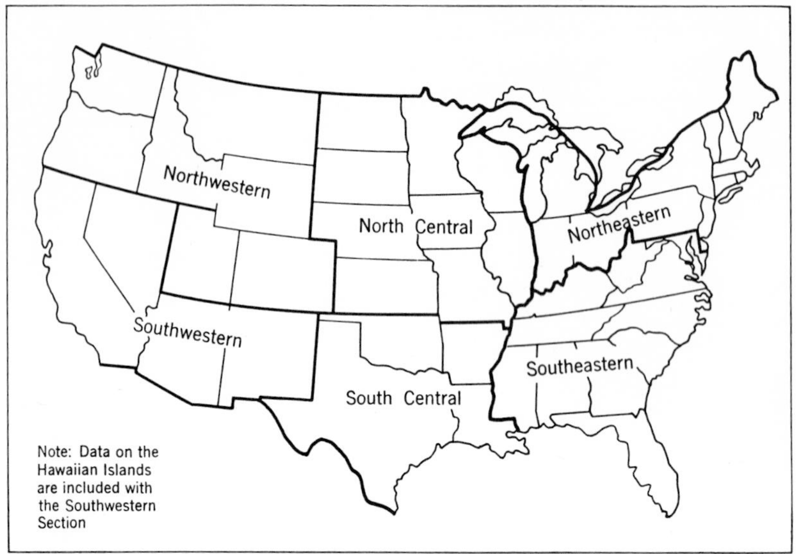

Fig. 1.3. Outline map of the United States showing areas included in *Geological Survey Water-Supply Papers* on water levels and artesian pressures in observation wells.

delineate present or potential areas of detrimentally high or low ground-water levels, to aid in the prediction of base flow of streams, to determine the several forces that act on a ground-water body, and to demonstrate the interplay of these forces in the ground-water regimen, to furnish information for use in basic research, and to provide long-term continuous records of fluctuations of water levels in representative wells.

Besides these *Water-Supply Papers,* the Geological Survey publishes at irregular intervals other papers on the geology and ground water resources of local areas. Invariably these intensive investigations concern areas containing important ground water problems and are carried out in cooperation with local agencies. Published information on a particular problem or area can be found in the ground water bibliographies of the Geological Survey [40, 41] or in the latest issue of *Publications of the Geological Survey.*

A second source of basic data on ground water is state geological and water resources agencies. Various states differ widely in their degree of activity, but California and Illinois, for example, maintain large water resources agencies and have made extensive ground water investigations in their respective states.

Two comprehensive bibliographies of hydrology have appeared in recent years which provide brief annotations of literature in the United States and Canada. The first covers the period 1941–1950,[3] and the second, 1951–1954.[4] It is anticipated that additional ones will be prepared in the future.

The professional literature on ground water hydrology embraces many fields of interest. Important contributions can be found in journals of civil engineering, water supply, geology, geophysics, agriculture, and soil science. Pertinent papers on flow in porous media also appear in chemical engineering, mechanics, and physics journals. The only organization in the United States recognizing hydrology as a distinct science is the American Geophysical Union; its *Transactions*, dating from 1920, contain a wealth of ground water papers. Similarly, publications of the International Association of Scientific Hydrology, an organization within the International Union of Geodesy and Geophysics, have served as the major media for exchange of ground water information on a world-wide basis.

Selected references are listed at the end of each chapter. These provide sources for additional material on topics treated within each chapter. Several general ground water references, including foreign texts, are listed in the references of this chapter.

References

1. Adams, F. D., Origin of springs and rivers—an historical review, *Fennia*, vol. 50, no. 1, 16 pp., 1928.
2. Agadjanov, A. M., *Hydrogeology and hydraulics of ground water and oil* (in Russian), Gostoptekhizdat, Moscow, 280 pp., 1950.
3. Amer. Geophysical Union, *Annotated bibliography of hydrology 1941–1950*, Washington, D. C., 408 pp., 1952
4. Amer. Geophysical Union, *Annotated bibliography of hydrology 1951–54 and sedimentation 1950–54*, Washington, D. C., 207 pp., 1955.
5. Amer. Soc. Civil Engrs., Hydrology Handbook, *Manual of Engineering Practice* 28, New York, 184 pp., 1949.
6. Anon., Water use in the United States, 1900–1975, *Supplement to Willing Water* 38, Amer. Water Works Assoc., 8 pp., 1956.
7. Baker, M. N., and R. E. Horton, Historical development of ideas regarding the origin of springs and ground-water, *Trans. Amer. Geophysical Union*, vol. 17, pp. 395–400, 1936.
8. Bennison, E. W., *Ground water, its development, uses, and conservation*, Edward E. Johnson, St. Paul, Minn., 507 pp., 1947
9. Bogomolov, G. V., and A. I. Silin-Bekcurin, *Special hydrogeology* (in Russian), Gosgeoltekhizdat, Moscow, 247 pp., 1955.

10. Dachler, R., *Grundwasserströmung,* J. Springer, Vienna, 141 pp., 1936.
11. Ferris, J. G., Ground water, in *Hydrology* (by C. O. Wisler and E. F. Brater), John Wiley and Sons, New York, pp. 198–272, 1949.
12. Houk, I. E., *Irrigation engineering,* vol. 1, John Wiley and Sons, New York, 545 pp., 1951.
13. Imbeaux, E., *Essai d'hydrogéologie,* Dunod, Paris, 704 pp., 1930.
14. Keilhack, K., *Lehrbuch der Grundwasser- und Quellenkunde,* 3rd ed., Gebr. Borntraeger, Berlin, 575 pp., 1935
15. Koechlin, R., and A. Koechlin, *Les eaux souterraines,* Libraire Rouge, Lausanne, 48 pp., 1945.
16. Koehne, W., *Grundwasserkunde,* E. Nagele, Stuttgart, 291 pp., 1928.
17. Kollbrunner, C. F., *Grundwasser und Filterbrunnen,* Leeman & Co., Zurich, 79 pp., 1943.
18. Linares, J. G.-Y., *Aguas subterraneas,* Libreria Dossat, Madrid, 342 pp., 1945.
19. MacKichan, K. A., Estimated use of water in the United States, 1955, *Jour. Amer. Water Works Assoc.,* vol. 49, pp. 369–391, 1957.
20. Martel, E. A., *Nouveau traité des eaux souterraines,* Doin Octave, Paris, 838 pp., 1921.
21. Mason, B., *Principles of geochemistry,* 2nd ed., John Wiley and Sons, New York, 310 pp., 1958.
22. McGuinness, C. L., The water situation in the United States with special reference to ground water, *U. S. Geological Survey Circular* 114, Washington, D. C., 127 pp., 1951.
23. Meinzer, O. E., Outline of ground-water hydrology with definitions, *U. S. Geological Survey Water-Supply Paper* 494, Washington, D. C., 71 pp., 1923.
24. Meinzer, O. E., The history and development of ground-water hydrology, *Jour. Washington Acad. Sci.,* vol. 24, pp. 6–32, 1934.
25. Miron, F., *Les eaux souterraines,* Gauthier-Villars, Masson & Cie., Paris, 188 pp., no date.
26. Müller-Delitzsch, G., *Grundlagen der Grundwassergewinnung,* Fachbuchverlag GMBH, Leipzig, 72 pp., 1951.
27. Petit, V., *L'eau souterraine—recherche, captage par sondages,* C. Beranger, Paris, 128 pp., 1930.
28. Pfalz, R., *Grundgewässerkunde,* Wilhelm Knapp, Halle (Saale), 175 pp., 1951.
29. Prinz, E., *Handbuch der Hydrologie,* 2nd ed., J. Springer, Berlin, 422 pp., 1923.
30. Sayre, A. N., Ground-water investigations in the United States, *Econ. Geol.,* vol. 43, pp. 547–552, 1948.
31. Sayre, A. N., Ground water, *Sci. Amer.,* vol. 183, no. 5, pp. 14–19, 1950.
32. Schneider, H., C. Truelsen, and H. Thiele, *Die Wassererschliessung,* Vulkan Verlag Dr. W. Classen, Essen, 421 pp., 1952
33. Semikhatov, A. N., *Hydrogeology* (in Russian), Sel'Khozgiz, Moscow, 328 pp., 1954.
34. Thomas, H. E., *The conservation of ground water,* McGraw-Hill, New York, 327 pp., 1951.
35. Todd, D. K., and F. B. Clendenen (eds.), *The California ground water situation,* Committee on Research in Water Resources, Univ. California, Berkeley, 212 pp., 1956.
36. Tolman, C. F., *Ground water,* McGraw-Hill, New York, 593 pp., 1937.

37. Trombe, F., *Les eaux souterraines,* Presses universitaires de France, Paris, 118 pp., 1951.
38. U. S. Dept. Agriculture, Water, *Yearbook of Agriculture,* Washington, D. C., 751 pp., 1955.
39. U. S. Geological Survey, Water levels and artesian pressures in observation wells in the United States, *Water-Supply Papers,* Washington, D. C., published annually.
40. Vorhis, R. C., Bibliography of publications relating to ground water prepared by the Geological Survey and cooperating agencies 1946–55, *U. S. Geological Survey Water-Supply Paper* 1492, Washington, D. C., 203 pp., 1957.
41. Waring, G. A., and O. E. Meinzer, Bibliography and index of publications relating to ground water prepared by the Geological Survey and cooperating agencies, *U. S. Geological Survey Water-Supply Paper* 992, Washington, D. C., 412 pp., 1947.

Occurrence of Ground Water

CHAPTER 2

To describe the occurrence of ground water necessitates a review of where and how ground water exists; subsurface distribution, in both vertical and areal extents, needs to be considered. The geologic zones important to ground water must be identified as well as their structure in terms of water-holding and water-yielding capabilities. Assuming hydrologic conditions furnish water to the underground zone, the subsurface strata govern its distribution and movement; hence the important role of geology in ground water hydrology cannot be overemphasized. Springs and water in permanently frozen ground constitute special ground water occurrences.

Origin of Ground Water

Almost all ground water can be thought of as a part of the hydrologic cycle, including surface and atmospheric (meteoric) waters. Relatively minor amounts of ground water, however, may enter this cycle from other origins. Connate water is water entrapped in the interstices of sedimentary rock at the time it was deposited. It may have been derived from the ocean or fresh water sources and, typically, is highly mineralized. New water of magmatic, volcanic, or cosmic origin added to the terrestrial water supply is juvenile water. In referring to water from a particular source, specific designations are appropriate: magmatic water, volcanic water, and cosmic water.

Rock Properties Affecting Ground Water

Ground water occurs in permeable geologic formations known as aquifers,* that is, formations having structures that permit appreciable water to move through them under ordinary field conditions. Ground water reservoir and water-bearing formation (also: bed, stratum, or deposit) are commonly used synonyms. In contradistinction, an aquiclude is an impermeable formation which may contain water but is incapable of transmitting significant water quantities; clay is an example. An aquifuge is an impermeable formation neither containing nor transmitting water; solid granite belongs in this category.

That portion of a rock or soil not occupied by solid mineral matter may be occupied by ground water. These spaces are known as voids, interstices, pores, or pore space. Because interstices can act as ground water conduits, they are of fundamental importance to the study of ground water. Typically, they are characterized by their size, shape, irregularity, and distribution. Original interstices [21] were created by geologic processes governing the origin of the geologic formation and are found in sedimentary and igneous rocks. Secondary interstices developed after the rock was formed; examples include joints, fractures, solution openings, and openings formed by plants and animals. With respect to size, interstices may be classed as capillary, supercapillary, and subcapillary. Capillary interstices are sufficiently small so that surface tension forces will hold water within them; supercapillary interstices are those larger than capillary ones; and subcapillary interstices are so small that water is held primarily by adhesive forces. Depending upon the connection of interstices with others, they may be classed as communicating or isolated.

The porosity of a rock or soil is a measure of the contained interstices. It is expressed as the percentage of void space to the total volume of the mass. If α is the porosity, then

$$\alpha = \frac{100w}{V} \tag{2.1}$$

* The word *aquifer* can be traced to its Latin origin. *Aqui-* is a combining form of *aqua,* meaning water, and *-fer* comes from *ferre,* to bear. Hence, an aquifer, literally, is a water bearer. The suffix *-clude* of aquiclude is derived from the Latin *claudere,* to shut or close. Similarly, the suffix *-fuge* of aquifuge comes from *fugere,* to drive away.

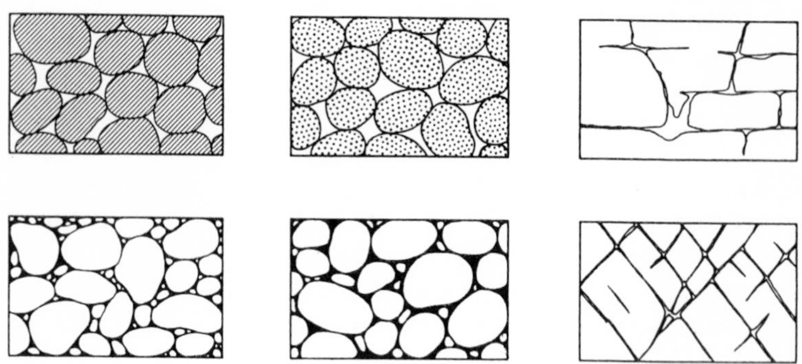

Fig. 2.1. Examples of rock interstices and the relation of rock texture to porosity (after Meinzer[22]).

where w is the volume of water required to fill, or saturate, all of the pore space, and V is the total volume of the rock or soil.

Figure 2.1 shows several types of interstices and their relation to porosity. In terms of ground water supply, granular sedimentary deposits are of major importance. Porosities in these deposits depend on the shape and arrangement of individual particles, distribution by size, and degree of cementation and compaction. In consolidated formations, removal of mineral matter by solution and degree of fracture are also important. Porosities range from near zero to more than 50 per cent,

TABLE 2.1 Representative Porosity Ranges for Sedimentary Materials

Material	Porosity, per cent
Soils	50–60
Clay	45–55
Silt	40–50
Medium to coarse mixed sand	35–40
Uniform sand	30–40
Fine to medium mixed sand	30–35
Gravel	30–40
Gravel and sand	20–35
Sandstone	10–20
Shale	1–10
Limestone	1–10

depending upon the above factors and the type of material. Representative porosity ranges for sedimentary materials are listed in Table 2.1.

Vertical Distribution of Ground Water

The subsurface occurrence of ground water may be divided into zones of saturation and aeration. In the zone of saturation all interstices are filled with water under hydrostatic pressure. The zone of aeration consists of interstices occupied partially by water and partially by air. Over most of the land masses of the earth a single zone of aeration overlies a single zone of saturation and extends upward to the ground surface, as shown in Fig. 2.2. The saturated zone is bounded at the top by either a limiting surface of saturation or overlying impermeable strata, and extends down to underlying impermeable strata such as clay beds or bedrock. In the absence of overlying impermeable strata, the upper surface of the zone of saturation is the water table, or phreatic surface.* This is defined as the surface of atmospheric pressure and would be revealed by the level at which water stands in a well penetrating the aquifer. Actually, saturation extends slightly above the water table owing to capillary attraction; however, water is held here at less than atmospheric pressure.

Water occurring in the zone of saturation is commonly referred to simply as ground water. In the zone of aeration suspended, or vadose, † water occurs. This general zone may be further subdivided into the soil water zone, intermediate zone, and the capillary zone (Fig. 2.2). The extent and water distribution of each zone are described in the following sections.

Soil Water Zone. Water in the soil water zone exists at less than saturation except temporarily when excessive water reaches the ground surface as from rainfall or irrigation. The zone extends from the ground surface down through the major root zone. Its thickness varies with soil type and vegetation. Because of the agricultural importance of soil water in supplying moisture to roots, agriculturists and soil scientists have studied soil moisture distribution and movement extensively.

Soil water was classified by Briggs[7] into three categories dependent upon its concentration in the soil zone. Hygroscopic water, adsorbed from the air, forms thin films of moisture on soil particle surfaces. The adhesive forces are very large, so that this water is unavailable

* *Phreatic* is derived from the Greek *phrear, -atos,* meaning a well.

† *Vadose* is derived from the Latin *vadosus,* meaning shallow.

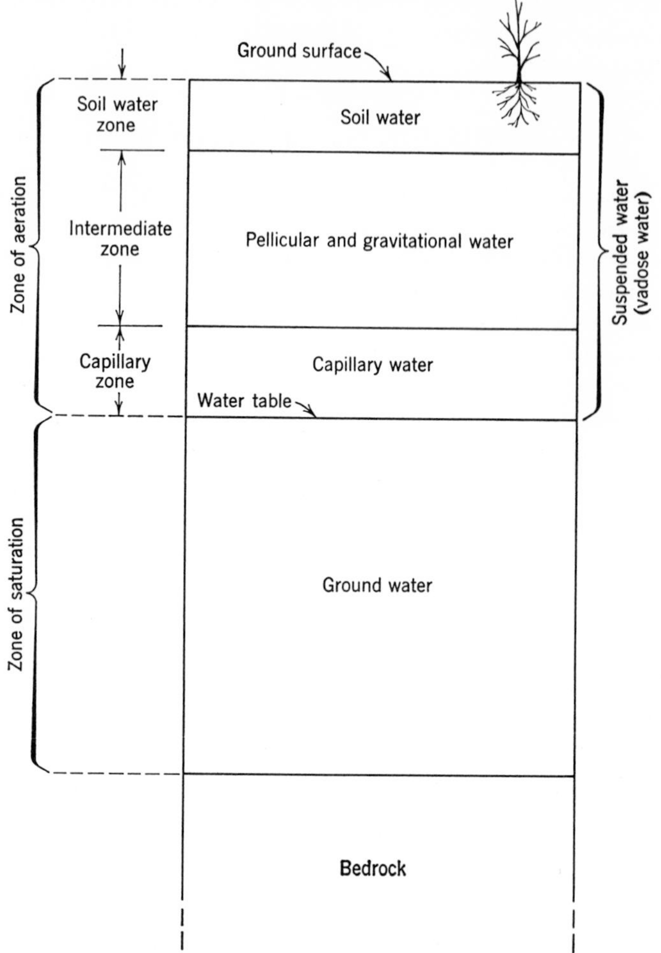

Fig. 2.2. Divisions of subsurface water.

to plants. Capillary water exists as continuous films around the soil particles. It is held by surface tension, is moved by capillary action, and is available to plants. Gravitational water is excess soil water which drains through the soil under the influence of gravity.

Several degrees, or equilibrium points, of soil moisture content in relation to agricultural and laboratory studies of soils are generally known. These represent efforts to define the above classes of soil water; however, as can be noted, the arbitrary definitions of some of these points prevent specific physical determinations. A moisture diagram, shown schematically in Fig. 2.3, indicates the relative positions of the soil water classes and equilibrium points. All of the following moisture contents are expressed as a percentage by weight of the moisture to the dry weight of the soil. Conversion to percentage by volume for comparing them with porosity can be made by multiplying by the specific gravity of the dry soil.

The hygroscopic coefficient is the maximum moisture which an initially dry soil will adsorb in contact with an atmosphere of 50 per cent relative humidity at 25° C. The wilting point is that moisture content at which permanent wilting of plants occurs. Experiments have proved that this is not a unique value, but rather depends upon the plant, the climate, the root system, and volume of soil tested. Field capacity is defined as the amount of water held in the soil after the excess gravitational water has drained away and after the rate of downward movement of water has materially decreased. Moisture equivalent is the amount of water which a saturated soil will retain after being centrifuged at a centrifugal force 1000 times that of gravity. The field capacity for sands is higher than the moisture equivalent, but about the same for loams.[43] Because field capacity and wilting point represent the upper and lower limits, respectively, of moisture for plant growth, the difference between these points is the available

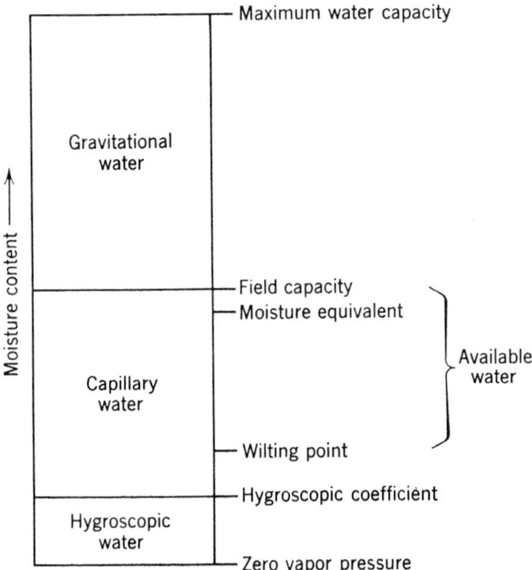

Fig. 2.3. Soil water diagram showing classes and equilibrium points.

water for plant growth. The water required to saturate all of the soil voids is the maximum possible water content. This is known as the maximum water capacity.

Studies of soil moisture have led to important advances in methods for measuring soil moisture in place and its variations with time.[15,19,34] The most accurate method is the gravimetric measurement of soil samples, in which samples are weighed, dried, and reweighed. A modification of this method utilizes gravimetric sorption blocks which may be inserted and removed from the soil. These porous blocks develop moisture equilibrium with the soil so that their weight can be correlated to that of the soil moisture. Richards [30] and others have developed tensiometers to measure tensions, or capillary potentials, of the soil. These measurements can be expressed in terms of moisture content for a given soil and provide continuous records of soil moisture variations. A tensiometer consists essentially of a porous cup inserted in the soil and connected by a water-filled tube to a manometer. Tensiometric measurements of soil moisture are limited to tensions in the range from zero (at saturation) to about 0.85 atmosphere. This encompasses half or more of the available water range, depending upon the soil texture. A variety of instruments have been built utilizing the principle of measuring the electrical resistance of a material imbedded in the soil and relating it to the soil moisture content.[5,6,11,12,48] Plaster of paris, nylon, and fiberglas, among others, have been used as absorbent materials to enclose electrodes. Because the heat conductivity of soil furnishes a measure of the soil moisture,[35] several units have been developed in which a heating element is imbedded in the soil.

The neutron scattering method is a promising new procedure for soil moisture determinations.[3,14] It is known that fast neutrons are slowed by collisions with hydrogen more effectively than with any other common element, and that hydrogen in most soils occurs almost entirely in the form of water. Applying these facts, a combined fast neutron source and a slow neutron counter are lowered into a specially cased hole in the soil. The counting rate of neutrons slowed by soil hydrogen is a measure of the soil moisture content. Once a hole has been calibrated, time and depth variations of moisture can be determined with ease.

Intermediate Zone. The intermediate zone extends from the lower edge of the soil water zone to the upper limit of the capillary zone (Fig. 2.2). This zone may vary in thickness from zero, when the bounding zones merge with a high water table approaching the ground surface, to several hundred feet under deep water table conditions.

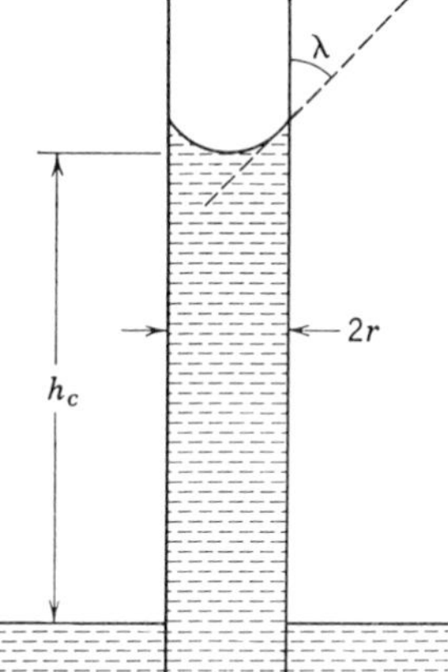

Fig. 2.4. Rise of water in a capillary tube.

The zone serves primarily as a region connecting the zone near the ground surface to that near the water table through which water moving vertically downward must pass. Non-moving, or pellicular,* water in the intermediate zone is held in place by hygroscopic and capillary forces, and is equivalent to field capacity in the soil water zone. Excess water is gravitational water, which moves downward under the influence of gravity.

Capillary Zone. The capillary zone extends from the water table up to the limit of capillary rise of water. Several investigators have studied the rise and distribution of water in the capillary zone in terms of the properties of porous media.[18, 20, 36, 37] If a pore space could be idealized to represent a capillary tube, the capillary rise h_c (Fig. 2.4) can be derived from an equilibrium between surface tension of water and the weight of water raised. Thus,

$$h_c = \frac{2\tau}{r\gamma} \cos \lambda \tag{2.2}$$

where τ is surface tension, γ is the specific weight of water, r is the tube radius, and λ is the angle of contact between the meniscus and the wall of the tube. Taking $\tau = 0.074$ gm/cm at 50° F, $\gamma = 1$ gm/cm^3, then the capillary rise in centimeters is approximately

$$h_c = \frac{0.15}{r} \cos \lambda \tag{2.3}$$

* *Pellicular* comes from the Latin *pellicula,* a diminutive form of *pellis,* meaning skin.

The angle of contact varies with the chemical composition of the liquid and wall, as well as with impurities on the wall, but approaches zero for pure water on clean glass. Assuming this value, the capillary rise might range from a fraction of an inch in gravel, to a foot in a sand, and to several feet in clay. From a study of four different sands under a variety of packings, Mavis and Tsui [20] found that the maximum capillary rise, in inches, could be approximated by

$$h_c = \frac{2.2}{d_H}\left(\frac{1-\alpha}{\alpha}\right)^{2/3} \tag{2.4}$$

where d_H is the harmonic mean grain diameter in millimeters and α is porosity.

Not only will the thickness of the capillary zone vary with soil or rock texture but, for a given stratum containing innumerable pores of a wide range in size, the upper limit will also form a jagged edge when studied microscopically. Taken macroscopically, however, there results a gradual decrease in moisture content with height. That is, just above the water table almost all pores contain capillary water; higher, only the smaller connected pores contain water; and still higher, only the few smallest connected pores contain water lifted above the water table. This distribution of moisture above the water table is shown in Fig. 2.5 from drainage test data on a fine sand by Lambe.[18] Note that saturation occurs above the water table, that the visual line of saturation differs from the actual line of saturation, and that

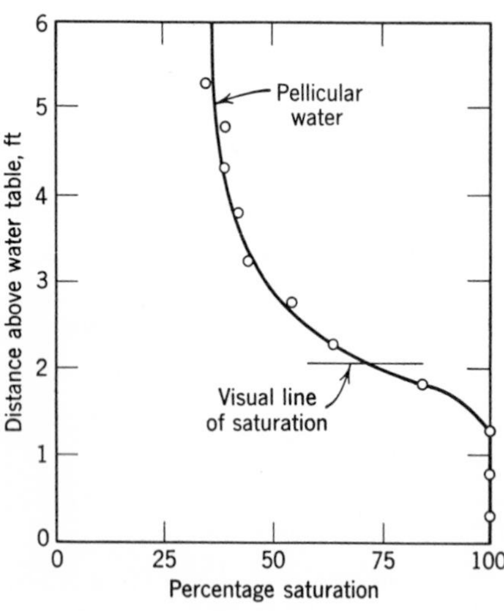

Fig. 2.5. Distribution of moisture in a fine sand above the water table after drainage (after Lambe [18]).

the upper portion of the curve becomes asymptotic to the pellicular water content.

Saturated Zone. Ground water fills all of the interstices in the saturated zone, hence the porosity is a direct measure of the water contained per unit volume. Not all of this water may be removed from the ground by drainage or pumping from a well, however, as molecular and surface tension forces will hold a portion of the water in place. Thus, retained water is that held in place against gravity.* The specific retention of a rock or soil is the ratio expressed as a percentage of the volume of water it will retain after saturation against the force of gravity to its own volume. If S_r is the specific retention, then

$$S_r = \frac{100w_r}{V} \tag{2.5}$$

where w_r is the volume occupied by retained water, and V is the gross volume of the rock or soil. On the other hand, the water which can be drained is expressed as the specific yield S_y. The term, effective porosity, has a synonymous meaning. It may be defined as the ratio expressed as a percentage of the volume of water which, after being saturated, can be drained by gravity to its own volume.

Therefore,

$$S_y = \frac{100w_y}{V} \tag{2.6}$$

where w_y is the volume of water drained. Because $w_r + w_y = w$, it is apparent that

$$\alpha = S_r + S_y \tag{2.7}$$

Thus, specific yield is a fraction of the porosity of an aquifer. Values depend upon grain size, shape and distribution of pores, and compaction of the stratum. For uniform sand, specific yield may equal up to 30 per cent, but most alluvial aquifers give values in the range of 10 to 20 per cent.

Meinzer[24] outlined seven methods for determining specific yield:

(1) Saturating samples in the laboratory and allowing them to drain.

(2) Saturating in the field a considerable body of material situated above the water table and above the capillary zone and allowing it to drain downward naturally.

* The reader should note that the terms *field capacity, pellicular water,* and *retained water* refer to the same water content but differ by the zone in which they occur.

(3) Collecting samples immediately above the capillary zone after the water table has gone down an appreciable distance.

(4) Ascertaining the volume of sediments drained by pumping a known quantity of water from a well.

(5) Ascertaining the volume of sediments saturated by a measured amount of seepage from one or more streams.

(6) Estimating specific yield indirectly by centrifuging to measure moisture equivalent.

(7) Making mechanical analyses and determinations of porosity and estimating therefrom the specific retention and specific yield.

All of these methods have limitations. Thus, laboratory samples may be disturbed or not representative; in field tests it is difficult to control and measure variables; and estimates often lack accuracy. A method based on a well pumping test is described in Chapter 4 which generally gives the best result for a field measurement.

Quantitative information on specific yield was obtained from an intensive field investigation of the South Coastal Basin in the Los Angeles area of California.[13] Numerous samples were taken from surface exposures, test holes, and wells. Porosities and specific re-

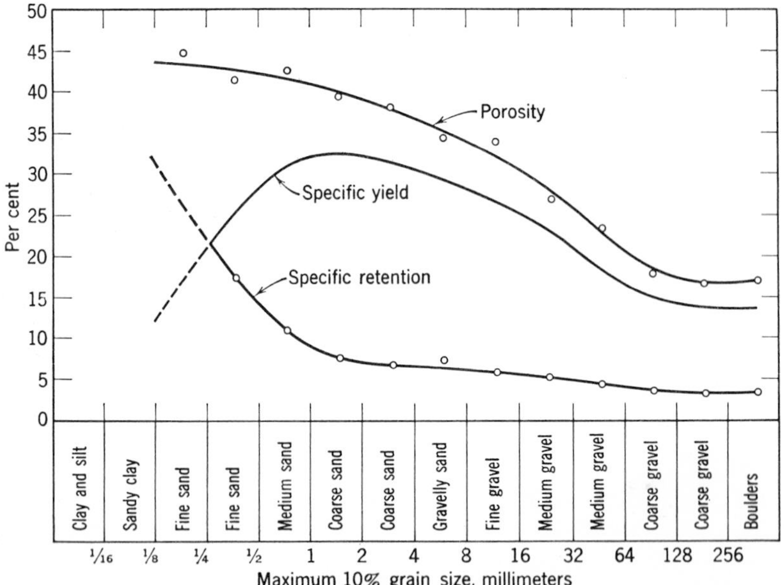

Fig. 2.6. Porosity, specific yield, and specific retention variations with grain size, South Coastal Basin, Calif. (after Eckis [13]).

TABLE 2.2 Specific Yields of Water-Bearing Deposits in Sacramento Valley, California

(After Poland and others [28])

Material	Specific Yield, per cent
Gravel	25
Sand, including sand and gravel, and gravel and sand	20
Fine sand, hard sand, tight sand, sandstone, and related deposits	10
Clay and gravel, gravel and clay, cemented gravel, and related deposits	5
Clay, silt, sandy clay, lava rock, and related fine-grained deposits	3

tentions were determined in the laboratory and specific yields were obtained as the difference. Mean curves showing porosity, specific yield, and specific retention variations with grain size appear in Fig. 2.6.

Poland and others, in another investigation, estimated the total ground water storage capacity of the Sacramento Valley in California.[28] Approximately 3000 well logs, giving information on subsurface strata, were classified as to material. Specific yields were as-

TABLE 2.3 Estimated Specific Yields for Storage Groups in Sacramento Valley, California

(After Poland and others [28])

	Specific Yield, per cent			
Storage Group	20–50 Ft Depth Zone	50–100 Ft Depth Zone	100–200 Ft Depth Zone	All Zones (20–200 ft)
River flood-plain and channel deposits	11.7	10.5	8.0	9.3
Low alluvial-plain and alluvial-fan deposits	8.0	7.5	6.9	7.3
Dissected alluvial deposits	6.2	6.0	6.2	6.2
Basin deposits	5.0	4.5	6.0	5.4
Entire valley	7.9	7.2	6.9	7.1

signed as shown in Table 2.2 and specific yields were determined for depths of 20 to 200 feet. The results, shown in Table 2.3, were classed by storage groups possessing certain common physiographic and geologic characteristics. Decreasing values with depth, associated with compaction, can be noted in the river and alluvial deposits. The valley, exceeding 2,500,000 acres in area, was estimated to have a mean specific yield of 7.1 per cent and a ground water storage capacity in the 20- to 200-foot depth zone of 33,700,000 acre-ft.

Geologic Formations as Aquifers

A rock formation or material which will yield significant quantities of water has been defined as an aquifer. Various geologic formations acting as aquifers are described in the following paragraphs based on work by Thomas.[41]

Probably 90 per cent of all developed aquifers consist of unconsolidated rocks, chiefly gravel and sand. These aquifers may be divided into four categories, based on manner of occurrence: water courses, abandoned or buried valleys, plains, and intermontane valleys. Water courses consist of the alluvium that forms and underlies stream channels, as well as forming the adjacent flood plains. Wells located in highly permeable strata bordering streams produce large quantities of water, as infiltration from the streams augment ground water supplies. Abandoned or buried valleys are valleys no longer occupied by streams that formed them. Although such valleys may resemble water courses in permeability and quantity of ground water storage, the recharge and capabilities for perennial yield are usually less. Extensive plains underlain by unconsolidated sediments exist in the United States. In some places gravel and sand beds form important aquifers under these plains; in other places they are relatively thin and have limited productivity. These plains flank highlands or other features that served as the source of the sedimentary deposits. The ground water reservoirs are recharged chiefly in areas accessible to downward percolation of water from precipitation and from occasional streams. Intermontane valleys are underlain by tremendous volumes of unconsolidated rock materials derived by erosion of bordering mountains. Many of these more or less individual basins, separated by mountain ranges, occur in the Western United States. The sand and gravel beds of these aquifers produce large quantities of water, most of which is replenished by seepage from streams into alluvial fans at mouths of mountain canyons.

Limestones vary widely in density, porosity, and permeability, depending upon degree of consolidation and development of permeable zones after deposition. Those most important as aquifers contain sizable proportions of the original rock which have been dissolved and removed. Openings in limestone may range from microscopic original pores to large solution caverns forming subterranean channels sufficiently large to carry the entire flow of a stream. The term, *lost river,* has been applied to a stream which disappears completely underground in a limestone terrane. Large springs are frequently found in limestone areas. The solution of calcium carbonate by water causes prevailingly hard ground water to be found in limestone aquifers; also, by dissolving the rock, water tends to increase the pore space and permeability with time. Ultimate development of a limestone terrane forms a karst region, where subterranean drainage through the limestone creates large ground water reservoirs. Although uncommon, gypsum is another soluble rock that has been developed to a limited extent as aquifers.

Volcanic rocks may form permeable aquifers. Basalt flows are very permeable, corresponding to limestones in this regard. Other permeable zones in volcanic rocks include flow breccias, porous zones between lava beds, lava tubes, shrinkage cracks, and joints. Most of the largest springs in the United States are associated with basalt deposits. Rhyolites are less permeable than basalt, whereas shallow intrusive rocks may be regarded as practically impermeable to flow.

Sandstone and conglomerate are cemented forms of sand and gravel. As such, their porosity and yield have been reduced by the cement. The best sandstone aquifers are those which are only partially cemented, or those which yield water through their joints. Conglomerates have limited distribution and are unimportant as aquifers.

Crystalline and metamorphic rocks are relatively impermeable and are poor aquifers. Where such rocks occur near the surface under fractured and decayed conditions they have been developed with small wells for domestic purposes.

Clay and coarser materials mixed with clay are generally porous, but their pores are so small that they may be regarded as relatively impermeable. Clayey soils have provided small domestic water supplies from shallow wells.

Types of Aquifers

Most aquifers are of large areal extent and may be visualized as underground storage reservoirs. Water enters a reservoir from natural or artificial recharge; it flows out under the action of gravity

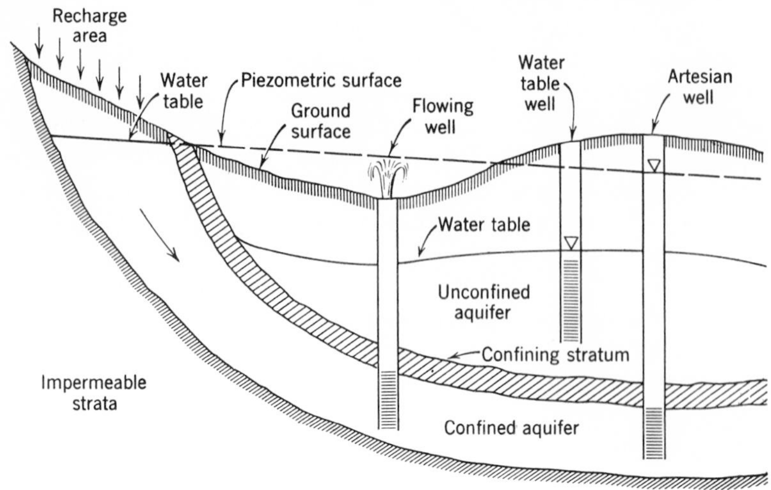

Fig. 2.7. Unconfined and confined aquifers.

or is extracted by wells. Ordinarily, the annual volume of water removed or replaced represents only a small fraction of the total storage capacity. Aquifers may be classed as unconfined or confined, depending upon the presence or absence of a water table.

An unconfined aquifer is one in which a water table serves as the upper surface of the zone of saturation. It is also known as a free, phreatic, or nonartesian aquifer. The water table varies in undulating form and in slope, depending upon areas of recharge and discharge, pumpage from wells, and permeability. Rises and falls in the water table correspond to changes in the volume of water in storage within an aquifer. Figure 2.2 is an idealized section through an unconfined aquifer; the upper aquifer in Fig 2.7 is unconfined also. Contour maps and profiles of the water table can be prepared from elevations of water in wells tapping the aquifer to determine the quantities of water available, its distribution, and movement.

Confined aquifers, also known as artesian * or pressure aquifers, occur where ground water is confined under pressure greater than atmospheric by overlying, relatively impermeable strata. In a well pene-

* The word *artesian* has an interesting origin. It is derived from the French *artésien,* meaning of or pertaining to Artois, the northernmost province of France. Here the first deep wells to tap confined aquifers, dating from about 1750, were drilled and investigated. Originally the term referred to a well with freely flowing water, but at present it is applied to any well penetrating a confined aquifer or simply the aquifer itself.

trating such an aquifer, the water level will rise above the bottom of the confining bed, as shown in the artesian and flowing wells of Fig. 2.7. Water enters a confined aquifer in an area where the confining bed rises to the surface or ends underground and the aquifer becomes unconfined. A region supplying water to a confined aquifer is known as a recharge area. Rises and falls of water in wells penetrating confined aquifers result primarily from changes in pressure rather than changes in storage volumes. Hence confined aquifers have only small changes in storage and serve mainly as conduits for conveying water from recharge areas to locations of natural or artificial discharge. The piezometric surface of a confined aquifer is an imaginary surface coinciding with the hydrostatic pressure level of the water in the aquifer (Fig. 2.7). The water level in a well penetrating a confined aquifer defines the elevation of the piezometric surface at that point. Should the piezometric surface lie above ground surface, a flowing well results. Contour maps and profiles of the piezometric surface can be prepared from well data similar to those for the water table in an unconfined aquifer. It should be noted that a confined aquifer becomes an unconfined aquifer when the piezometric surface falls below the bottom of the upper confining bed. Also, quite commonly an unconfined aquifer exists above a confined one, as shown in Fig. 2.7.

A special case of an unconfined aquifer is the perched aquifer, which is illustrated by Fig. 2.8. This occurs wherever a ground water

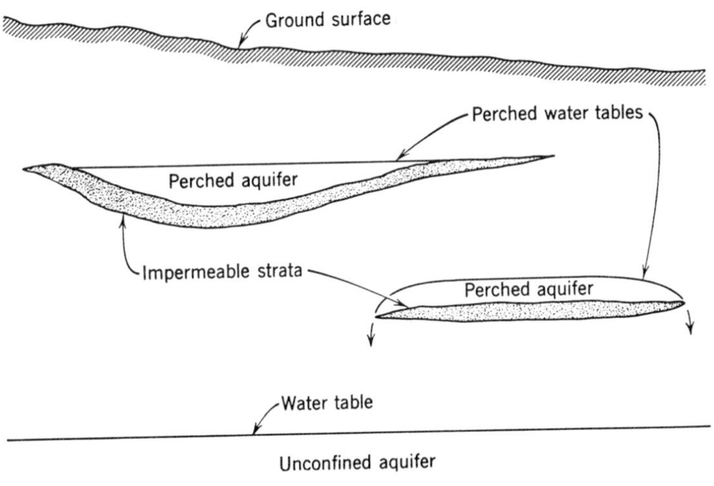

Fig. 2.8. Perched aquifers.

body is separated from the main ground water by a relatively impermeable stratum of small areal extent and by the zone of aeration above the main body of ground water. Clay lenses in sedimentary deposits often have shallow perched water bodies overlying them. Wells tapping perched aquifers yield only temporary or small quantities of water.

Water recharged to, or discharged from, an aquifer represents a change in the storage volume within the aquifer. For unconfined aquifers this is simply expressed by the product of the volume of aquifer lying between the water table at the beginning and at the end of a period of time and the average specific yield of the formation. In confined aquifers, however, assuming the aquifer remains

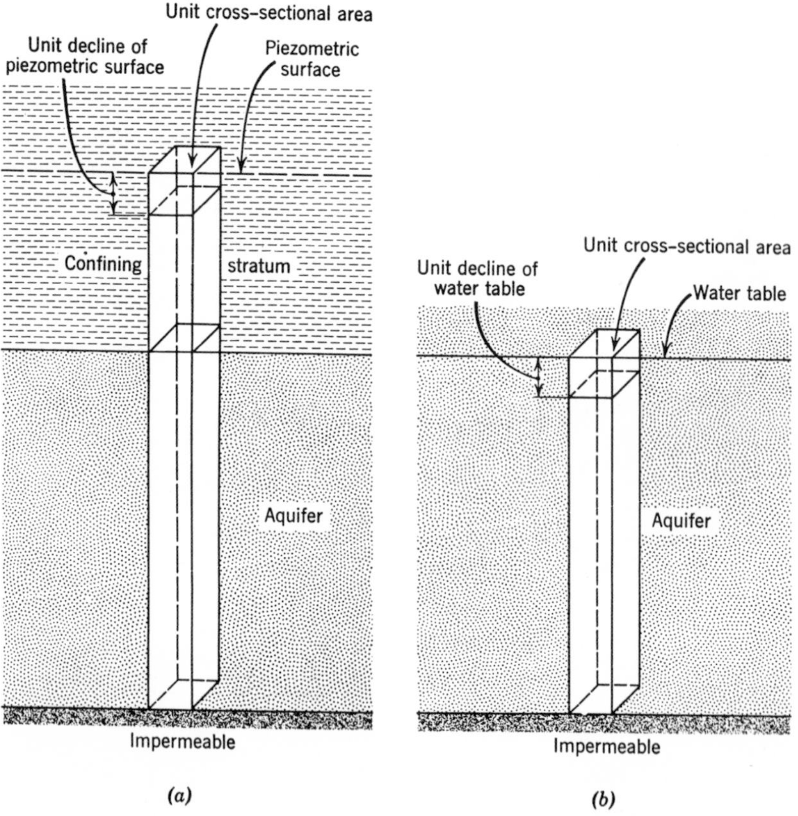

Fig. 2.9. Illustrative sketches for defining storage coefficient of (*a*) confined and (*b*) unconfined aquifers.

saturated, changes in pressure produce only small changes in storage volume. Thus, the hydrostatic pressure within an aquifer partially supports the weight of the overburden while the solid structure of the aquifer provides the remaining support. When the hydrostatic pressure is reduced, such as by pumping water from a well penetrating the aquifer, the aquifer load increases. A compression of the aquifer results which forces some water from it. In addition, lowering of the pressure causes a small expansion and subsequent release of water. The water-yielding capacity of a confined aquifer can be expressed in terms of its storage coefficient.

Storage coefficient is defined as the volume of water that an aquifer releases from or takes into storage per unit surface area of aquifer per unit change in the component of head normal to that surface. For a vertical column one foot by one foot extending through a confined aquifer, as in Fig. 2.9*a*, the storage coefficient S equals the volume of water (in cubic feet) released from the aquifer when the piezometric surface declines one foot. In most confined aquifers, values fall in the range $0.00005 \leqq S \leqq 0.005$, indicating that large pressure changes over extensive areas are required to produce substantial water yields. Storage coefficients may be determined from pumping tests of wells (Chapter 4) and from ground water fluctuations in response to atmospheric pressure or ocean tide variations (see Chapter 6).

The storage coefficient for an unconfined aquifer corresponds to its specific yield, as shown in Fig. 2.9*b*.

Ground Water Basins

A ground water basin may be defined as a physiographic unit containing one large aquifer or several connected and interrelated aquifers.* In a valley between mountain ranges the drainage basin of the surface stream closely coincides with the ground water basin. In limestone and sand hill areas, the drainage and ground water basins may have entirely different configurations. The concept of a ground water basin has become important in recent years with the realization that overdevelopment of ground water in one portion of a basin directly affects water supplies throughout the remainder of the basin. This has led to basin-wide planning and development of ground water, which are described in Chapter 8.

* The term *basin* is used very loosely in practice, and, because of its vagueness, has no clear general definition; however, it implies an area containing a ground water reservoir capable of furnishing a substantial water supply.

Springs

A spring is a concentrated discharge of ground water appearing at the ground surface as a current of flowing water. To be distinguished from springs are seepage areas,* which indicate a slower movement of ground water to the ground surface. Water in seepage areas may pond and evaporate or flow, depending upon the magnitude of the seepage, the climate, and the topography.

Springs occur in many forms, and have been classified as to cause, rock structure, discharge, temperature, and variability. Bryan [8] divided all springs into (*a*) those resulting from nongravitational forces, and (*b*) those resulting from gravitational forces. Under the former category are included volcanic springs, associated with volcanic rocks, and fissure springs, resulting from fractures extending to great depths in the earth's crust. Such springs are usually thermal in that their water temperature exceeds that of the normal local ground water. The relative terms *warm springs* and *hot springs* are common. Waters of thermal springs are usually highly mineralized and may consist of juvenile water or a mixture of ground water and juvenile water. Extensive studies of thermal springs have been made in the United States [38, 46, 47] where more than 1000 such springs have been reported. Figure 2.10 shows their regional distribution.

Of the gravity springs, which result from water flowing under hydrostatic pressure, the following types [22] are recognized: depression springs—formed where the land surface intersects the water table; contact springs—created by a permeable water-bearing formation overlying a less permeable formation which intersects the ground surface; artesian springs—resulting from releases of water under pressure from confined aquifers either at an outcrop of the aquifer or through an opening in the confining bed; and tubular or fracture springs—issuing from rounded channels, such as lava tubes or solution channels, or fractures in impermeable rock connecting with a ground water supply.

To study magnitudes of springs, Meinzer proposed a classification by discharge.[23] The system, which has come into general acceptance, is outlined in Table 2.4. According to an investigation of large springs in the United States,[23] there are 65 of the first magnitude,

* *Seepage* is a general term describing the movement of water through the ground or other porous media to the ground surface or surface water bodies. The term is well established in the engineering literature in connection with ground water movement from and to surface water bodies, particularly where associated with structures such as dams, canals, and levees.

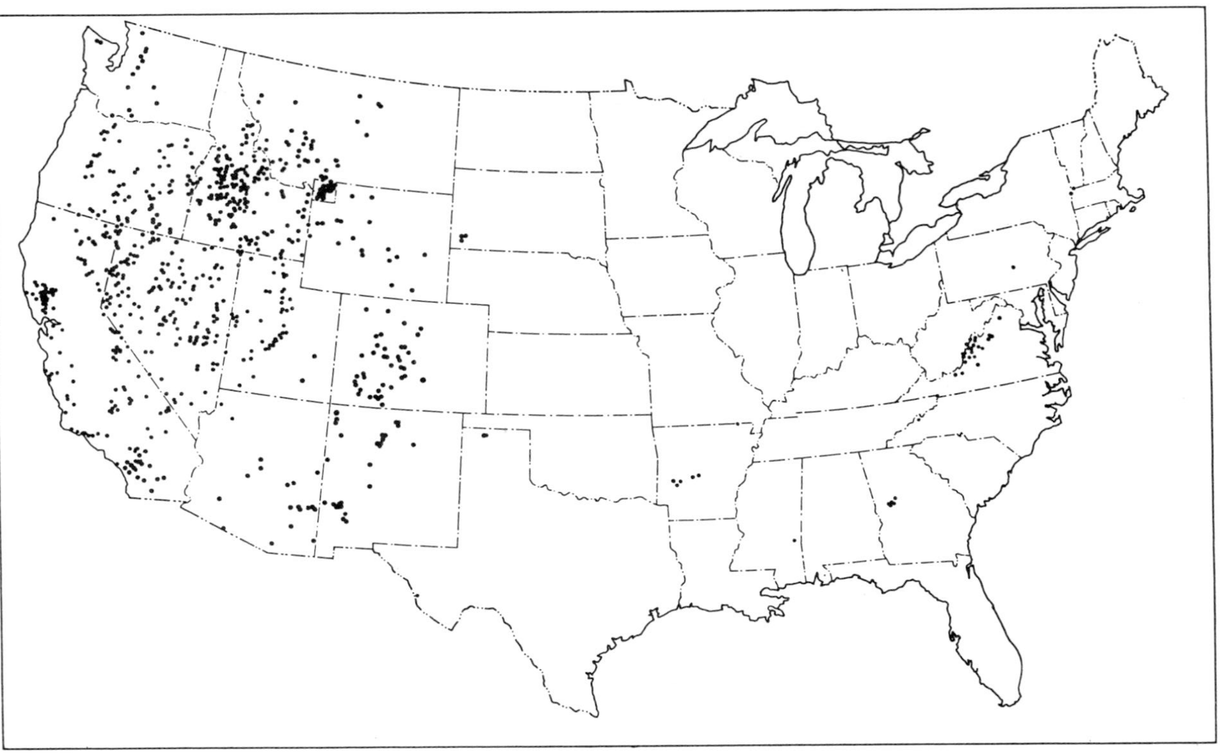

Fig. 2.10. Thermal springs in the United States (after Stearns, Stearns, and Waring[38]).

TABLE 2.4 Classification of Springs by Discharge

(After Meinzer [23])

Magnitude	Discharge
First	Greater than 100 cfs
Second	10 to 100 cfs
Third	1 to 10 cfs
Fourth	100 gal/min (0.22 cfs) to 1 cfs
Fifth	10 to 100 gal/min
Sixth	1 to 10 gal/min
Seventh	1 pt/min to 1 gal/min
Eighth	Less than 1 pt/min (180 gal/day)

several hundred of the second magnitude, and thousands of the third magnitude. Of the first-magnitude springs, 38 rise in volcanic rocks, 24 in limestone, and 3 in sandstone. Those in volcanic rocks are found in California, Idaho, and Oregon; those in limestone occur in the Missouri-Arkansas area, Texas, and Florida; and the three large sandstone springs rise through faults or other openings in Montana.

Most springs fluctuate in their rate of discharge. Fluctuations are in response to variations in rate of recharge with periods ranging from minutes to years, depending upon geologic and hydrologic conditions. Perennial springs drain extensive permeable aquifers and discharge throughout the year, whereas intermittent springs discharge only during portions of the year when sufficient ground water is recharged to maintain flow. Areas of volcanic rock and sand hills are noted for their perennial springs of nearly constant discharge. Springs which exhibit more or less regular discharge fluctuations not associated with rainfall or seasonal effects are periodic springs. Such fluctuations may be caused by variations in transpiration, by atmospheric pressure changes, by tides affecting confined aquifers, and by natural siphons acting in underground storage basins. A geyser is a periodic thermal spring resulting from the expansive force of superheated steam produced by water in contact with heated rock at great depths.

Ground Water in Permafrost Regions

Permafrost, or permanently frozen ground, exists over large areas in the polar regions of the earth. Sixty per cent of Alaska is occupied by permafrost. Here are found strata varying in thickness from a few to several hundred feet below ground surface, continuously frozen with the exception of a shallow surface layer which is seasonally thawed. The water supply and engineering problems associated with permafrost have been studied in the Soviet Union and Alaska.[10,17]

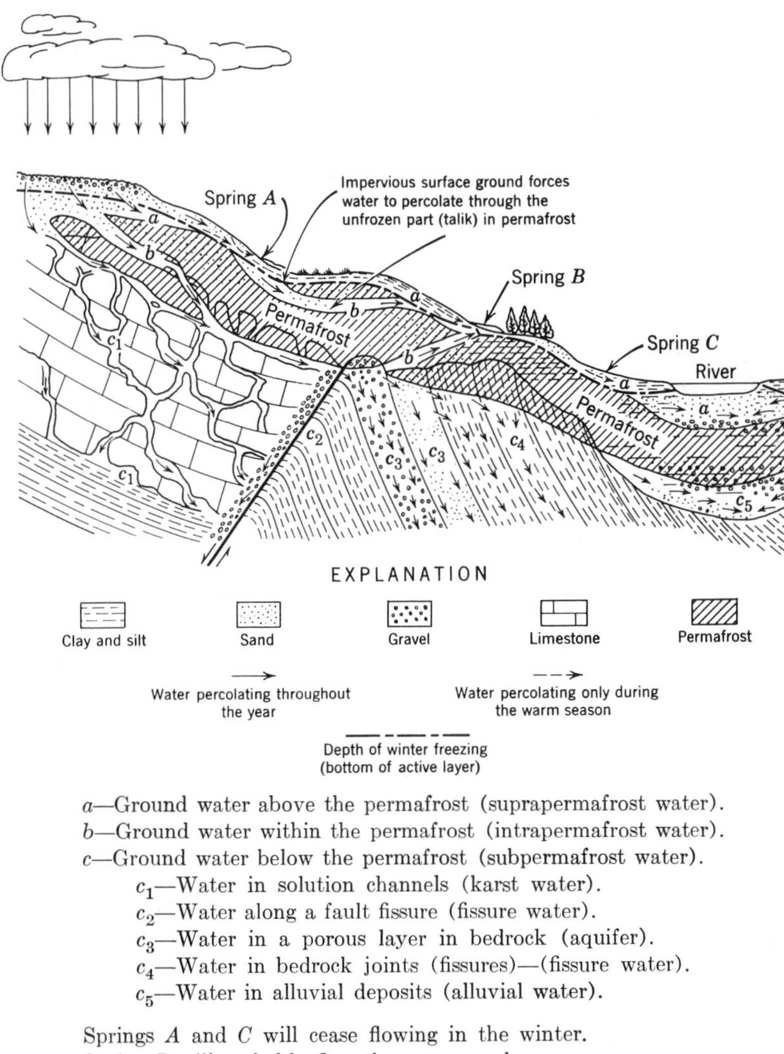

Fig. 2.11. Occurrence of ground water in permafrost regions (after Cederstrom, Johnston, and Subitzky [10]).

Water contained within a permafrost zone is obviously unavailable, hence usable ground water is described in terms of its location relative to the permafrost. Suprapermafrost, intrapermafrost, and subpermafrost water may be distinguished, as illustrated in Fig. 2.11. Suprapermafrost water, ground water above the permafrost layer, furnishes shallow temporary water supplies. It is subject to seasonal freezing in winter and may be readily contaminated by waste disposal facilities located above the permafrost. Entrapped or artesian water occurring within the permafrost is termed intrapermafrost water. This water occurs in openings of the permafrost, as near rivers, faults, or fractures in thin sections. The water usually is not a stable source, and for adequate development by wells it must be associated with suprapermafrost or subpermafrost waters. Subpermafrost water, located below the frozen ground, might appear as the most promising of permanent supplies; however, difficulties of location, costly development, and possible high mineralization are major obstacles to extensive utilization. Often permafrost extends to impermeable rock so that no subpermafrost water is available. Best ground water sources in permafrost regions are found in thawed ground near rivers, streams, and standing water bodies; in dry river beds and lakes; and on south-facing hillsides.

Ground Water in the United States

Ground water areas in the United States are shown in Fig. 2.12. This map, prepared by Thomas,[40] shows regions in which moderate to large supplies of usable water can be obtained from wells. Productive areas are identified as water courses, buried valleys, unconsolidated aquifers, and consolidated aquifers. The blank areas occupying about half of the country delineate generally those sections not known to produce yields of more than 50 gal/min to a well.

Areal distribution of ground water in the United States can best be described by dividing the country into ground water provinces, as shown in Fig. 2.13. These provinces were developed by the U. S. Geological Survey,[22, 25] based on the areal extent of either the important superficial water-bearing or bedrock formations, or a combination of the two if both held important water supplies. Brief geologic and ground water summaries [42] for each province follow.

A. Atlantic Coastal Plain Province. Water is derived in rather large quantities from Cretaceous, Tertiary, and Quaternary strata, chiefly sand and gravel interbedded with clay. Large supplies are obtained from alluvial gravels in the Mississippi Valley and adjacent areas. The province includes

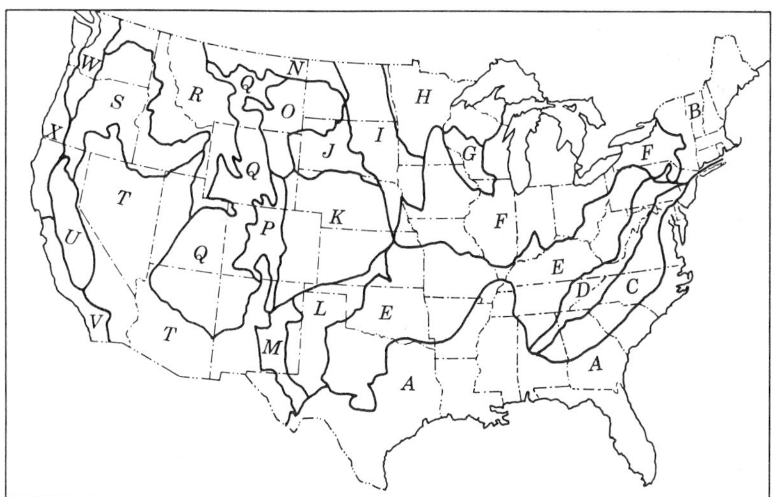

Fig. 2.13. Ground water provinces of the United States (after Meinzer[25]).

extensive areas of artesian flow. The ground water ranges from low to high in mineral content.

B. Northeastern Drift Province. Principal ground water supplies come from glacial drift. The till yields small supplies to many springs and shallow wells; the outwash gravels yield large supplies, notably on Long Island in New York. Many drilled rock wells receive small supplies, chiefly from joints in crystalline rocks or in Triassic sandstone. Ground water is generally soft and otherwise low in mineral content.

C. Piedmont Province. Water that is generally low in mineral matter is supplied in small quantities by the crystalline rocks and locally by Triassic sandstone. Many shallow dug wells are supplied from surface deposits or from the upper decomposed part of the bedrock. Many drilled wells of moderate depth are supplied from joints in the crystalline rocks. Some wells in Triassic sandstone yield rather large supplies.

D. Blue Ridge-Appalachian Valley Province. This is a region of rugged topography with numerous springs which generally yield water of good quality from Paleozoic strata, pre-Cambrian crystalline rocks, or post-Cambrian intrusive rocks. The water supplies are derived chiefly from springs, spring-fed streams, and shallow wells.

E. Southcentral Paleozoic Province. The ground water conditions are in general rather unsatisfactory. The principal sources of supply are the Paleozoic sandstones and limestones. Throughout a considerable part of the province the Paleozoic supplies are meager or of poor quality. Deep Paleozoic water is highly mineralized. In many of the valleys, large supplies are obtained from glacial outwash and other alluvial sands and gravels.

F. Northcentral Drift-Paleozoic Province. Most water supplies are derived from the glacial drift, where the water is generally hard but otherwise good. Numerous drilled wells obtain large supplies from glacial outwash or from gravel interbedded with till. Many drilled wells end in Paleozoic sandstone or limestone and receive ample supplies of water. The deeper Paleozoic waters are generally highly mineralized and in many places are unfit for use; the shallower Paleozoic waters are commonly of satisfactory quality except that they are hard. In many areas flowing wells can be obtained from drift and Paleozoic aquifers.

G. Wisconsin Paleozoic Province. Most of the water supplies are obtained from wells of moderate depth drilled into Cambrian or Ordovician sandstone or limestone. These wells as a rule yield ample supplies of hard but otherwise good water. In many of the valleys, artesian flows are obtained from the Paleozoic aquifers. The region is devoid of water-bearing drift except in the valleys, where there are water-bearing outwash gravels.

H. Superior Drift-Crystalline Province. In most parts of this province satisfactory water supplies are obtained from glacial drift. Where the drift is thin, water supplies are generally scarce because the pre-Cambrian crystalline rocks in most places yield only meager supplies, and as a rule there are no intervening Paleozoic, Mesozoic, or Tertiary formations that are thick enough to yield much water. The drift and rock waters range from soft waters of low mineralization in Wisconsin to highly mineralized waters in the western and northwestern parts of the province.

I. Dakota Drift-Cretaceous Province. The two important sources of ground water are the glacial drift and the Dakota sandstone. The drift supplies numerous wells with hard but otherwise good water. It is available for water supply in nearly all parts of the province. The Dakota sandstone has extensive areas of artesian flow which supply many strong flowing wells, a considerable number of which are more than 1000 feet deep. The Dakota sandstone waters are highly mineralized but are used for domestic supplies. The water from most parts of the formation is very hard, but the water from a few strata is soft.

J. Black Hills Cretaceous Province. The conditions in this province are, on the whole, unfavorable with respect to shallow-water supplies because most of the province is underlain by the Pierre shale or by shales of the White River group (Oligocene). The principal aquifer is the Dakota sandstone, which underlies the entire region except most of the Black Hills. This sandstone will probably yield water wherever it occurs, and over considerable parts of the province will give rise to flowing wells; however, throughout much of the province it is far below the surface. In some localities underlain by shale, small supplies are obtained from shallow wells. In the Black Hills water is obtained from a variety of sources, ranging from pre-Cambrian crystalline rocks to Cretaceous or Tertiary sedimentary rocks.

K. Great Plains Pliocene-Cretaceous Province. The principal aquifers of this province are the late Tertiary sands and gravels (Ogallalla formation and related deposits) and the Dakota sandstone. The Tertiary deposits underlying the extensive smooth and uneroded plains supply large quantities of water to shallow wells. The Dakota sandstone underlies nearly the entire province and gives rise to various areas of artesian flow. Throughout much of the province, however, it lies too far below the surface to be a practical source of water. Where the Tertiary beds are absent or badly eroded and the Dakota sandstone is buried beneath thick beds of shale, as in parts of eastern Colorado, it may be difficult to develop even small water supplies. Many of the valleys contain Quaternary gravels, which supply large quantities of good water. Considerable Tertiary and Quaternary well water is used for irrigation.

L. Great Plains Pliocene-Paleozoic Province. The principal aquifers of this province are the late Tertiary and Quaternary sands and gravels, which give the same favorable conditions as those in province K. The Tertiary deposits are underlain through practically the entire province by Permian or Triassic "Red Beds," which in most places yield little or only highly mineralized water. In localities where the Tertiary deposits are thin or absent, or where they have been badly eroded, the ground water conditions are generally unfavorable.

M. Trans-Pecos Paleozoic Province. The bedrock consists of Carboniferous and Triassic strata, including limestone, gypsum, red beds of shale and shaly sandstone, and some less shaly sandstone. In most of the province these rocks yield only meager supplies of highly mineralized waters to deep wells. In the Pecos Valley, however, Carboniferous limestones and sandstones yield large supplies to numerous flowing wells; the water is very hard, but good enough for irrigation, domestic, and livestock purposes. Locally the bedrock is overlain by Quaternary water-bearing gravels.

N. Northwestern Drift-Eocene-Cretaceous Province. Ground water supplies are obtained from glacial drift and from underlying Eocene and Upper Cretaceous formations. Where the drift is absent or not water bearing, wells are sunk into the underlying formations with variable success. The Eocene and latest Cretaceous, which underlie most of the eastern part of the province, generally include strata or lenses of sand, gravel, or coal that yield water. The Cretaceous formations that occur in the western part consist chiefly of alternating beds of shale and sandstone. The sandstones generally yield water, but the shales are unproductive, and where a thick shale formation immediately underlies the drift or is at the surface, it may be difficult to get successful wells. In certain localities, upland gravels yield water to shallow wells.

O. Montana Eocene-Cretaceous Province. Fairly good water in quantities adequate for domestic and livestock supplies and even for small municipal supplies is obtained from strata and lenses of sand, gravel, and coal in the Fort Union (Eocene) and Lance (late Cretaceous or Eocene) formations which underlie most of the province. These formations in this province usually rest on the Pierre shale, a thick dense shale of Upper Cretaceous age that yields no water or only meager amounts of generally poor quality water. Hence, locally, where the Fort Union and Lance are absent or do not yield adequately, there is great difficulty in obtaining satisfactory water supplies. In the northern part of the province, there is a little water-bearing glacial drift.

P. Southern Rocky Mountain Province. In this mountain province, underlain for the most part by crystalline rocks, water supplies are obtained chiefly from springs, from streams fed by springs and melted snow, or from very shallow wells near streams.

Q. Montana-Arizona Plateau Province. This large area is for the most part an arid to semiarid plateau region underlain by sedimentary formations ranging in age from Paleozoic to Tertiary, not violently deformed but sufficiently warped and broken to produce a close relation between rock structure and the occurrence of ground water and to cause rapid variation in ground water conditions from place to place. On the whole, water supplies are not plentiful and not of very satisfactory quality. Where thick formations of nearly impervious material are at the surface, or where the plateau is greatly dissected, as in the Grand Canyon region, water supplies are scarce. Locally, however, sandstone aquifers, such as those of the Kootenai formation, the Dakota sandstone, or the Mesaverde formation, can be developed and may yield very satisfactory supplies—in some places giving rise to flowing wells. There are also local deposits of water-bearing gravels of Quaternary age.

R. Northern Rocky Mountain Province. This is a relatively cold region, chiefly mountainous, but with extensive intermontane valleys and plains. It is underlain by a great variety of rocks with complicated and diverse structure. As in other mountain regions, water supplies are obtained largely from mountain springs and streams. Considerable water is available in places from valley fill, chiefly ordinary alluvial sand and gravel and the outwash deposits of mountain glaciers. A few supplies are also obtained from wells drilled into various rock formations of pre-Cambrian and Tertiary ages.

S. Columbia Plateau Lava Province. The principal aquifers of this province are the widespread Tertiary and Quaternary lava beds and interbedded or associated Tertiary sand and gravel, such as those of the Ellensburg formation. In general, the lava yields abundant supplies of good water. It gives rise to many large springs, especially along the Snake River in Idaho. Locally the lava or the interbedded sand and gravel give rise to flowing wells. However, much of the lava is so permeable and the relief of the region is so great that in many places the water table is too far below the surface to be reached except by deep wells. In certain parts of the province, glacial outwash and ordinary valley fill are also important sources of water.

T. Southwestern Bolson Province. The principal source of water supply in this arid province is the alluvial sand and gravel of the valley fill underlying the numerous intermontane valleys that characterize the region. In the elevated marginal parts of the valleys the water table may be far below the surface or ground water may be absent; in the lowest parts, underlain by clayey and alkaline beds, ground water may be meager in quantity and poor in quality; at intermediate levels, however, large supplies of good water are generally found. Most of the water in the valleys of this province is recovered by means of pumping wells, but there are many springs and areas of artesian flow. In mountain areas of the province there are many springs, small streams, and shallow wells that furnish valuable supplies. As a rule, the most favorable areas in the mountains for springs and shallow wells are those underlain by granitic rocks.

U. Central Valley of California Province. Ground water of good quality is found chiefly in alluvial cones formed by streams emerging from the Sierra Nevada, although water can be obtained throughout the valley floor. The yield of cones flanking the Coast Range is small, with poorer quality water generally occurring in the south and central sections, and better in the north. Underlying piedmont deposits consist of marine, lacustrine, and alluvial formations. Highly mineralized connate water is found in deep strata throughout the valley; in the center it occurs near ground surface. Extensive irrigation in the valley is dependent upon ground water pumped from wells.

V. Coastal Ranges of Central and Southern California Province. The principal ground water bodies are in the mountain valley and piedmont plains draining to the Pacific Ocean. Aquifers consist of valley fill and alluvial sand and gravel deposits. Locally, good water supplies are developed from underlying younger Tertiary sandstones. Heavy development of ground water along the coast for municipal and irrigation needs has resulted in the sea water entering and contaminating aquifers in several valley mouths.

W. Willamette Valley-Puget Sound Province. A large body of alluvium fills the structural trough forming this province. Abundant supplies of surface water have delayed investigation and exploitation of the extensive ground water resources of the area.

X. Northern Coast Range Province. Ground water is found in the alluvial fill of the valleys draining to the Pacific Ocean. A small area in the southern part of the province contains heated ground water, hot springs, and geysers. Because of the abundant surface water and the relatively undeveloped nature of the province, detailed information on ground water conditions is limited.

References

1. Alter, A. J., Water supply in Alaska, *Jour. Amer. Water Works Assoc.*, vol. 42, pp. 519–532, 1950.
2. Baver, L. D., *Soil physics*, 3rd ed., John Wiley and Sons, New York, 498 pp., 1956.
3. Belcher, D. J., T. R. Cuykendall, and H. S. Sack, The measurement of soil moisture and density by neutron and gamma-ray scattering, *Tech. Developm. Rep.* 127, Civil Aeronautics Admin., Indianapolis, Ind., 20 pp., 1950.
4. Bosazza, V. L., On storage of water in rocks in situ, *Trans. Amer. Geophysical Union*, vol. 33, pp. 42–48, 1952.

5. Bouyoucos, G. J., Nylon electrical resistance unit for continuous measurement of soil moisture in the field, *Soil Sci.,* vol. 67, pp. 319–330, 1949.
6. Bouyoucos, G. J., and A. H. Mick, A fabric absorption unit for continuous measurement of soil moisture in the field, *Soil Sci.,* vol. 66, pp. 217–232, 1948.
7. Briggs, L. J., The mechanics of soil moisture, *Bull.* 10, Div. Soils, U. S. Dept. Agric., Washington, D. C., 24 pp., 1897.
8. Bryan, K., Classification of springs, *Jour. Geol.,* vol. 27, pp. 522–561, 1919.
9. California Dept. Public Works, Ground-water basins in California, *Water Quality Investigations Rep.* 3, Div. Water Resources, Sacramento, 44 pp., 1952.
10. Cederstrom, D. J., P. M. Johnston, and S. Subitzky, Occurrence and development of ground water in permafrost regions, *U. S. Geological Survey Circular* 275, Washington, D. C., 30 pp., 1953.
11. Colman, E. A., The place of electrical soil-moisture meters in hydrologic research, *Trans. Amer. Geophysical Union,* vol. 27, pp. 847–853, 1946.
12. Colman, E. A., and T. M. Hendrix, The fiberglas electrical soil-moisture instrument, *Soil Sci.,* vol. 67, pp. 425–438, 1949.
13. Eckis, R., South Coastal Basin investigation, geology and ground-water storage capacity of valley fill, *Bull.* 45, Calif. Div. Water Resources, Sacramento, 279 pp., 1934.
14. Gardner, W., and D. Kirkham, Determination of soil moisture by neutron scattering, *Soil Sci.,* vol. 73, pp. 391–401, 1952.
15. Haise, H. R., How to measure the moisture in the soil, in *Water,* U. S. Dept. Agric., Washington, D. C., pp. 362–371, 1955.
16. Harding, S. T., Relation of the moisture equivalent of soils to the moisture properties under field conditions of irrigation, *Soil Sci.,* vol. 8, pp. 303–312, 1919.
17. Hopkins, D. M., T. N. V. Karlstrom, and others, Permafrost and ground water in Alaska, *U. S. Geological Survey Professional Paper* 264–F, Washington, D. C., pp. 113–146, 1955.
18. Lambe, T. W., Capillary phenomena in cohesionless soils, *Trans. Amer. Soc. Civil Engrs.,* vol. 116, pp. 401–432, 1951.
19. Lull, H. W., and K. G. Reinhart, Soil-moisture measurement, *Southern Forest Exp. Sta. Occasional Paper* 140, Forest Service, U. S. Dept. Agric., 56 pp., 1955.
20. Mavis, F. T., and T. P. Tsui, Percolation and capillary movements of water through sand prisms, *Bull.* 18, Univ. Iowa Studies in Eng., Iowa City, 25 pp., 1939.
21. Meinzer, O. E., Outline of ground-water hydrology with definitions, *U. S. Geological Survey Water-Supply Paper* 494, Washington, D. C., 71 pp., 1923.
22. Meinzer, O. E., The occurrence of ground water in the United States, *U. S. Geological Survey Water-Supply Paper* 489, Washington, D. C., 321 pp., 1923.
23. Meinzer, O. E., Large springs in the United States, *U. S. Geological Survey Water-Supply Paper* 557, Washington, D. C., 94 pp., 1927.
24. Meinzer, O. E., Outline of methods for estimating ground-water supplies, *U. S. Geological Survey Water-Supply Paper* 638-C, Washington, D. C., pp. 99–144, 1932.
25. Meinzer, O. E., Ground water in the United States—a summary, *U. S. Geological Survey Water-Supply Paper* 836-D, Washington, D. C., pp. 157–232, 1939.
26. Meinzer, O. E. (ed.), *Hydrology,* McGraw-Hill, New York, 712 pp., 1942.

27. Picard, L., Outline of ground-water geology in arid regions, *Proc. Ankara Symposium on Arid Zone Hydrology,* UNESCO, Paris, pp. 165–176, 1953.
28. Poland, J. F., G. H. Davis, F. H. Olmsted, and F. Kunkel, Ground-water storage capacity of the Sacramento Valley, California, in *Water Resources of California,* Bull. 1, Calif. State Water Resources Board, Sacramento, pp. 617–632, 1949.
29. Prinz, E., and R. Kampe, *Handbuch der Hydrologie,* Band II: Quellen, J. Springer, Berlin, 290 pp., 1934.
30. Richards, L. A., Methods of measuring soil moisture tension, *Soil Sci.,* vol. 68, pp. 95–112, 1949.
31. Rode, A. A., *Hydraulic properties of soils and rocks* (in Russian), Acad. Sci. USSR, Moscow, 131 pp., 1955.
32. Russell, W. L., The origin of artesian pressure, *Econ. Geol.,* vol. 23, pp. 132–157, 1928.
33. Sayre, A. N., Ground water, *Sci. Amer.,* vol. 183, no. 5, pp. 14–19, 1950.
34. Scofield, C. S., The measurement of soil water, *Jour. Agric. Research,* vol. 71, pp. 375–402, 1945.
35. Shaw, C. F., and L. D. Baver, Heat conductivity as an index of soil moisture, *Jour. Amer. Soc. Agronomy,* vol. 31, pp. 886–891, 1939.
36. Smith, W. O., The final distribution of retained liquid in an ideal uniform soil, *Physics,* vol. 4, pp. 425–438, 1933.
37. Smith, W. O., P. D. Foote, and P. F. Busang, Capillary rise in sands of uniform spherical grains, *Physics,* vol. 1, pp. 18–26, 1931.
38. Stearns, N. D., H. T. Stearns, and G. A. Waring, Thermal springs in the United States, *U. S. Geological Survey Water-Supply Paper* 679-B, Washington, D. C., pp. 59–191, 1937.
39. Suter, M., Ground-water reservoirs, *Assemblée Générale de Bruxelles, Assoc. Intl. d'Hydrologie Scientifique,* vol. 4, pp. 16–20, 1951.
40. Thomas, H. E., *The conservation of ground water,* McGraw-Hill, New York, 327 pp., 1951.
41. Thomas, H. E., *Ground-water regions of the United States—their storage facilities,* vol. 3, Interior and Insular Affairs Comm., House of Representatives, U. S. Congress, Washington, D. C., 78 pp., 1952.
42. Tolman, C. F., *Ground water,* McGraw-Hill, New York, 593 pp., 1937.
43. Veihmeyer, F. J., and A. H. Hendrickson, The moisture equivalent as a measure of the field capacity of soils, *Soil Sci.,* vol. 32, pp. 181–193, 1931.
44. Veihmeyer, F. J., and A. H. Hendrickson, The permanent wilting percentage as a reference for the measurement of soil moisture, *Trans. Amer. Geophysical Union,* vol. 29, pp. 887–896, 1948.
45. Veihmeyer, F. J., and A. H. Hendrickson, Methods of measuring field capacity and permanent wilting percentage of soils, *Soil Sci.,* vol. 68, pp. 75–94, 1949.
46. Waring, G. A., Summary of literature on thermal springs, *Assemblée Générale de Bruxelles, Assoc. Intl. d'Hydrologie Scientifique,* vol. 2, pp. 289–293, 1951.
47. White, D. E., and W. W. Brannock, The sources of heat and water supply of thermal springs, with particular reference to Steamboat Springs, Nevada, *Trans. Amer. Geophysical Union,* vol. 31, pp. 566–574, 1950.
48. Youker, R. E., and F. R. Dreibelbis, An improved soil-moisture measuring unit for hydrologic studies, *Trans. Amer. Geophysical Union,* vol. 32, pp. 447–449, 1951.

Ground Water Movement

CHAPTER 3

Ground water in its natural state is invariably moving. This movement is governed by established hydraulic principles. The flow through aquifers, most of which are natural porous media, can be expressed by what is known as Darcy's law. Permeability, which is a measure of the ease of flow through the media, is an important constant in the flow equation. Direct determination of permeability can be made from laboratory or field measurements. Information on ground water movement can be obtained by adding a substance to the flow and tracing its movement in space and time. From Darcy's law and the equation of continuity, general flow equations of ground water can be derived.

Darcy's Law

More than a century ago Henry Darcy,* a French hydraulic engineer, investigated the flow of water through horizontal beds of sand to be used for water filtration. He reported [11] in 1856:

I have attempted by precise experiments to determine the law of the flow of water through filters. . . . The experiments demonstrate positively that the volume of water which passes through a bed of sand of a given nature is proportional to the pressure and inversely proportional to the thickness of the bed

* An interesting summary of the life and accomplishments of Henry Darcy was prepared by Fancher.[15]

traversed; thus, in calling s the surface area of a filter, k a coefficient depending on the nature of the sand, e the thickness of the sand bed, $P - H_0$ the pressure below the filtering bed, $P + H$ the atmospheric pressure added to the depth of water on the filter; one has for the flow of this last condition $Q = (ks/e)(H + e + H_0)$, which reduces to $Q = (ks/e)(H + e)$ when $H_0 = 0$, or when the pressure below the filter is equal to the weight of the atmosphere.

This statement, that the flow rate through porous media is proportional to the head loss and inversely proportional to the length of the flow path, is known universally as Darcy's law. It, more than any other contribution, serves as the basis for present-day knowledge of ground water flow. Analysis and solution of problems relating to ground water movement and well hydraulics began after Darcy's work.

The experimental verification of Darcy's law can be performed with water flowing at a rate Q through a cylinder of cross-sectional area A packed with sand and having piezometer taps a distance L apart, as shown in Fig. 3.1.[31, 32, 36] Total energy heads, or fluid potentials, above a datum plane may be expressed by the Bernoulli equation

$$\frac{p_1}{\gamma} + \frac{v_1^2}{2g} + z_1 = \frac{p_2}{\gamma} + \frac{v_2^2}{2g} + z_2 + h_L \tag{3.1}$$

where p is pressure, γ is the specific weight of water, v is the velocity of flow, g is the acceleration of gravity, z is elevation, and h_L is head loss. Subscripts refer to points of measurement identified in Fig. 3.1.

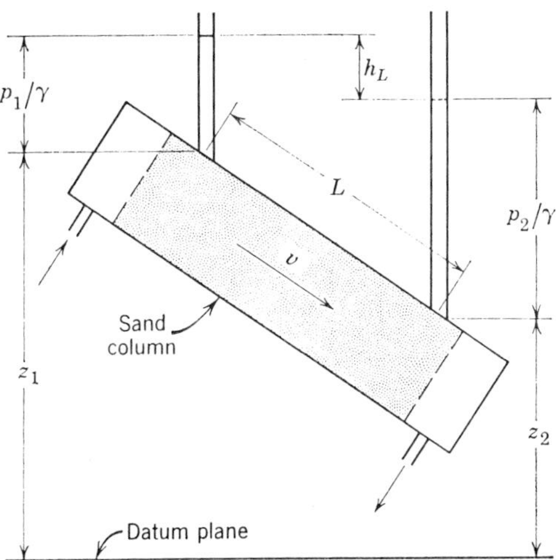

Fig. 3.1. Pressure distribution and head loss in flow through a sand column.

Because velocities in porous media are usually low, velocity heads may be neglected without appreciable error. Hence, by rewriting, the head loss becomes

$$h_L = \left(\frac{p_1}{\gamma} + z_1\right) - \left(\frac{p_2}{\gamma} + z_2\right) \tag{3.2}$$

Therefore, the resulting head loss is defined as the potential loss within the sand cylinder, this energy being lost by frictional resistance dissipated as heat energy. It follows that the head loss is independent of the inclination of the cylinder.

Now, Darcy's measurements showed that the proportionalities

$$Q \sim h_L \quad \text{and} \quad Q \sim \frac{1}{L}$$

exist. Introducing a proportionality constant K leads to the equation

$$Q = KA\frac{h_L}{L} \tag{3.3}$$

Expressed in general terms

$$Q = KA\frac{dh}{dL} \tag{3.4}$$

or simply

$$v = \frac{Q}{A} = K\frac{dh}{dL} \tag{3.5}$$

where dh/dL is the hydraulic gradient.* Equation 3.5 states Darcy's law in its simplest form, namely that the flow velocity v is equal to the product of the constant K, known as the coefficient of permeability,† and the hydraulic gradient. This velocity is an apparent one, defined by the quotient of the discharge divided by the cross-sectional area of the porous media through which it is flowing. The actual velocity varies from point to point throughout the media.

It should be noted that ground water flows in accordance with the hydraulic gradient. A common misinterpretation of Darcy's law involves the statement that flow takes place from high to low pressure. For horizontal flow this is true from Eq. 3.2 when $z_1 = z_2$, but for

* Darcy's law is sometimes written with a negative sign, as $v = -K(dh/dL)$, to indicate that the flow is in the direction of decreasing head. This convention, however, is unnecessary and often confusing for practical applications.

† The coefficient of permeability is also referred to as hydraulic conductivity, because of its analogy to electrical and thermal conductivity.

inclined flow, water may actually flow in the direction of increasing pressure. Figure 3.1 is a case in point.

Range of Validity of Darcy's Law. In applying Darcy's law it is important to know the range of validity within which it is applicable. Because velocity in laminar flow, such as water flowing in a capillary tube, is proportional to the first power of the hydraulic gradient (Poiseuille's law), it seems reasonable to believe that Darcy's law applies to laminar flow in porous media. For flow in pipes and other large sections, the Reynolds number, which expresses the dimensionless ratio of inertial to viscous (or resistive) forces, serves as a criterion to distinguish between laminar and turbulent flow. Hence, by analogy, the Reynolds number has been employed to establish the limit of flows described by Darcy's law, corresponding to the value where the linear relationship is no longer valid.

Reynolds number is expressed as

$$N_R = \frac{\rho v D}{\mu} \tag{3.6}$$

where ρ is the fluid density, v the velocity, D the diameter (of a pipe), and μ the viscosity of the fluid. To adapt this criterion to flow in porous media, the apparent velocity defined by Darcy's law is used for v and an average grain diameter d is substituted for D. Certainly a grain diameter represents only an approximation of the critical flow dimension, or average pore diameter, for which it is intended; however, measuring a representative pore rather than a representative grain is much more difficult from a practical standpoint.

For very low velocities, laminar flow occurs; consequently, from both theory and experiment, no lower limit is known to exist for Darcy's law.[50] On the contrary, however, an upper limit has been identified by experiments on sands and small spheres.[4, 5, 32, 46, 49, 60, 61, 62] The limit can be found by plotting the dimensionless Fanning friction factor f, used in hydraulics, against N_R. The factor f is defined by

$$f = \frac{d\,\Delta p}{2\rho L v^2} \tag{3.7}$$

where Δp is the pressure difference over a length of porous media L measured along the line of flow and other quantities are as defined above. Data from several investigations are plotted in Fig. 3.2. Departures from a linear relationship appear when N_R reaches the range between about 1 and 10, thus indicating an upper limit for the validity of Darcy's law. A range of values rather than a unique value must be stated because the distribution of grain sizes of natural media for a specified average grain diameter is limitless. Then too, grain shapes and packings may vary widely so that deviations can only be stated within the range where they are most frequently observed. For almost all natural ground water motion, $N_R < 1$; therefore, Darcy's law is applicable. Deviations from Darcy's law may be found in rock aquifers, in unconsolidated aquifers with steep hydraulic gradients, or in those containing large diameter solution openings. Flows in the immediate vicinity of open bodies of water, such as to streams and wells, are often associated with steep gradients.

From the application by analogy of Reynolds number to flow in porous media, it is sometimes assumed [52] that turbulent flow begins at the upper limit of Darcy's law. Recent experimental investigations by Schneebeli [65] and Hubbert [32] indicate otherwise.

Schneebeli found from visual observations of flow in porous media that the first appearance of turbulence occurred at a Reynolds number of about 60, whereas Hubbert found it in the range of 600 to 700. Despite the discrepancy between these observations, both suggest that the inception of turbulence exists at a Reynolds number many times greater than that of the upper limit of Darcy's law. This implies first, that the Reynolds number is not a good criterion for judging the beginning of turbulence in porous media flow, and second, that laminar flows which do not obey Darcy's law exist in porous media. Each particle of fluid moving through a porous medium follows a continuously curvilinear path at a continuously varying speed, and therefore with a continuously varying acceleration.[32] At a relatively slow rate of flow (near $N_R = 1$ to 10), the inertial forces in this essentially nonuniform flow becomes significant.[46] Darcy's law governs flows only when resistive forces predominate; therefore, when the inertial forces approach the same order of magnitude of the resistive forces, Darcy's law is inapplicable. This transition occurs before and separate from the incidence of turbulence.

The transitions from laminar flow where resistive forces govern to laminar flow where inertial forces govern and to turbulent flow are gradual as evidenced by the mild curvature in Fig. 3.2 between $N_R = 1$ and $N_R = 1000$. The explanation for the gradual transition into turbulent flow hinges upon the microstructure of porous media flow. In a natural sand, pores vary widely in magnitude, shape, and orientation. As the hydraulic gradient increases, turbulent flow occurs initially in only isolated pores associated with highest velocities. With further increases turbulence occurs in a correspondingly larger portion of the medium; the result is a gradual transition in flow type.

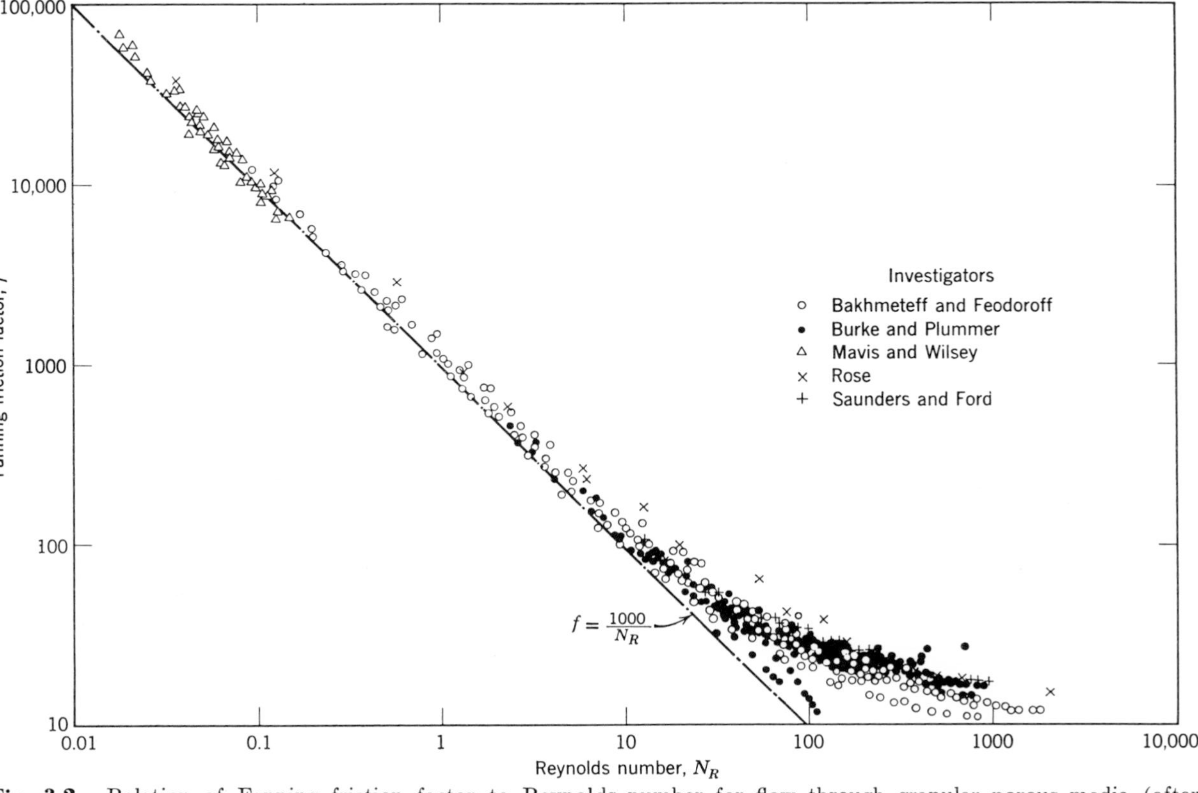

Fig. 3.2. Relation of Fanning friction factor to Reynolds number for flow through granular porous media (after Rose [60]).

Coefficient of Permeability

Solving Darcy's law, expressed by Eq. 3.4, for the coefficient of permeability leads to

$$K = \frac{Q}{A(dh/dL)} \tag{3.8}$$

which shows that K has the dimensions of $[L/T]$, or velocity. A variety of means for expressing the coefficient of permeability have been used; however, the leadership of the U. S. Geological Survey in the field of ground water has done much to standardize definitions. The laboratory (or standard) coefficient of permeability K_s is defined as the flow of water at 60° F in gallons per day through a medium having a cross-sectional area of 1 ft^2 under a hydraulic gradient of 1 ft/ft. Laboratory tests by the Geological Survey [71] have yielded coefficients varying from 2×10^{-4} to 9×10^4, but for most natural aquifers values range between 10 and 5000. For field investigations, the field coefficient of permeability K_f is defined as the flow of water in gallons per day through a cross-section of aquifer 1 ft thick and 1 mile wide under a hydraulic gradient of 1 ft/1 mile at field temperature.*

Taking the ratio of these two coefficients reveals that the only difference is that of temperature. Neglecting the effect of temperature on density, and recalling that viscosity varies inversely with temperature, enables the relation to be expressed as

$$\frac{K_s}{K_f} = \frac{\mu_f}{\mu_{60}} \tag{3.9}$$

where μ_f is the viscosity at field temperature and μ_{60} that at 60° F. Figure 3.3 simplifies the conversion of coefficients of permeability without reference to viscosity tables. The coefficient of transmissibility T equals the field coefficient of permeability multiplied by the aquifer thickness in feet.

Permeability of a porous medium refers to the ease with which a fluid will pass through it. Nevertheless, the coefficients just defined depend not only upon the medium but also upon the fluid. A more rational concept of permeability, therefore, could be expressed by a coefficient which is independent of those fluid properties governing the

* The U. S. Geological Survey employs the term *meinzer,* honoring the late Dr. O. E. Meinzer, as a synonym for coefficient of permeability. At present, however, it has not been established whether this applies to the laboratory or the field coefficient, or to both with a qualifying adjective.

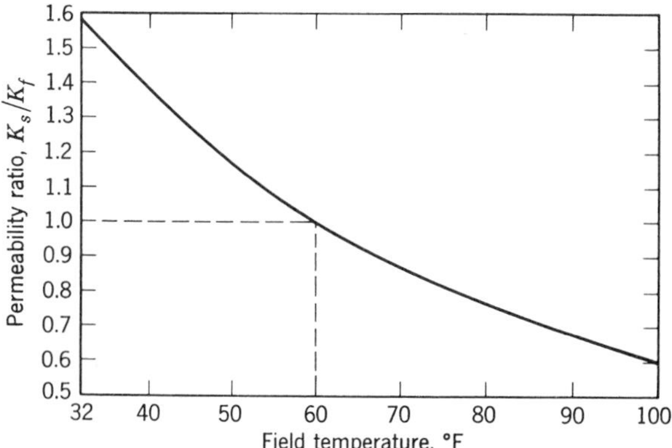

Fig. 3.3. Ratio of laboratory to field coefficient of permeability as a function of field temperature.

flow. The properties involved are viscosity μ, expressing the shear resistance, and specific weight γ, expressing the driving force of the fluid. For the medium the flow should be related to a pore diameter which can be assumed proportionate to a representative grain diameter d. From these the functional equation

$$K = f(\mu, \gamma, d) \tag{3.10}$$

can be written, and by dimensional analysis becomes

$$K = \frac{Cd^2\gamma}{\mu} \tag{3.11}$$

where C is a dimensionless constant. Because the product Cd^2 is a property of the porous medium only, a specific (or intrinsic) permeability [37, 52] k of the medium may be defined as

$$k = Cd^2 \tag{3.12}$$

which, when substituted in Darcy's law, gives

$$Q = A\,\frac{k\gamma}{\mu}\,\frac{dh}{dL} \tag{3.13}$$

The dimensions of k are $[L^2]$, or area, which can be roughly interpreted as a unique pore area governing the flow. The constant C is controlled by the various properties of the medium which affect flow other than grain diameter, including porosity, packing, and grain size distribution and shape. Experimental data yielding the same value of k for different liquids and gases flowing through a given medium [52] demonstrate the more rational nature of specific permeability.

The value of k when expressed as ft^2 or cm^2 is usually extremely small, so that the *darcy* has been adopted as a more practical unit. First introduced in the petroleum industry, the darcy has in recent years gained acceptance in ground water literature [37, 52, 58] because of its rational interpretation. Solving for k in Eq. 3.13 gives

$$k = \frac{\mu Q/A}{\gamma(dh/dL)} \tag{3.14}$$

Based upon this equation, the darcy is defined as

$$1 \text{ darcy} = \frac{\dfrac{1 \text{ centipoise} \times 1 \text{ cm}^3/\text{sec}}{1 \text{ cm}^2}}{1 \text{ atmosphere}/1 \text{ cm}}$$

The transformation to area units can be obtained by inserting *

$$1 \text{ centipoise} = 0.01 \text{ poise} = 0.01 \frac{\text{dyne sec}}{\text{cm}^2}$$

and

$$1 \text{ atmosphere} = 1.0132 \times 10^6 \frac{\text{dynes}}{\text{cm}^2}$$

These substitutions lead to the conversion factor

$$1 \text{ darcy} = 0.987 \times 10^{-8} \text{ cm}^2$$

or its equivalent

$$1 \text{ darcy} = 1.062 \times 10^{-11} \text{ ft}^2$$

Noting that

$$K = \frac{k\gamma}{\mu} \tag{3.15}$$

and inserting appropriate values of γ and μ for water at 60° F result in the conversion factor relating the darcy to the laboratory coefficient of permeability,[75]

$$1 \text{ darcy} = 18.2K_s$$

Magnitudes of specific permeability, in darcys, and laboratory coefficient of permeability for different soil classes are shown in Fig. 3.4.

* Water has a viscosity of 1 centipoise at 68.4° F (20.20° C).

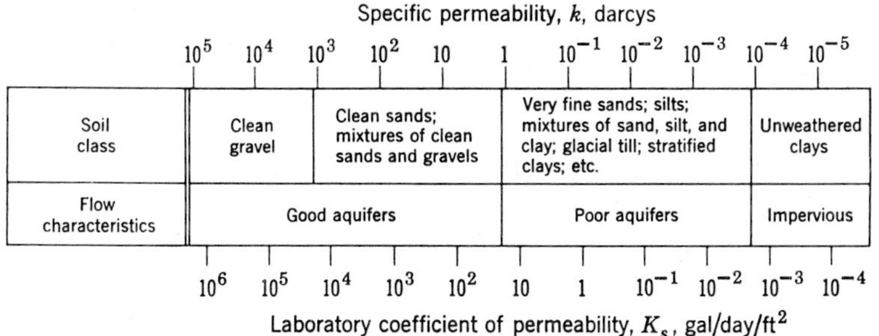

Fig. 3.4. Magnitude of specific permeability and laboratory coefficient of permeability for different classes of soils.

Ground Water Flow Rates

It has been shown that the rate of ground water movement is governed by the permeability of the aquifer and the hydraulic gradient. To obtain an idea of the order of magnitude of natural flow rates, assume a slope of 10 ft/mile (0.0019) and a low permeability of $K_s = 10$. This results in a rate of 0.0025 ft/day, whereas a slope of 100 ft/mile (0.019) and a high permeability of $K_s = 5000$ yields a velocity of 12.7 ft/day. As suggested by these, ground water velocities vary widely. Field tests have reported velocities of more than 100 ft/day; however, a normal range is from 5 ft/year to 5 ft/day. Of course, where natural flows are modified, as by pumping wells or drains, steeper water table or piezometric slopes produce higher velocities.

Permeability Formulas

Numerous investigators have studied the problem of relating permeability to the properties of porous media. Several formulas have resulted based on analytic or experimental work. Not all are general, and few give exact results because of the difficulty of including all of the possible variations of porous media. Basically, the problem reduces to relating the factor C of Eq. 3.12 to media properties. For an ideal medium, such as an assemblage of spheres of uniform diameter, the permeability can be accurately evaluated from known porosity and packing conditions. The results, however, when applied even to a selected sand require modification.

Early investigations leading to permeability formulas were conducted by Hazen[28] and Slichter.[67, 68] More recent studies have resulted in formulas by Terzaghi,[72] Smith,[70] Fair and Hatch,[14, 27] Hulbert and Feben,[33] Bakhameteff and Feodoroff,[4, 5] and Rose,[60, 62] among others.

The Fair and Hatch permeability formula[14] can be considered typical of many of the contributions. It was developed from dimensional considerations and verified experimentally. The specific permeability is given by

$$k = \frac{1}{m\left[\frac{(1-\alpha)^2}{\alpha^3}\left(\frac{\theta}{100}\sum\frac{P}{d_m}\right)^2\right]} \tag{3.16}$$

where α is porosity. The factor m is a packing factor, found experimentally to be about 5; θ is a sand shape factor, varying from 6.0 for spherical grains to 7.7 for angular grains; P is the percentage of sand held between adjacent sieves; and d_m is the geometric mean of rated sizes of adjacent sieves. The equation is dimensionally correct so that any consistent system of units may be introduced. Basically similar expressions have been developed by several other investigators. All have included variables designed to express the significant factors of porous media governing permeability.

Laboratory Measurement of Permeability

Several types of permeameters have been developed for laboratory determinations of permeability from small samples of aquifers.[75] Although conducted under controlled conditions, such measurements may have little relation to field permeabilities. When unconsolidated samples are disturbed and repacked, porosities, packings, and grain orientations are markedly changed; consequently, permeabilities are modified. Then too, one or even several samples from an aquifer may not represent the overall permeability of an aquifer. Samples of sand and gravel collected at different depths in a well near Grand Island, Nebr., were analyzed in the laboratory and found to have K_s values ranging from 150 to 4350.[74] This result, which may be considered typical of many aquifers, points out the importance of stratifications and irregularities which modify any assumed uniform subsurface flow pattern.

The constant-head permeameter shown in Fig. 3.5*a* can be used to measure permeabilities of consolidated or unconsolidated formations under low heads. Water enters the medium cylinder from the bottom

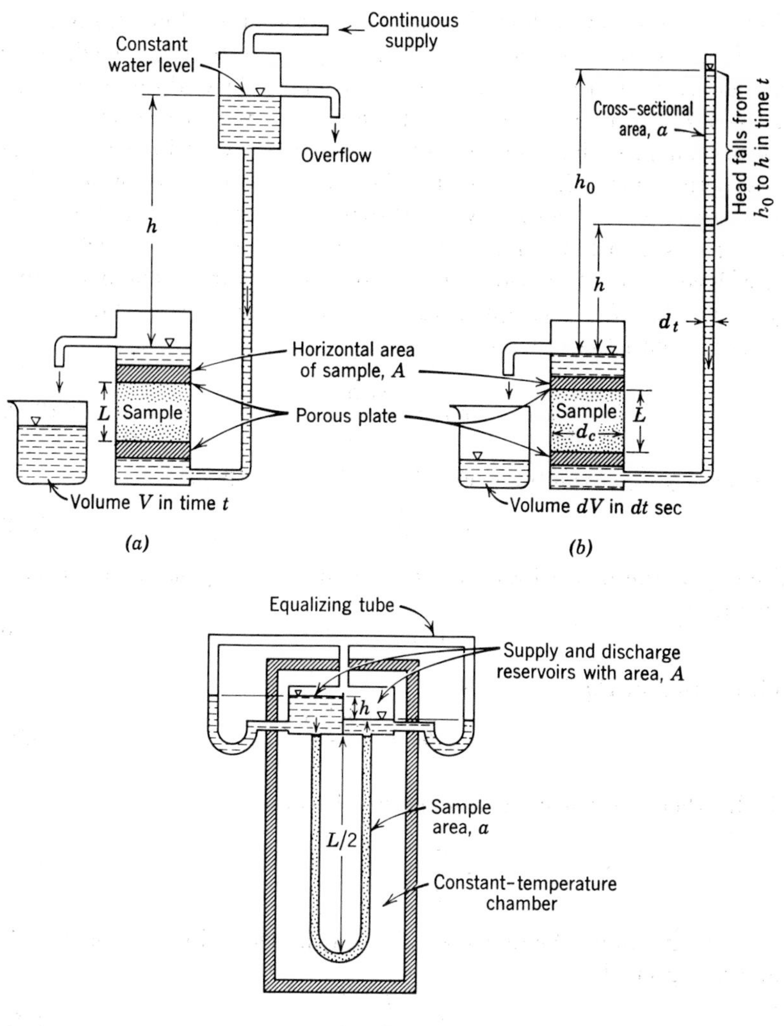

Fig. 3.5. Permeameters: (*a*) constant-head, (*b*) falling-head, and (*c*) nondischarging.

and is collected as overflow after passing upward through the material. From Darcy's law it follows that the permeability can be obtained from

$$K = \frac{VL}{Ath} \tag{3.17}$$

where V is the flow volume in time t, and the other dimensions, A, L, and h, are shown in Fig. 3.5a. It is important that the medium be thoroughly saturated to remove entrapped air. Several different heads in a series of tests provide a reliable permeability measurement.

A second procedure for measuring permeability utilizes the falling head permeameter illustrated in Fig. 3.5b. Here water is added to the tall column; it flows upward through the medium cylinder and is collected as overflow. The test consists of noting times at which the water level lowers to various graduations on the tube. The permeability expression for this apparatus can be derived from Darcy's law beginning with the differential form

$$dV = \frac{KhA\,dt}{L} \tag{3.18}$$

If a is the area of the tube (Fig. 3.5b), then a volume

$$V = a(h_0 - h) \tag{3.19}$$

where h_0 is the initial head and h is the head at any later time t, or in general,

$$dV = -a\,dh \tag{3.20}$$

Substituting in Eq. 3.18 gives

$$-a\,dh = \frac{KhA\,dt}{L} \tag{3.21}$$

which, when rearranged and simplified, becomes

$$-\frac{dh}{h} = \frac{Kd_c^2\,dt}{d_t^2L} \tag{3.22}$$

where d_c and d_t are the diameters of the cylinder and tube, respectively. Integrating yields

$$-\ln h = \frac{K\,d_c^2t}{d_t^2L} + C \tag{3.23}$$

When $t = 0$, $h = h_0$, thus

$$C = -\ln h_0$$

Inserting this in Eq. 3.23 and rearranging gives

$$K = \frac{d_t^2L}{d_c^2t}\ln\frac{h_0}{h} \tag{3.24}$$

Both unconsolidated and consolidated samples can be tested in this manner.

For measurements of permeability of unconsolidated formations under very low heads, a nondischarging permeameter may be used.[75] As shown in Fig. 3.5*c*, a long U-tube containing the medium is connected to supply and receiving reservoirs at the top. The entire instrument is submerged in a constant temperature chamber, while the top is covered to avoid evaporation losses from the reservoirs. The permeability is derived similar to that above, giving

$$K = \frac{AL}{2at} \ln \frac{h_0}{h} \tag{3.25}$$

where A, L, and a are identified in Fig. 3.5*c*, h_0 is the head at $t = 0$, and h is the head at a later time t. Investigations by Meinzer and Fishel [19,50] with this equipment showed the applicability of Darcy's law to gradients of less than one foot per mile.

Field Measurement of Permeability

By introducing a tracer substance into ground water at an upstream location and observing the time required for it to appear at a downstream point, estimates of ground water velocity can be obtained. This information, together with the existing hydraulic gradient, provides a measure of the permeability of an aquifer. Because flow occurs only within the pores of a porous medium, the flow rate

$$Q = \alpha A v_a \tag{3.26}$$

results where α is porosity, A is the gross area of the flow cross-section, and v_a is the average velocity measured by the tracer flow. Substituting this in the equation for Darcy's law and solving for K, gives

$$K = \frac{\alpha v_a \, dL}{dh} \tag{3.27}$$

Measurements with tracers in the field usually have been limited to distances of a few feet, and results obtained are approximate only. Tracers are discussed more fully in the following section.

Natural permeabilities at shallow depths intersected by water tables can be measured directly. Piezometer, tube, and auger hole methods have been developed by Reeve and Kirkham [54] and others. A cylindrical cavity is formed to below the water table and pumped out to open all water passages. A test involves pumping to lower the water level then observing the rate of rise, or adding water and observing its rate of fall. From this information the permeability coefficient can be computed by means of a suitable formula. These methods have the advantages of simplicity and economy; also, they measure in-place permeability.

The most reliable method for estimating aquifer permeability is by means of pumping tests with wells.[75] Based upon observations of water levels in connection with pumping, an integrated permeability value over a sizable aquifer section can be obtained. Then too, because the aquifer is not disturbed, the reliability of such determinations is superior to laboratory methods. Pumping test methods and computations are described in Chapter 4.

Tracing Ground Water Movement

In essence, the concept of a tracer to follow the movement of ground water is very simple. Such methods, using dyes[13] and salts, have been employed for many years. The early experiments of Slichter[69] using tracers for measuring ground water flow are well known. However, when examined in detail, tracer techniques often prove to have serious limitations.

Dispersion. Velocities vary widely across any single pore in porous media, just as in a capillary tube where the velocity distribution of laminar flow is parabolic. The result is that the concentration of a tracer will vary in the flow direction, becoming more widely

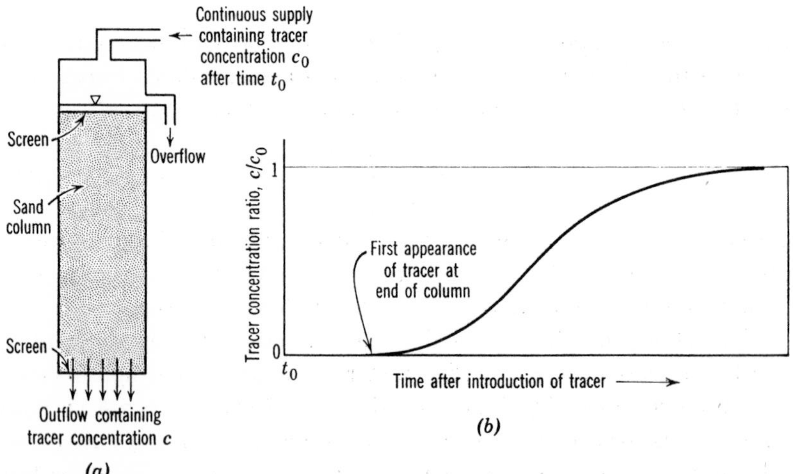

Fig. 3.6. Longitudinal dispersion of a tracer passing through a sand column; (*a*) sand column, and (*b*) dispersion curve.

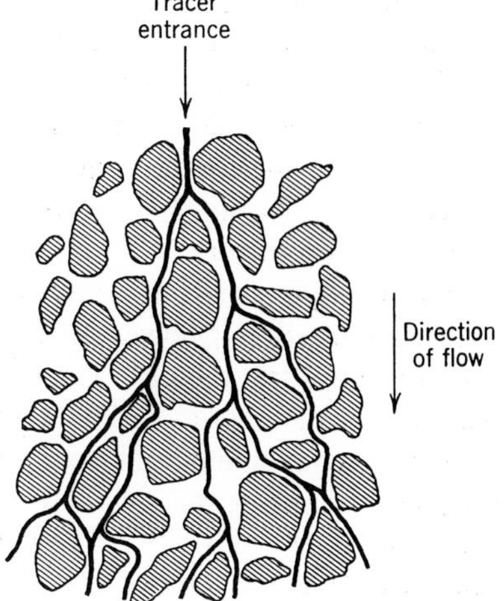

Fig. 3.7. Lateral dispersion of a tracer originating from a point source in a porous medium.

dispersed the longer and the farther it travels.[59] By means of a column packed with sand (see Fig. 3.6*a*) and supplied continuously after a time t_0 with water containing a tracer of concentration c_0, the longitudinal tracer dispersion can be measured. From samples of the water emerging from the column, a tracer concentration c is found. Figure 3.6*b* shows a typical dispersion curve based on the tracer concentration ratio, c/c_0. Besides longitudinal dispersion, a lateral dispersion of tracer concentration also occurs because water is continually dividing and reuniting as it flows around and among grains of a medium, as illustrated in Fig. 3.7. The combined effects of these two types of dispersion, when pictured in three dimensions beginning at a point tracer source, form a cone opening outward in the direction of flow. According to experiments by Danel[10] the surface of this cone, representing the limit of the tracer, was inclined about 3° to the axis.

Dispersion of a tracer is caused by the microvelocity variations inherent in laminar flow through porous media. Molecular diffusion may contribute to the phenomenon, but only when flow velocities are quite small. The problem can be analyzed statistically on a probability basis.[38, 59, 63] Results, confirmed experimentally,[10, 43, 59] indicate that a tracer introduced instantaneously at a point source will tend to form a normal distribution of concentration both parallel and perpendicular to the flow direction as it moves downstream.

Tracers. An ideal tracer must be susceptible to quantitative determination in very low concentrations, should be absent or nearly so from the natural water, must not react with the natural water to form a precipitate, must not be absorbed by porous media, and must be cheap and readily available.[39,40] No tracer completely meets all these requirements, but a reasonably satisfactory tracer can be selected to fit the needs of a particular situation. Tracers may be classified as to method of detection—colorimetry, chemical determination, electrical conductivity, nuclear radiation, mass spectrography, and flame spectrophotometry. Table 3.1 lists substances which may be of value for ground water tracers.

Organic dyes, such as sodium fluorescein, may be detected in very low concentrations; however, they may be adsorbed by clay fractions present in natural media. The chloride ion, used in low concentrations, has proved to be a satisfactory tracer.[40] Radioactive substances provide a convenient and very sensitive means of detection,[20,30,39] as they can be measured by their nuclear radiations at mass concentrations of 10^{-16} to 10^{-18}. They do not modify the flow properties of porous media, but are affected by base exchange and adsorption phenomena. Certain radioisotopes, tritium in particular, can be used as a field tracer without danger of contamination, but others must be carefully controlled or restricted to laboratory studies because of

TABLE 3.1 Classification by Method of Detection of Substances Which May Be Useful as Ground Water Tracers

Colorimetry	Chemical Determination
Organic dyes and stains, water soluble	Soluble chloride salts
Soluble chromate salts	Boron, borax, and boric acid
Amaranth dye	Copper sulfate
Basic fuchsin	Dextrose
Congo red	Ethanethiol
Eosine	Sodium glyceral phosphate
Magenta	Sodium iodide
Methylene blue	
Sodium fluorescein	

Mass Spectrography	Nuclear Radiation
Helium	Bromine 82
Hydrogen 2	Calcium 45
Oxygen 18	Cobalt 60
	Hydrogen 3 (Tritium)
	Iodine 131
	Phosphorus 32
	Rubidium 86

Flame Spectrophotometry	Electrical Conductivity
Soluble lithium salts	Any strong electrolyte

dangerous radiation levels. A radioactive rubidium tracer was used by Fox [20] to ascertain that seepage from springs seven miles distant appeared at a reservoir site under investigation. Concern with the necessity of disposing of radioactive waste products from nuclear fission [73] has prompted studies of the feasibility of underground storage and the possible subsequent contamination of ground water.

Dating Ground Water. An interesting possibility for dating ground water, using natural tritium as a tracer, has been suggested by Libby.[45] Tritium is produced in the atmosphere by cosmic radiation (and thermonuclear explosions), and its abundance in rain varies roughly with the distance ocean water vapor must travel before precipitation. After rainfall infiltrates into the ground, no further additions of tritium occur; moreover, a predictable exponential diminution of the radioactive isotope concentration occurs. Thus, from well samples of ground water, estimates of time which the water has been underground can be obtained. The method would be most feasible in confined aquifers recharged from a single recharge area. In fact, from several samples taken from wells scattered over a basin, the direction and rate of movement might be calculated. Because of the expensive radiation measuring equipment and the time required to measure the extremely low levels of natural occurring tritium, the method has not been adequately investigated to date.*

General Flow Equations

In general form Darcy's law may be written

$$v = K \frac{\partial h}{\partial s} \tag{3.28}$$

where v, K, and h are as previously defined, and s is distance along the average direction of flow. A porous medium may have permeabilities which vary with flow direction. Such a condition is termed anisotropic permeability,† and velocity components in a rectangular coordinate system may be given by

* For a recent contribution to the subject, see: von Buttlar, H., and I. Wendt, "Ground-Water Studies in New Mexico Using Tritium as a Tracer," *Trans Amer. Geophysical Union,* vol. 39, pp. 660–668, 1958.

† Anisotropic permeability is a common occurrence in unconsolidated sedimentary deposits, where the horizontal permeability may exceed that of the vertical from 2 to 10 times or more. An excellent discussion of the theoretical and practical aspects of flow through anisotropic media is presented in Maasland, M., "Soil Anisotropy and Land Drainage," in *Drainage of agricultural lands* (J. N. Luthin, ed.), Amer. Soc. Agronomy, Madison, Wis., pp. 216–285, 1957.

$$v_x = K_x \frac{\partial h}{\partial x}, \qquad v_y = K_y \frac{\partial h}{\partial y}, \qquad v_z = K_z \frac{\partial h}{\partial z} \tag{3.29}$$

where K_x, K_y, and K_z, are the coefficients of permeability in the x, y, and z directions, respectively. The velocity at any point in an aquifer may be taken as the vector sum of the component velocities. To simplify mathematical treatment, aquifers will be assumed homogenous with isotropic permeability; that is, the same in all directions. Hence,

$$v_x = K \frac{\partial h}{\partial x}, \qquad v_y = K \frac{\partial h}{\partial y}, \qquad v_z = K \frac{\partial h}{\partial z} \tag{3.30}$$

In hydrodynamics a velocity potential ϕ is defined as a scalar function of space and time such that its negative derivative with respect to any direction is the fluid velocity in that direction. If, for the present purpose $\phi = -Kh$, then it follows from Eq. 3.30

$$v_x = -\frac{\partial \phi}{\partial x}, \qquad v_y = -\frac{\partial \phi}{\partial y}, \qquad v_z = -\frac{\partial \phi}{\partial z} \tag{3.31}$$

and it is apparent from the definition that a velocity potential exists for ground water flow. Existence of a velocity potential implies irrotational flow.* Because ground water is known to flow around individual grains of a medium, inasmuch as the grains may be regarded as submerged bodies within the fluid, the statement may be misleading. On a macroscopic basis, however, rotations within the interstices balance out statistically so that the flow becomes irrotational.

Steady Flow. All ground water flow must satisfy the equation of continuity, which in general form may be expressed as

$$-\left[\frac{\partial(\rho v_x)}{\partial x} + \frac{\partial(\rho v_y)}{\partial y} + \frac{\partial(\rho v_z)}{\partial z}\right] = \frac{\partial \rho}{\partial t} \tag{3.32}$$

where ρ is fluid density and t is time. For steady flow there is no change in conditions with respect to time, and regarding water as an incompressible fluid makes ρ a constant; therefore, Eq. 3.32 reduces to

$$\frac{\partial v_x}{\partial x} + \frac{\partial v_y}{\partial y} + \frac{\partial v_z}{\partial z} = 0 \tag{3.33}$$

When the conditions for existence of irrotational flow, given by Eq. 3.31, are substituted in Eq. 3.33, the Laplace equation

* For proof of this statement the reader is referred to any elementary text on hydrodynamics.

$$\frac{\partial^2 \phi}{\partial x^2} + \frac{\partial^2 \phi}{\partial y^2} + \frac{\partial^2 \phi}{\partial z^2} = 0 \tag{3.34}$$

results. Replacing ϕ by $-Kh$ leads to

$$\frac{\partial^2 h}{\partial x^2} + \frac{\partial^2 h}{\partial y^2} + \frac{\partial^2 h}{\partial z^2} = 0 \tag{3.35}$$

which is the general partial differential equation for steady flow of water in homogeneous and isotropic media.

Unsteady Flow. In order to derive the corresponding equation for unsteady flow,[36] it will be necessary to consider the storage coefficient S. For an unconfined aquifer this was defined in Chapter 2 as the specific yield, but for confined aquifers it is a measure of the aquifer compressibility β. The defining equation,

$$\beta = \frac{-\partial V/V}{\partial p} \tag{3.36}$$

where V is volume and p is pressure, can be evaluated in terms of changes within a column of unit cross-sectional area extending upward through a confined aquifer (see Fig. 2.9a). It is assumed that the compressive force acts in a vertical direction (or, in general, normal to the plane of the aquifer) over a large areal extent so that changes in horizontal (lateral) directions are negligible. When the piezometric surface is lowered a unit distance, the quantity of water released from the column by the pressure change is S; hence $S = \partial V$. The volume of the aquifer column is $V = 1 \cdot b = b$ where b is the aquifer thickness, and the change in pressure $\partial p = -\gamma(1) = -\gamma$. Inserting these values in Eq. 3.36 gives

$$\beta = \frac{S}{\gamma b} \tag{3.37}$$

Now for an elastic material,*

$$\frac{\partial V}{V} = -\frac{\partial \rho}{\rho} \tag{3.38}$$

which, when combined with Eq. 3.36, gives

$$\partial \rho = \rho \beta \, \partial p \tag{3.39}$$

* It is assumed that water is compressed and that the grains of porous media are rigid; however, they may be packed more closely together by the compressive force (see Chapter 6).

and by replacing β with its equivalent from Eq. 3.37,

$$\partial\rho = \frac{\rho S}{b\gamma}\,\partial p \tag{3.40}$$

Inserting this expression in the continuity equation (Eq. 3.32) gives

$$-\left[\frac{\partial(\rho v_x)}{\partial x} + \frac{\partial(\rho v_y)}{\partial y} + \frac{\partial(\rho v_z)}{\partial z}\right] = \frac{\rho S}{b\gamma}\frac{\partial p}{\partial t} \tag{3.41}$$

This equation may be expanded and values of velocity components inserted to give

$$K\left(\frac{\partial^2 h}{\partial x^2} + \frac{\partial^2 h}{\partial y^2} + \frac{\partial^2 h}{\partial z^2}\right) = \frac{S}{b\gamma}\frac{\partial p}{\partial t} \tag{3.42}$$

when ρ is assumed constant. Rewriting and substituting $p = \gamma h$,

$$\frac{\partial^2 h}{\partial x^2} + \frac{\partial^2 h}{\partial y^2} + \frac{\partial^2 h}{\partial z^2} = \frac{S}{Kb}\frac{\partial h}{\partial t} \tag{3.43}$$

which is the approximate partial differential equation governing the unsteady flow of water in a compressible confined aquifer of uniform thickness b. The corresponding equation for an unconfined aquifer has a nonlinear form,[36] which makes direct solution impossible. By approximation, however, Eq. 3.43 can be applied to unconfined aquifers where variations in the saturated thickness are relatively small.

Application to Aquifers. The equations derived above will be applied subsequently to obtain analytic solutions to particular ground water flow problems. For solution of any problem, idealization of the aquifer and of the boundary conditions of the flow system is necessary. Results may only approximate field conditions, nevertheless known deviations from assumptions frequently allow analytic solutions to be modified to obtain an answer which otherwise would not have been possible. A common assumption regarding the aquifer is that it is homogeneous and isotropic. Often aquifers can be assumed to be infinite in areal extent; if not, boundaries are assumed to be (*a*) impermeable, such as underlying or overlying rock or clay layers, dikes, faults, or valley walls, or (*b*) permeable, including surface water bodies in contact with the aquifer, ground surfaces where water emerges from underground, and wells.

Ground Water Flow Lines

Flow Nets. For specified boundary conditions flow lines * and equipotential lines can be mapped in two dimensions to form a flow

* A flow line is defined here as a line such that the macroscopic velocity vector is everywhere tangent to it.

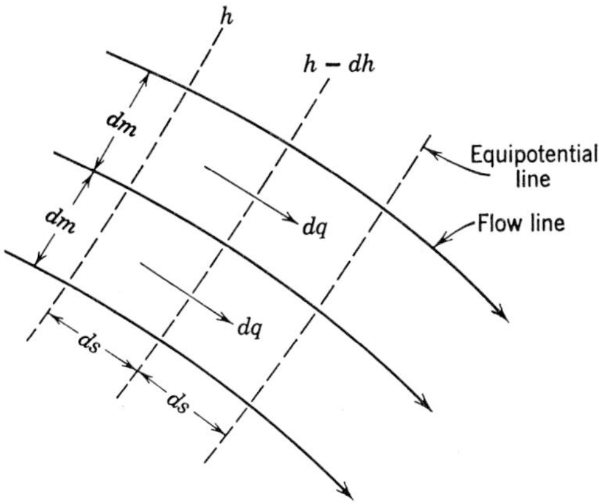

Fig. 3.8. Portion of an orthogonal flow net formed by flow and equipotential lines.

net. The two sets of lines form an orthogonal pattern of small squares. In a few simplified cases, the differential equation governing flow can be solved to obtain the flow net.[52] Generally, however, graphical solutions based on trial-and-error approximations or laboratory model studies are necessary. Suggestions for graphical construction of flow nets have been given by Casagrande; [8] model studies are described in Chapter 14.

Consider the portion of a flow net shown in Fig. 3.8. The hydraulic gradient i is given by

$$i = \frac{dh}{ds} \tag{3.44}$$

and the constant flow dq between two adjacent flow lines by

$$dq = K \frac{dh}{ds} dm \tag{3.45}$$

for unit thickness. But for the squares of the flow net, the approximation

$$ds \cong dm \tag{3.46}$$

can be made so that Eq. 3.45 reduces to

$$dq = K\, dh \tag{3.47}$$

Applying this to an entire flow net where the total head loss h is divided into n squares between any two adjacent flow lines, then

$$dh = \frac{h}{n} \tag{3.48}$$

If the flow is divided into m channels by flow lines, then the total flow

$$Q = m\,dq = \frac{Kmh}{n} \tag{3.49}$$

Thus the geometry of the flow net, together with the permeability and head loss, enables the total flow in the section to be computed directly.

Flow in Relation to Ground Water Contours. Because no flow crosses an impermeable boundary, flow lines must parallel it. Similarly, if no flow crosses the water table of an unconfined aquifer, it becomes a bounding flow surface. The energy head h_E, or fluid potential, from Eq. 3.2 at any point on the water table can be approximated by

$$h_E = \frac{p}{\gamma} + z \tag{3.50}$$

so that by letting the atmospheric pressure reference be zero, $p = 0$, and $h_E = z$. Therefore, under steady state conditions the elevation at any point on the water table equals the energy head and, as a consequence, flow lines lie perpendicular to water table contours.

With only three ground water elevations known from wells, estimates of local ground water contours and flow directions can be determined as demonstrated by Fig. 3.9. From field measurements of static water levels in wells within a basin, a water table contour map can be constructed. Flow lines, sketched perpendicular to contours, show directions of movement. An example appears in Fig. 3.10. A similar procedure may be followed for piezometric surfaces of confined aquifers.

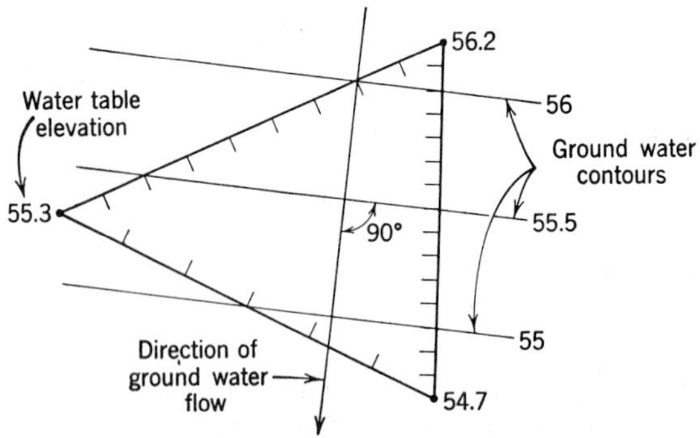

Fig. 3.9. Estimate of ground water contours and flow direction from water table elevations in three wells.

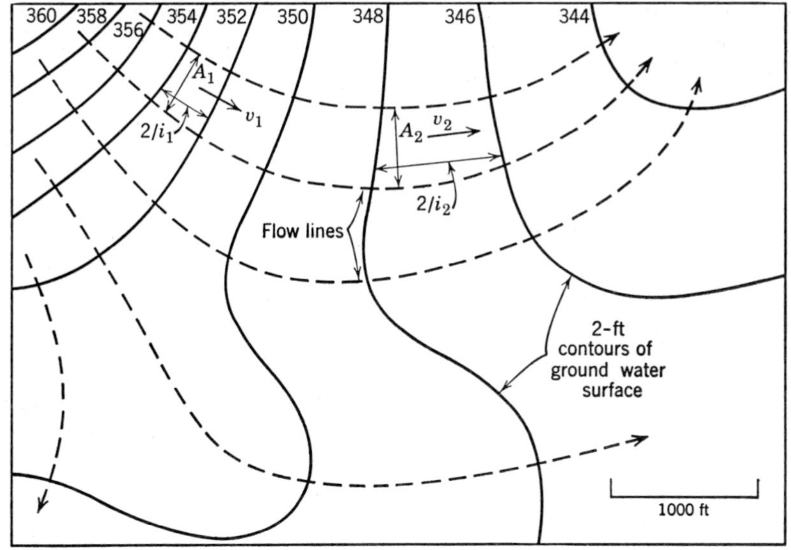

Fig. 3.10. Contour map of a ground water surface and showing flow lines.

Contour maps of water tables or piezometric surfaces, together with the flow lines, are useful data for locating new wells. Not only can areas be selected which suggest the best possible sources of ground water supply, but also areas of favorable permeability can be ascertained. The procedure can be illustrated by treating two adjacent flow lines as impermeable boundaries, for there is no velocity across these lines. The flow at sections 1 and 2 in Fig. 3.10 equals

$$Q = A_1 v_1 = A_2 v_2 \tag{3.51}$$

where v is velocity and A is the saturated area perpendicular to the flow. From Darcy's law,

$$A_1 K_1 i_1 = A_2 K_2 i_2 \tag{3.52}$$

which can be rewritten

$$\frac{K_1}{K_2} = \frac{A_2 i_2}{A_1 i_1} \tag{3.53}$$

where K is coefficient of permeability and i is hydraulic gradient. The ratio A_2/A_1 can be estimated from the distances between flow lines at the two sections (see Fig. 3.10) for an unconfined aquifer if the difference in elevation of the water table at the two sections is small compared to the saturated aquifer thickness, or for a confined aquifer of uniform thickness. Similarly, i_2/i_1 can be estimated from the respective contour spacings. For the special case of nearly parallel flow lines, Eq. 3.53 reduces to

$$\frac{K_1}{K_2} = \frac{i_2}{i_1} \tag{3.54}$$

This equation may be interpreted as indicating for an area of uniform ground water flow that portions having wide contour spacings (flat gradients) will have higher permeabilities than those with narrow spacings (steep gradients). In Fig. 3.10, therefore, prospects for a good-yielding well are better near section 2 than 1.

Natural permeable boundaries of aquifers include surface water bodies and the ground surface. In a surface water body the energy head is constant everywhere within the water body and equals the elevation of the water surface; consequently, aquifer flow lines must intersect normal to such a bounding surface. For the ground surface this does not apply as only atmospheric pressure exists at the ground surface. Hence in Eq. 3.50 by letting $p = 0$, $h_E = z$, which is identical to the case for a water table boundary.

Flow Across a Water Table. As long as no flow crosses a water table, it serves as a ground water boundary; however, if flow, such as percolating water, reaches the water table, flow lines no longer parallel the surface as an impermeable boundary.[31, 36] To illustrate this re-

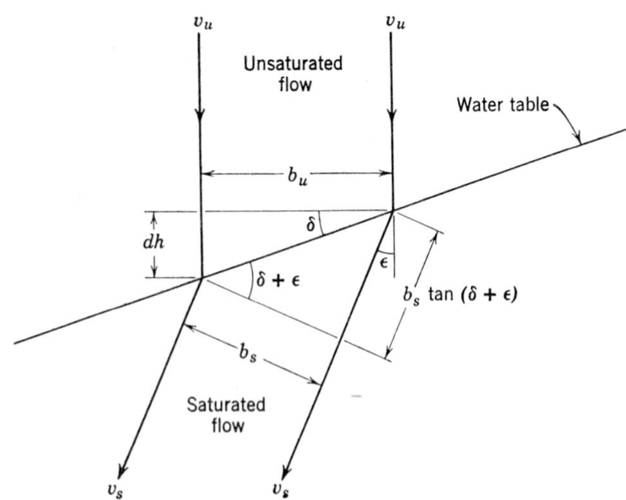

Fig. 3.11. Refraction of flow lines across a water table (after Jacob[36]).

fraction effect let v_u represent the unsaturated vertical velocity approaching the water table and v_s the saturated velocity below the water table (Fig. 3.11). The head loss dh for flow along the left flow line below the water table occurs in a distance of $b_s \tan(\delta + \epsilon)$, as defined in Fig. 3.11. Thus

$$v_s = Ki = K \frac{dh}{b_s \tan(\delta + \epsilon)} \tag{3.55}$$

but

$$dh = b_u \tan \delta \tag{3.56}$$

hence

$$v_s = K \frac{b_u \tan \delta}{b_s \tan(\delta + \epsilon)} \tag{3.57}$$

From continuity

$$\frac{b_u}{b_s} = \frac{v_s}{v_u} \tag{3.58}$$

where b_u and b_s are as shown in Fig. 3.11, so that

$$v_s = K \frac{v_s \tan \delta}{v_u \tan(\delta + \epsilon)} \tag{3.59}$$

which, when solved for ϵ, gives

$$\epsilon = \tan^{-1}\left(\frac{K}{v_u} \tan \delta\right) - \delta \tag{3.60}$$

This states that for $v_u > 0$, flow lines will form an angle of $(90° - \delta - \epsilon)$ below the water table. For the case of no percolating flow, $v_u = 0$ and $\epsilon = 90° - \delta$, thus paralleling the water table.

Flow Across a Boundary of Permeability. Similar to the above analysis, where flow passes from a region of permeability K_1 to one of K_2, a change in flow direction results. The change of direction can be derived from continuity considerations and expressed in terms of the two permeabilities. Visualizing a flow field as shown in Fig. 3.12, it is clear that the normal components of flow approaching and leaving the boundary must be equal, hence the normal velocities v_n must be such that

$$v_{n_1} = v_{n_2} \tag{3.61}$$

or

$$K_1 \frac{dh_1}{dL_1} \cos \theta_1 = K_2 \frac{dh_2}{dL_2} \cos \theta_2 \tag{3.62}$$

where θ_1 and θ_2 are angles with the normal shown in Fig. 3.12. Also, the distance b along the boundary between two adjacent flow lines must be the same on each side of the boundary. From Fig. 3.12 the distance b can be given as

$$b = \frac{dL_1}{\sin \theta_1} = \frac{dL_2}{\sin \theta_2} \tag{3.63}$$

which can be rearranged

$$dL_1 \sin \theta_2 = dL_2 \sin \theta_1 \tag{3.64}$$

Dividing this equation by Eq. 3.62, and noting that $dh_1 = dh_2$ between two equipotential lines, gives

$$\frac{K_1}{K_2} = \frac{\tan \theta_1}{\tan \theta_2} \tag{3.65}$$

Thus, for saturated flow passing from a medium of one permeability to another of different permeability, a refraction in flow lines occurs such that the permeability ratio equals the ratio of the tangents of the angles the flow lines make with the normal to the boundary. Consequences of this relation are illustrated in Fig. 3.13.

Unsaturated Flow

Movement of water under conditions of less than saturation takes place in the zone of aeration as a result of capillary and gravitational

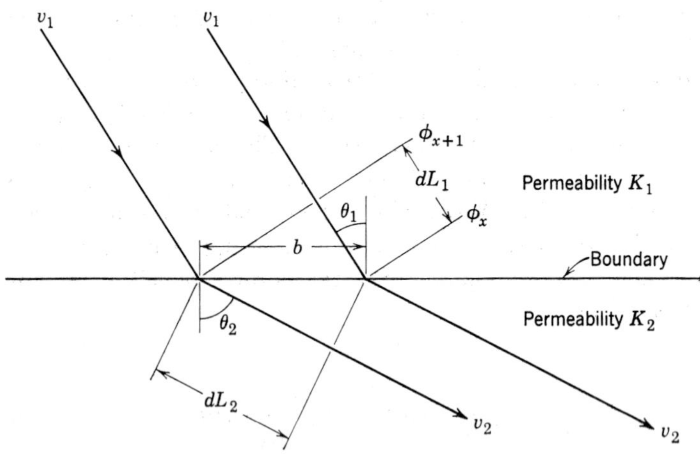

Fig. 3.12. Refraction of flow lines across a boundary between media of different permeabilities.

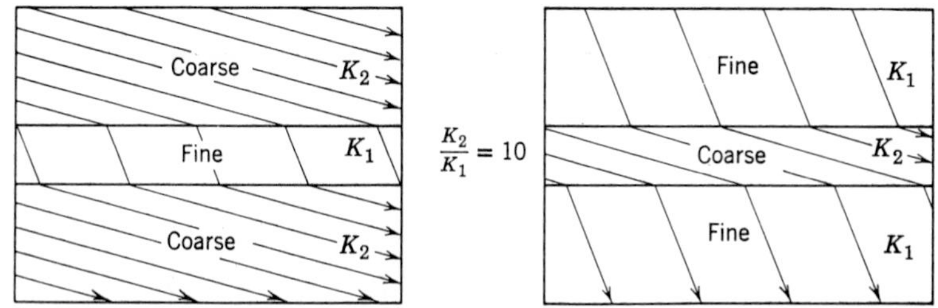

Fig. 3.13. Refraction across layers of coarse and fine sand with a permeability ratio of 10 (after Hubbert [31]).

forces. Experimental evidence indicates that unsaturated flow obeys Darcy's law but with a different permeability than for saturated flow.

Specific permeability k, previously defined, applies only to saturated flow; however, a similar expression—unsaturated specific permeability k_u—can be defined for unsaturated flow.* Experimental studies of flow of liquid-gas mixtures by Wyckoff and Botset [76] showed a consistent relation between the degree of saturation and specific permeability for sands of widely different permeabilities. Irmay [34] showed that these data could be expressed by

$$k_u = Cd_e^2(S_s - S_0)^3 \frac{\alpha^3}{(1 - \alpha)^2} \tag{3.66}$$

where C is a constant which equals approximately 0.01, depending on the shape of grains and the soil structure; d_e is the effective grain diameter (the diameter such that 10 per cent of the material is finer than this size); S_s is the degree of saturation; S_0 is the threshold saturation, being that part of the voids which is filled with non-moving water; and α is porosity. The curve for k_u/k plotted against S_s is shown in Fig. 3.14 for $S_0 = 0.20$, which fits the Wyckoff and Botset data well.

It should be noted that permeabilities associated with unsaturated flow are less than those for saturated flow. In fact, the lower the degree of saturation, the lower the permeability. Physically this is logical, because with a portion of the voids occupied by air, water is impeded in its passage through porous media. Permeability approaches zero near the threshold saturation, indicating no flow. At this lower limit, water is held primarily by capillary forces and is distributed in individual concentrations in the smaller pore spaces; hence it is retained against external forces.

* An unsaturated coefficient of permeability K_u can also be defined by $K_u = k_u\gamma/\mu$. This is generally referred to as capillary conductivity.

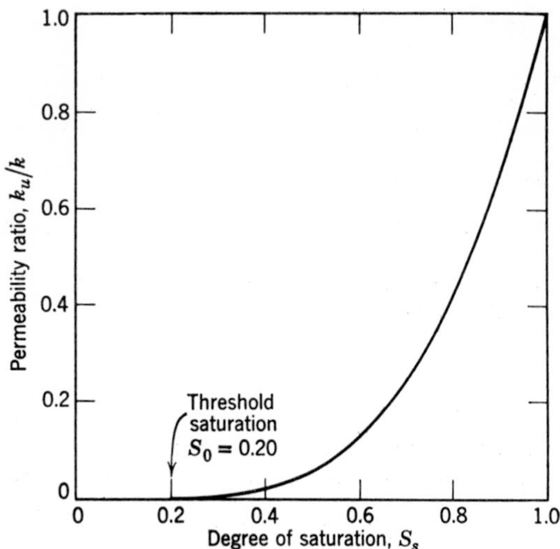

Fig. 3.14. Ratio of unsaturated to saturated specific permeability as a function of saturation (after Irmay [34]).

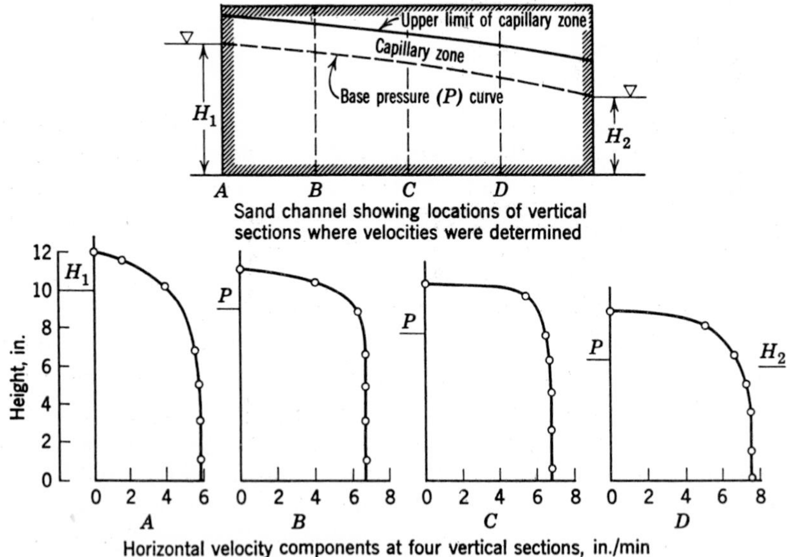

Fig. 3.15. Horizontal velocity distribution along a channel containing coarse sand, showing flow in capillary zone (after Mavis and Tsui [48]).

Laboratory experiments with sand channels by Mavis and Tsui [48] demonstrated that flow parallel to the water table occurs in the capillary zone. Data presented in Fig. 3.15 show the horizontal velocity components at the entry and quarter points along a channel filled with coarse sand. As might be anticipated, velocities in the unsaturated zone decrease with distance above the water table (base pressure curve).

It has been shown from experimental evidence [26] that unsaturated horizontal flow into a dry medium originating from a constant saturated source can be expressed by

$$v = Ct^{-1/2} \tag{3.67}$$

where v is velocity, C is a constant, and t is time. For upward and downward flow more complex expressions relating velocity to time have been derived. For upward flow $v \to 0$ as $t \to \infty$; whereas, for downward flow $v \to$ constant as $t \to \infty$. Laboratory studies of one-directional flow from a free surface through unsaturated soil indicate three distinct moisture zones. First the wetting front, indicating the initial capillary fringe of the advancing water, arrives. The wetting zone follows, beginning with moisture in the conducting pores and extending until a moisture equilibrium is reached. Finally, the transmission zone is formed, containing an essentially constant moisture content which approximates 80 per cent of saturation.

References

1. Ambrose, A. W., Use of detectors for tracing movement of underground water, *U. S. Bureau Mines Bull.* 195, Washington, D. C., pp. 106–120, 1921.
2. Amer. Soc. for Testing Materials, Symposium on permeability of soils, *Spec. Tech. Publ.* 163, 136 pp., 1955.
3. Aravin, V. I., and S. N. Numerov, *Theory of movement of liquids and gases in consolidated porous media* (in Russian), Gostekhizdat, Moscow, 616 pp., 1953.
4. Bakhameteff, B. A., and N. V. Feodoroff, Flow through granular media, *Jour. Appl. Mech.*, vol. 4A, pp. 97–104; discussion, vol. 5A, pp. 86–90, 1937.
5. Bakhameteff, B. A., and N. V. Feodoroff, Flow through granular media, *Proc. 5th Intl. Cong. Appl. Mech.*, pp. 555–560, 1938.
6. Boreli, M., Contribution à l'étude des milieux poreux, *Publications Scientifiques et Techniques du Ministère de l'Air* 305, Paris, 129 pp., 1955.
7. Brownell, L. E., and D. L. Katz, Flow of fluids through porous media, I—Single homogeneous fluids, *Chem. Eng. Progress*, vol. 43, pp. 537–548, 1947.
8. Casagrande, A., Seepage through dams, *Jour. New England Water Works Assoc.*, vol. 51, pp. 131–172, 1937.

9. Christiansen, J. E., Effect of entrapped air upon the permeability of soils, *Soil Sci.*, vol. 58, pp. 355–365, 1944.
10. Danel, P., The measurement of ground-water flow, *Proc. Ankara Symposium on Arid Zone Hydrology,* UNESCO, Paris, pp. 99–107, 1953.
11. Darcy, H., *Les fontaines publiques de la ville de Dijon,* V. Dalmont, Paris, 647 pp., 1856.
12. Day, P. R., Dispersion of a moving salt-water boundary advancing through saturated sand, *Trans. Amer. Geophysical Union,* vol. 37, pp. 595–601, 1956.
13. Dole, R. B., Use of fluorescein in the study of underground water, *U. S. Geological Survey Water-Supply Paper* 160, Washington, D. C., pp. 73–86, 1906.
14. Fair, G. M., and L. P. Hatch, Fundamental factors governing the streamline flow of water through sand, *Jour. Amer. Water Works Assoc.*, vol. 25, pp. 1551–1565, 1933.
15. Fancher, G., Henry Darcy—engineer and benefactor of mankind, *Jour. Petr. Tech.*, vol. 8, pp. 12–14, Oct. 1956.
16. Fancher, G. H., and J. A. Lewis, Flow of simple fluids through porous materials, *Ind. and Eng. Chem.*, vol. 25, pp. 1139–1147, 1933.
17. Fancher, G. H., J. A. Lewis, and K. B. Barnes, Some physical characteristics of oil sands, *Bull.* 12, Penn. State College Mineral Industries Exp. Sta., State College, pp. 65–171, 1933.
18. Fireman, M., Permeability measurements on disturbed soil samples, *Soil Sci.*, vol. 58, pp. 337–353, 1944.
19. Fishel, V. C., Further tests of permeability with low hydraulic gradients, *Trans. Amer. Geophysical Union,* vol. 16, pp. 499–503, 1935.
20. Fox, C. S., Using radioactive isotopes to trace movement of underground waters, *Municipal Utilities,* vol. 90, no. 4, pp. 30–32, 1952.
21. Franzini, J. B., Porosity factor for case of laminar flow through granular media, *Trans. Amer. Geophysical Union,* vol. 32, pp. 443–446, 1951.
22. Fraser, H. J., Experimental study of the porosity and permeability of elastic sediments, *Jour. Geol.*, vol. 43, pp. 910–1010, 1935.
23. Givan, C. V., Flow of water through granular materials, *Trans. Amer. Geophysical Union,* vol. 15, pp. 572–579, 1934.
24. Graton, L. C., and H. J. Fraser, Systematic packing of spheres with particular relation to porosity and permeability, *Jour. Geol.*, vol. 43, pp. 785–909, 1935.
25. Hall, W. A., An analytical derivation of the Darcy equation, *Trans. Amer. Geophysical Union,* vol. 37, pp. 185–188, 1956.
26. Hansen, V. E., Infiltration and water movement during irrigation, *Soil Sci.*, vol. 79, pp. 93–105, 1955.
27. Hatch, L. P., Flow through granular media, *Jour. Appl. Mech.*, vol. 7A, pp. 109–112, 1940.
28. Hazen, A., Some physical properties of sands and gravels with special reference to their use in filtration, *24th Ann. Rep.*, Mass. State Bd. Health, Boston, pp. 541–556, 1893.
29. Hickox, G. H., Flow through granular materials, *Trans. Amer. Geophysical Union,* vol. 15, pp. 567–572, 1934
30. Hours, R., Radioactive tracers in hydrology, *La Houille Blanche,* vol. 10, no. A, pp. 14–24, 1955.
31. Hubbert, M. K., The theory of ground-water motion, *Jour. Geol.*, vol. 48, pp. 785–944, 1940.

32. Hubbert, M. K., Darcy's law and the field equations of the flow of underground fluids, *Trans. Amer. Inst. Min. and Met. Engrs.*, vol. 207, pp. 222–239, 1956.
33. Hulbert, R., and D. Feben, Hydraulics of rapid filter sand, *Jour. Amer. Water Works Assoc.*, vol. 25, pp. 19–65, 1933.
34. Irmay, S., On the hydraulic conductivity of unsaturated soils, *Trans. Amer. Geophysical Union*, vol. 35, pp. 463–467, 1954.
35. Irmay, S., Extension of Darcy law to unsteady unsaturated flow through porous media, *Symposia Darcy*, Publ. 41, Assoc. Intl. d'Hydrologie Scientifique, pp. 57–66, 1956.
36. Jacob, C. E., Flow of ground water, in *Engineering hydraulics* (H. Rouse, ed.), John Wiley and Sons, New York, pp. 321–386, 1950.
37. Jacob, C. E., V. C. Fishel, and M. K. Hubbert, Report of committee on ground water—Appendices on permeability, *Trans. Amer. Geophysical Union*, vol. 27, pp. 245–273, 1946.
38. de Josselin de Jong, G., Longitudinal and transverse diffusion in granular deposits, *Trans. Amer. Geophysical Union*, vol. 39, pp. 67–74, 1958.
39. Kaufman, W. J., and G. T. Orlob, Measuring ground water movement with radioactive and chemical tracers, *Jour. Amer. Water Works Assoc.*, vol. 48, pp. 559–572, 1956.
40. Kaufman, W. J., and D. K. Todd, Methods of detecting and tracing the movement of ground water, *Inst. Eng. Research Rep.* 93-1, Univ. Calif., Berkeley, 130 pp., 1955.
41. King, F. H., Principles and conditions of the movements of ground water, *U. S. Geological Survey 19th Ann. Rep.*, pt. 2, Washington, D. C., pp. 59–294, 1899.
42. Kirkham, D., and C. L. Feng, Some tests of the diffusion theory, and laws of capillary flow, in soils, *Soil Sci.*, vol. 67, pp. 29–40, 1949.
43. Kitagawa, K., Sur le dispersement et l'écart moyen de l'écoulement des eaux souterraines, *Mem. College Sci.*, Kyoto Imp. Univ., Ser. A, vol. 17, pp. 37–42, 431–441, 1934; and vol. 18, pp. 129–135, 1935.
44. Krumbein, W. C., and G. D. Monk, Permeability as a function of the size parameters of unconsolidated sands, *Trans. Amer. Inst. Min. and Met. Engrs.*, vol. 151, pp. 153–163, 1943.
45. Libby, W. F., Tritium in nature, *Sci. Amer.*, vol. 190, no. 4, pp. 38–42, 1954.
46. Lindquist, E., On the flow of water through porous soil, *1er Congrès des Grands Barrages*, vol. 5, Stockholm, pp. 81–101, 1933.
47. Luthin, J. N., and P. R. Day, Lateral flow above a sloping water table, *Proc. Soil Sci. Soc. Amer.*, vol. 19, pp. 406–410, 1955.
48. Mavis, F. T., and T. P. Tsui, Percolation and capillary movements of water through sand prisms, *Bull.* 18, Univ. Iowa Studies in Eng., Iowa City, 25 pp., 1939.
49. Mavis, F. T., and E. F. Wilsey, A study of the permeability of sand, *Bull.* 7, Univ. Iowa Studies in Eng., Iowa City, 29 pp., 1936.
50. Meinzer, O. E., and V. C. Fishel, Tests of permeability with low hydraulic gradients, *Trans. Amer. Geophysical Union*, vol. 15, pp. 405–409, 1934.
51. Moore, R. E., Water conduction from shallow water tables, *Hilgardia*, vol. 12, pp. 383–426, 1939.
52. Muskat, M., *The flow of homogeneous fluids through porous media*, McGraw-Hill, New York, 763 pp., 1937.

53. Polubarinova-Kochina, P. Y., and S. B. Falkovich, Theory of filtration of liquids in porous media in *Advances in applied mechanics,* vol. 2, Academic Press, New York, pp. 153–225, 1951.

54. Reeve, R. C., and D. Kirkham, Soil anisotropy and some field methods for measuring permeability, *Trans. Amer. Geophysical Union,* vol. 32, pp. 582–590, 1951.

55. Remson, I., and G. S. Fox, Capillary losses from ground water, *Trans. Amer. Geophysical Union,* vol. 36, pp. 304–310, 1955.

56. Richards, L. A., Capillary conduction of liquids through porous mediums, *Physics,* vol. 1, pp. 318–333, 1931.

57. Richards, L. A., Laws of soil moisture, *Trans. Amer. Geophysical Union,* vol. 31, pp. 750–756, 1950.

58. Richards, L. A., Report of the Subcommittee on Permeability and Infiltration, Committee on Terminology, *Proc. Soil Sci. Soc. Amer.,* vol. 16, pp. 85–88, 1952.

59. Rifai, M. N. E., W. J. Kaufman, and D. K. Todd, Dispersion phenomena in laminar flow through porous media, *Inst. Eng. Research Rep.* 93-2, Univ. Calif., Berkeley, 157 pp., 1956.

60. Rose, H. E., An investigation into the laws of flow of fluids through beds of granular materials, *Proc. Inst. Mech. Engrs.,* vol. 153, pp. 141–148, 1945.

61. Rose, H. E., On the resistance coefficient—Reynolds number relationship for fluid flow through a bed of granular material, *Proc. Inst. Mech. Engrs.,* vol. 153, pp. 154–168, 1945.

62. Rose, H. E., and A. M. A. Rizk, Further researches in fluid flow through beds of granular material, *Proc. Inst. Mech. Engrs.,* vol. 160, pp. 493–511, 1949.

63. Scheidegger, A. E., Statistical hydrodynamics in porous media, *Jour. App. Physics,* vol. 25, pp. 994–1001, 1954.

64. Scheidegger, A. E., *The physics of flow through porous media,* Univ. Toronto Press, Toronto, 236 pp., 1957.

65. Schneebeli, G., Expériences sur la limite de validité de la loi de Darcy et l'apparition de la turbulence dans un écoulement de filtration, *La Houille Blanche,* vol. 10, pp. 141–149, 1955.

66. Slater, C. S., The flow of water through soil, *Agric. Eng.,* vol. 29, pp. 119–124, 1948.

67. Slichter, C. S., Theoretical investigation of the motion of ground waters, *U. S. Geological Survey 19th Ann. Rep.,* pt. 2, Washington, D. C., pp. 295–384, 1899.

68. Slichter, C. S., The motions of underground waters, *U. S. Geological Survey Water-Supply Paper* 67, Washington, D. C., 106 pp., 1902.

69. Slichter, C. S., Field measurements of the rate of movement of underground water, *U. S. Geological Survey Water-Supply Paper* 140, Washington, D. C., pp. 9–85, 1905.

70. Smith, W. O., Capillary flow through an ideal uniform soil, *Physics,* vol. 3, pp. 139–146, 1933.

71. Stearns, N. D., Laboratory tests on physical properties of water-bearing materials, *U. S. Geological Survey Water-Supply Paper* 596, Washington, D. C., pp. 121–176, 1928.

72. Terzaghi, C., Principles of soil mechanics, *Eng. News-Record,* vol. 95, p. 832, 1925.

73. Warde, J., and R. M. Richardson, Waste disposal—vital to atomic power development, *Min. Eng.,* vol. 7, pp. 450–461, 1955.
74. Wenzel, L. K., The Thiem method for determining permeability of water-bearing materials and its application to the determination of specific yield, *U. S. Geological Survey Water-Supply Paper* 679-A, Washington, D. C., 57 pp., 1936.
75. Wenzel, L. K., Methods for determining permeability of water-bearing materials with special reference to discharging-well methods, *U. S. Geological Survey Water-Supply Paper* 887, Washington, D. C., 192 pp., 1942.
76. Wyckoff, R. D., and H. G. Botset, The flow of gas-liquid mixtures through unconsolidated sands, *Physics,* vol. 7, pp. 325–345, 1936.
77. Wyckoff, R. D., H. G. Botset, M. Muskat, and D. W. Reed, The measurement of the permeability of porous media for homogeneous fluids, *Review Sci. Instruments,* vol. 4, pp. 394–405, 1933.
78. Wyckoff, R. D., H. G. Botset, and M. Muskat, Flow of liquids through porous media under the action of gravity, *Physics,* vol. 3, pp. 90–113, 1932.

Ground Water and Well Hydraulics

CHAPTER 4

Having introduced Darcy's law and the fundamental equations for ground water movement, these can now be applied to particular situations. To obtain a solution for a ground water flow problem, assumptions regarding permeability, type of flow, and boundary conditions must be made. Although such solutions often only approximate field conditions, they provide valuable insight into the intricacies of ground water flow. The extensive development of ground water supplies by means of pumping wells makes it important that practical solutions to well flow problems be obtainable. The present knowledge of well hydraulics has been contributed by a chain of investigators working over the past century.[19]

Steady Unidirectional Flow

Confined Aquifer. Let ground water flow with a velocity v in the x-direction of a confined aquifer of uniform thickness. Then for steady flow, Eq. 3.35 reduces to

$$\frac{\partial^2 h}{\partial x^2} = 0 \tag{4.1}$$

which has for its solution

$$h = C_1 x + C_2 \tag{4.2}$$

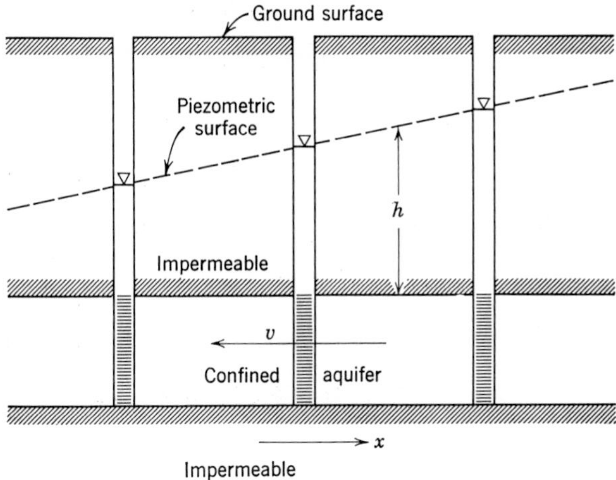

Fig. 4.1. Steady unidirectional flow in a confined aquifer of uniform thickness.

where h is the head above a given datum and C_1 and C_2 are constants of integration. Assuming $h = 0$ when $x = 0$ and $\frac{\partial h}{\partial x} = \frac{v}{K}$ from Darcy's law, then

$$h = \frac{vx}{K} \tag{4.3}$$

This states that the head decreases linearly, as sketched in Fig. 4.1, with flow in the negative x-direction

Unconfined Aquifer. For the similar flow situation in an unconfined aquifer, direct analytic solution of the Laplace equation is not possible. The difficulty arises from the fact that the water table in the two-dimensional case represents a flow line. The shape of the water table determines the flow distribution, but at the same time the flow distribution governs the water table shape. To obtain a solution Dupuit [12] assumed (a) the velocity of the flow to be proportional to the tangent of the hydraulic gradient instead of the sine as defined in Eq. 3.28, and (b) the flow to be horizontal and uniform everywhere in a vertical section. These assumptions, although permitting a solution to be obtained, limit the application of the results. For unidirectional flow, as sketched in Fig. 4.2, the discharge per unit width q at any vertical section can be given as

$$q = Kh\frac{dh}{dx} \tag{4.4}$$

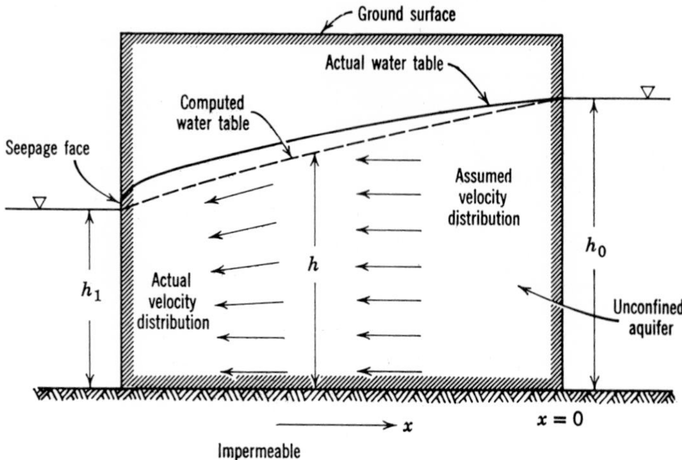

Fig. 4.2. Steady flow in an unconfined aquifer between two water bodies with vertical boundaries.

where K is the permeability coefficient and h is the height of the water table above an impervious base, and x is the direction of flow. Integrating,

$$qx = \frac{K}{2} h^2 + C \tag{4.5}$$

and, if $h = h_0$ where $x = 0$, then the Dupuit equation

$$q = \frac{K}{2x} (h^2 - h_0{}^2) \tag{4.6}$$

results, which indicates that the water table is parabolic in form.

For flow between two fixed bodies of water of constant heads h_0 and h_1 as in Fig. 4.2, the water table slope at the upstream boundary of the aquifer (neglecting the capillary zone)

$$\frac{dh}{dx} = \frac{q}{Kh_0} \tag{4.7}$$

But the boundary $h = h_0$ is an equipotential line because the fluid potential in a water body is constant; consequently, the water table must be horizontal at this section, which is inconsistent with Eq. 4.7. In the direction of the flow, the parabolic water table described by Eq. 4.6 increases in slope. By so doing, the two Dupuit assumptions, previously stated, become increasingly poor approximations to the actual flow; therefore, the actual water table deviates more and more from the computed position in the direction of flow as indicated in Fig. 4.2. The fact that the actual water table lies above the computed one can be explained by the fact that the Dupuit flows are all assumed horizontal, whereas the actual velocities of the same magnitude have a downward vertical component so that a greater saturated thickness is required for the same discharge. At the downstream boundary a discontinuity in flow forms because no consistent flow pattern can connect a water table directly to a downstream free-water surface. The water table actually approaches the boundary tangentially above the water body surface and forms a seepage face.

The above discrepancies indicate that the water table does not follow the parabolic form of Eq. 4.6; nevertheless, for flat slopes, where the sine and tangent are nearly equal, it closely predicts the water table position except near the outflow. The equation, however, accurately determines q or K for given boundary heads.[40]

Steady Radial Flow to a Well

When a well is pumped, water is removed from the aquifer surrounding the well and the water table or piezometric surface, depending upon the type of aquifer, is lowered. The drawdown at a given point is the distance the water level is lowered. A drawdown curve shows the variation of drawdown with distance from the well (see Fig. 4.3).

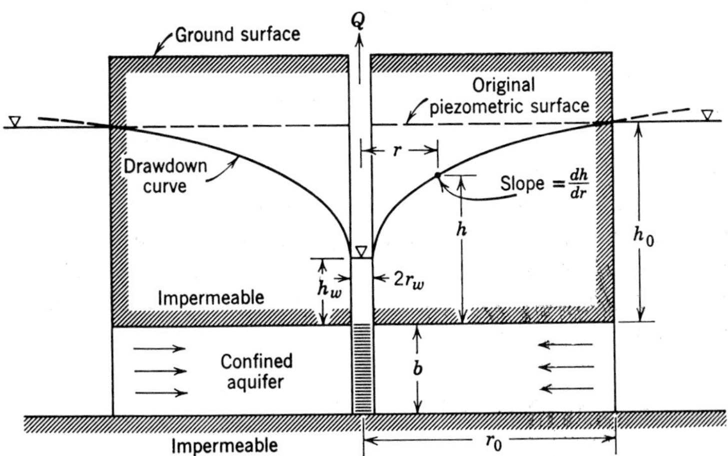

Fig. 4.3. Steady radial flow to a well penetrating a confined aquifer on an island.

In three dimensions the drawdown curve describes a conic shape known as the cone of depression. Also, the outer limit of the cone of depression defines the area of influence of the well.

Confined Aquifer. To derive the radial flow equation (which relates the well discharge to drawdown) for a well completely penetrating a confined aquifer, reference to Fig. 4.3 will prove helpful. The flow is assumed two-dimensional to a well centered on a circular island and penetrating a homogeneous and isotropic aquifer. Because the flow is everywhere horizontal, the Dupuit assumptions apply without error. Using plane polar coordinates with the well as the origin, the well discharge Q at any distance r equals

$$Q = Av = 2\pi rbK \frac{dh}{dr} \tag{4.8}$$

for steady radial flow to the well. Rearranging and integrating for the boundary conditions at the well, $h = h_w$ and $r = r_w$, and at the edge of the island, $h = h_0$ and $r = r_0$, yields

$$h_0 - h_w = \frac{Q}{2\pi Kb} \ln \frac{r_0}{r_w} \tag{4.9}$$

or

$$Q = 2\pi Kb \frac{h_0 - h_w}{\ln (r_0/r_w)} \tag{4.10}$$

In the more general case of a well penetrating an extensive confined aquifer, as in Fig. 4.4, there is no external limit for r. From the above derivation at any given value of r,

$$Q = 2\pi Kb \frac{h - h_w}{\ln (r/r_w)} \tag{4.11}$$

which shows that h increases indefinitely with increasing r. Yet, the maximum h is the initial uniform head h_0. Thus, from a theoretical aspect, steady radial flow in an extensive aquifer does not exist. However, from a practical standpoint, h approaches h_0 with distance from the well. As a close approximation, assume a radius of influence $r = r_0$ where $h = h_0$ so that Q for these limits is given by Eq. 4.10. By eliminating Q between Eqs. 4.10 and 4.11

$$h - h_w = (h_0 - h_w) \frac{\ln (r/r_w)}{\ln (r_0/r_w)} \tag{4.12}$$

which shows that the head varies linearly with the logarithm of the distance, regardless of the rate of discharge.

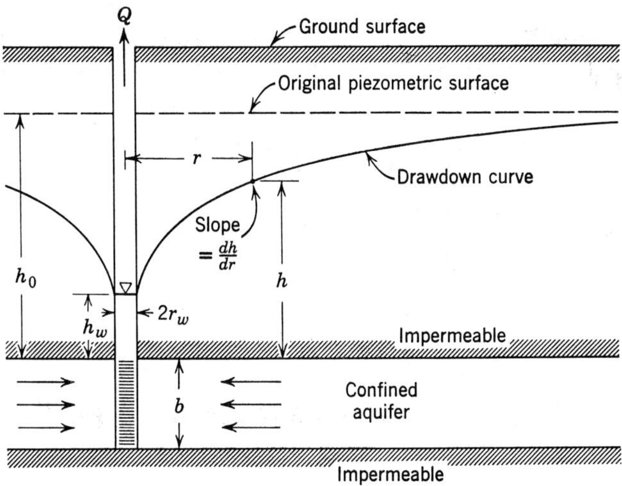

Fig. 4.4. Radial flow to a well penetrating an extensive confined aquifer.

Equation 4.11, known as the equilibrium, or Thiem,[56] equation, enables the aquifer permeability to be determined from a pumped well. Because any two points will define the logarithmic drawdown curve, the method consists of measuring drawdowns in two observation wells at different distances from a well pumped at a constant rate. The coefficient of permeability is given by

$$K = \frac{Q}{2\pi b(h_2 - h_1)} \ln \frac{r_2}{r_1} \tag{4.13}$$

where r_1 and r_2 are the distances and h_1 and h_2 are the heads of the respective observation wells. In order to apply the equation, pumping must continue at a uniform rate for a sufficient time to approach a steady-state condition, that is, one in which the drawdown changes negligibly with time. The observation wells should be located close enough to the pumping well so that their drawdowns are appreciable and can be readily measured. The derivation assumes that the aquifer is homogeneous and isotropic and is of infinite areal extent, that the well penetrates the entire aquifer, and that the flow is laminar. In spite of these restrictive assumptions, the equilibrium equation has been widely applied for permeability determinations.

Unconfined Aquifer. An equation for steady radial flow to a well in an unconfined aquifer also can be derived with the help of the Dupuit assumptions. As shown in Fig. 4.5, the well completely pene-

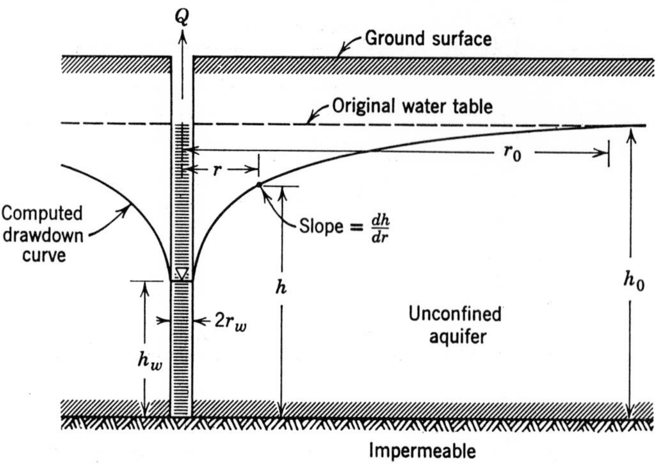

Fig. 4.5. Radial flow to a well penetrating an unconfined aquifer.

trates the aquifer to the horizontal base and a concentric boundary of constant head surrounds the well. The well discharge is

$$Q = 2\pi rKh \frac{dh}{dr} \tag{4.14}$$

which, when integrated between the limits $h = h_w$ at $r = r_w$ and $h = h_0$ at $r = r_0$, yields

$$Q = \pi K \frac{h_0^2 - h_w^2}{\ln (r_0/r_w)} \tag{4.15}$$

Because of large vertical flow components, this equation fails to describe accurately the drawdown curve near the well; however, estimates of Q for given heads are good. In practice, the selection of the radius of influence r_0 is approximate and arbitrary, but the variation in Q is small for a wide range of r_0. Suggested values of r_0 fall in the range of 500 to 1000 feet. These distances do not indicate the limits within which drawdown can be observed but, rather, they serve as approximations for practical application of the equation. Any pair of distances and heads also can be substituted, as was done in Eq. 4.13.

Well in a Uniform Flow

Drawdown curves for well flow presented heretofore have assumed an initially horizontal ground water surface. A practical situation

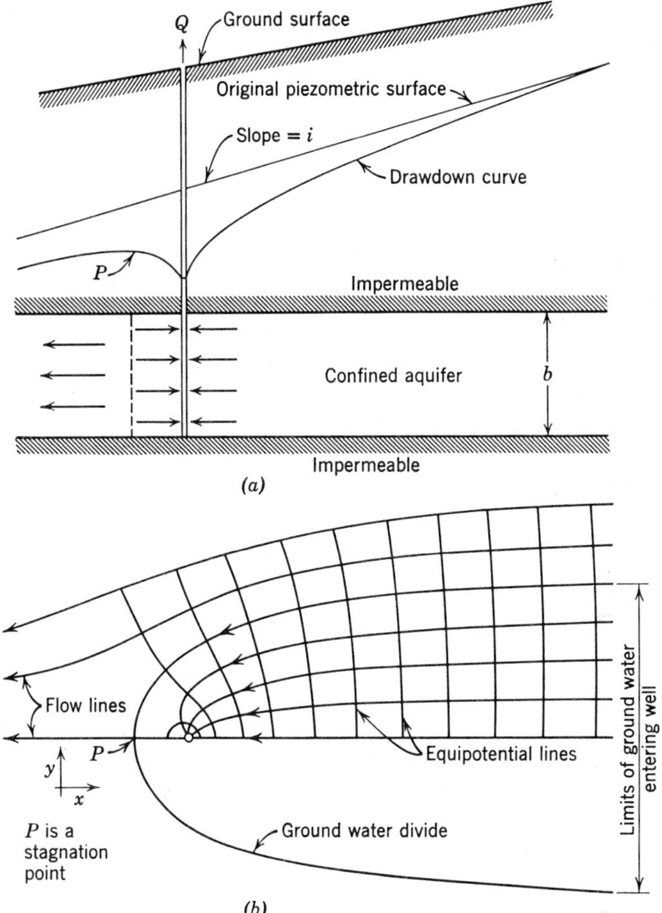

Fig. 4.6. Flow to a well penetrating a confined aquifer having a sloping plane piezometric surface; (*a*) vertical section, and (*b*) plan view.

is that of a well pumping from an aquifer having a uniform flow field, as indicated by a plane sloping piezometric surface or water table. Figure 4.6 shows sectional and plan views of a well penetrating a confined aquifer with a sloping piezometric surface. It is apparent that the circular area of influence associated with a radial flow pattern becomes distorted; however, for most relatively flat natural slopes the Dupuit radial flow equation can be applied without appreciable error.

From field investigations of wells pumping from aquifers having sloping hydraulic gradients, Wenzel[59] found that the permeability could be determined by averaging hydraulic gradients on each side of the pumped well and lying along a line parallel to the natural flow direction. The resulting expression, known as the gradient formula, has the form

$$K = \frac{2Q}{\pi r(h_u + h_d)(i_u + i_d)} \tag{4.16}$$

for an unconfined aquifer where Q is the pumping rate, h_u and h_d are the saturated thicknesses, and i_u and i_d are the water table slopes at distance r upstream and downstream, respectively, from the well. For a confined aquifer, piezometric slopes replace water table slopes, and $(h_u + h_d)$ is replaced by $2b$ where b is the aquifer thickness.

In Fig. 4.6 the ground water divide marking the boundary of the region producing inflow to the well is shown. For a well pumping an infinite time, the boundary would extend up to the limit of the aquifer. Based upon the Dupuit assumptions, the expression for the boundary of the region producing inflow can be derived[16] as

$$-\frac{y}{x} = \tan\left(\frac{2\pi Kbi}{Q}y\right) \tag{4.17}$$

where the rectangular coordinates are as shown in Fig. 4.6 with the origin at the well, b is the aquifer thickness, Q is the discharge rate, i is the natural piezometric slope, and K is permeability. It follows from Eq. 4.17 that the boundary asymptotically approaches

$$y = \pm\frac{Q}{2Kbi} \tag{4.18}$$

as $x \rightarrow \infty$. The boundary of the contributing area extends downstream to a stagnation point where

$$x = -\frac{Q}{2\pi Kbi} \tag{4.19}$$

Equations 4.17 to 4.19 also apply to unconfined aquifers by replacing b by the uniform saturated aquifer thickness h_0, providing the drawdown is small in relation to the aquifer thickness.

Steady Flow with Uniform Recharge

Figure 4.7 shows a well penetrating an unconfined aquifer which is recharged uniformly at rate W from rainfall, excess irrigation water, or other surface water sources.[51] The flow Q toward the well increases

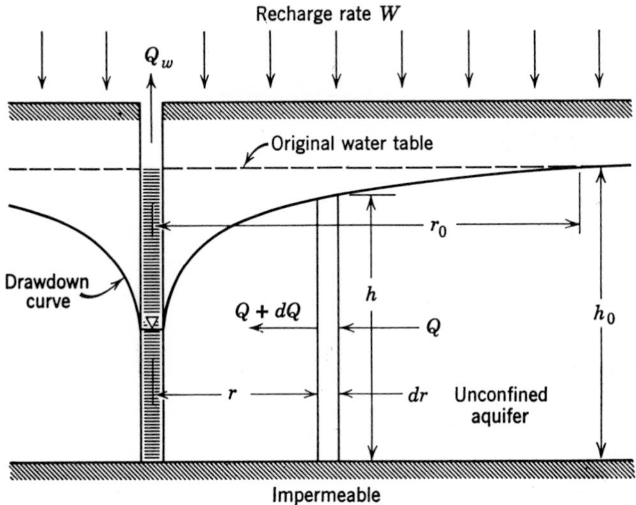

Fig. 4.7. Steady flow to a well penetrating a uniformly recharged unconfined aquifer.

as the well is approached, reaching a maximum of Q_w at the well. The increase in flow dQ through a cylinder of thickness dr and radius r comes from the recharged water entering the cylinder from above, hence

$$dQ = -2\pi r\,dr\,W \tag{4.20}$$

Integrating,

$$Q = -\pi r^2 W + C \tag{4.21}$$

but at the well $r \to 0$ and $Q = Q_w$, so that

$$Q = -\pi r^2 W + Q_w \tag{4.22}$$

Substituting this flow in the equation for flow to the well (Eq. 4.14), gives

$$2\pi r K h \frac{dh}{dr} = -\pi r^2 W + Q_w \tag{4.23}$$

Integrating, and noting that $h = h_0$ at $r = r_0$, yields the equation for the drawdown curve

$$h_0^2 - h^2 = \frac{W}{2K}(r^2 - r_0^2) + \frac{Q_w}{\pi K} \ln \frac{r_0}{r} \tag{4.24}$$

By comparing Eq. 4.24 with Eq. 4.15, the effect of the vertical recharge becomes apparent.

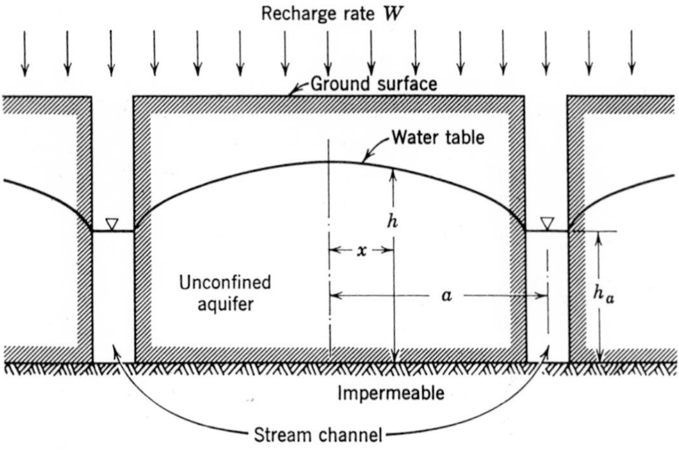

Fig. 4.8. Steady flow to two parallel streams from a uniformly recharged unconfined aquifer.

The above analysis can be carried one step further to yield the radius of influence r_0 independent of the permeability K. Differentiating Eq. 4.24 with respect to r,

$$-2h\frac{dh}{dr} = \frac{rW}{K} - \frac{Q_w}{\pi K}\frac{1}{r} \tag{4.25}$$

But for an extensive aquifer, $dh/dr = 0$ where $r = r_0$; hence Eq. 4.25 reduces to

$$Q_w = \pi r_0^2 W \tag{4.26}$$

Thus, total flow of the well equals the recharge within the circle defined by the radius of influence; conversely, the radius of influence is a function of the well pumpage and the recharge rate only.

Estimates of the base flow of streams (see Chapter 6) or the average ground water recharge can be computed for particular situations. For example, picture the idealized boundaries shown in Fig. 4.8 of two infinitely long parallel streams completely penetrating an unconfined aquifer with a continuous recharge rate W occurring uniformly over the aquifer. It can be shown [29] that the steady-state profile of the water table is expressed by

$$h^2 = h_a^2 + \frac{W}{K}(a^2 - x^2) \tag{4.27}$$

where h, h_a, x, and a are as defined in Fig. 4.8, and K is permeability. From symmetry and continuity

$$Q_b = 2aW \tag{4.28}$$

where Q_b is the base flow entering the stream per unit length of stream channel. If h is known at any point, Q_b or W can be computed provided K is known.

Unsteady Radial Flow to a Well

When a well penetrating an extensive aquifer is pumped at a constant rate, the influence of the discharge extends outward with time. The rate of decline of head times the storage coefficient summed over the area of influence equals the discharge. Because the water must come from a reduction of storage within the aquifer, the head will continue to decline as long as the aquifer is effectively infinite; therefore, no steady state flow can exist. The rate of decline, however, decreases continuously as the area of influence expands.

The differential equation which applies to this situation is Eq. 3.43, which in plane polar coordinates becomes

$$\frac{\partial^2 h}{\partial r^2} + \frac{1}{r}\frac{\partial h}{\partial r} = \frac{S}{T}\frac{\partial h}{\partial t} \tag{4.29}$$

where T is the coefficient of transmissibility ($T = Kb$, where b is the aquifer thickness) and t is the time since beginning of pumping. Theis [53] obtained a solution for Eq. 4.29 based on the analogy between ground water flow and heat conduction. By assuming that the well is replaced by a mathematical sink of constant strength, that $h = h_0$ before pumping begins (see Figs. 4.4 and 4.5), and that $h \to h_0$ as $r \to \infty$ after pumping begins ($t \geq 0$), the solution

$$h_0 - h = \frac{Q}{4\pi T}\int_{r^2S/4Tt}^{\infty} \frac{e^{-u}\,du}{u} \tag{4.30}$$

is obtained where $u = r^2S/4Tt$ and Q is the constant well discharge. Equation 4.30 is known as the nonequilibrium, or Theis, equation. The integral is a function of the lower limit and is known as an exponential integral. It can be expanded as a convergent series so that Eq. 4.30 becomes

$$h_0 - h = \frac{Q}{4\pi T}\left[-0.5772 - \ln u + u - \frac{u^2}{2 \cdot 2!} + \frac{u^3}{3 \cdot 3!} - \frac{u^4}{4 \cdot 4!} + \cdots\right] \tag{4.31}$$

Simpler approximate solutions, described below, have been developed which are sufficiently accurate for field purposes.

Nonequilibrium Equation for Pumping Tests

The nonequilibrium equation permits determination of the formation constants S and T by means of pumping tests of wells, or if the constants are known, the drawdown can be computed for a given well discharge. The assumptions required in applying Eq. 4.30 should be noted: the aquifer is homogeneous and isotropic * and is of infinite areal extent; the well penetrates the entire aquifer; the well diameter is infinitesimal; and the water removed from storage is discharged instantaneously with decline of head. Average values of S and T are obtained in the vicinity of the pumped well by measuring in one or more observation wells the decline of head with time under the influence of a constant pumping rate. Because of the mathematical difficulties encountered in applying Eq. 4.30, or its equivalent Eq. 4.31, several investigators have developed approximate solutions which can be readily applied to obtain desired answers. Three methods, by Theis,[53,60] Jacob,[10,29] and Chow,[9] are described in the following sections with the necessary tables and/or graphs. An illustrative example accompanies each method.

Theis Method of Solution. Using field values, Eq. 4.30 may be expressed as

$$h_0 - h = \frac{114.6Q}{T} W(u) \tag{4.32}$$

where $h_0 - h$ is the drawdown in feet, Q is the well discharge in gal/min, T is the coefficient of transmissibility in gal/day/ft, and $W(u)$ is the exponential integral termed a "well function." The argument u is given by

$$u = \frac{1.87r^2S}{Tt} \tag{4.33}$$

where S is the dimensionless storage coefficient, r is the distance in feet from the discharging well to the observation well, and t is the time in days since pumping started. To obtain the formation constants from pumping test data, Theis [53] suggested an approximate solution based on a graphical method of superposition.

A plot on logarithmic paper of $W(u)$ versus u, known as a "type curve," is prepared. Table 4.1 gives values of $W(u)$ for a wide range

* Aquifers composed of limestone, sandstone, and other types of rock with secondary openings exhibit homogeneous characteristics if sufficiently large volumes are considered. On this basis it has been observed that pumping tests of wells in rock aquifers yield excellent results.

TABLE 4.1 Values of $W(u)$ for Values of u

(After Wenzel [60])

u	1.0	2.0	3.0	4.0	5.0	6.0	7.0	8.0	9.0
$\times 1$	0.219	0.049	0.013	0.0038	0.0011	0.00036	0.00012	0.000038	0.000012
$\times 10^{-1}$	1.82	1.22	0.91	0.70	0.56	0.45	0.37	0.31	0.26
$\times 10^{-2}$	4.04	3.35	2.96	2.68	2.47	2.30	2.15	2.03	1.92
$\times 10^{-3}$	6.33	5.64	5.23	4.95	4.73	4.54	4.39	4.26	4.14
$\times 10^{-4}$	8.63	7.94	7.53	7.25	7.02	6.84	6.69	6.55	6.44
$\times 10^{-5}$	10.94	10.24	9.84	9.55	9.33	9.14	8.99	8.86	8.74
$\times 10^{-6}$	13.24	12.55	12.14	11.85	11.63	11.45	11.29	11.16	11.04
$\times 10^{-7}$	15.54	14.85	14.44	14.15	13.93	13.75	13.60	13.46	13.34
$\times 10^{-8}$	17.84	17.15	16.74	16.46	16.23	16.05	15.90	15.76	15.65
$\times 10^{-9}$	20.15	19.45	19.05	18.76	18.54	18.35	18.20	18.07	17.95
$\times 10^{-10}$	22.45	21.76	21.35	21.06	20.84	20.66	20.50	20.37	20.25
$\times 10^{-11}$	24.75	24.06	23.65	23.36	23.14	22.96	22.81	22.67	22.55
$\times 10^{-12}$	27.05	26.36	25.96	25.67	25.44	25.26	25.11	24.97	24.86
$\times 10^{-13}$	29.36	28.66	28.26	27.97	27.75	27.56	27.41	27.28	27.16
$\times 10^{-14}$	31.66	30.97	30.56	30.27	30.05	29.87	29.71	29.58	29.46
$\times 10^{-15}$	33.96	33.27	32.86	32.58	32.35	32.17	32.02	31.88	31.76

of u. Values of drawdown $h_0 - h$ are plotted against values of r^2/t on logarithmic paper of the same size as for the type curve. The observed data curve is superimposed on the type curve, keeping the coordinate axes of the two curves parallel, and adjusted until a position is found by trial whereby most of the plotted points of the observed data fall on a segment of the type curve. An arbitrary point is selected on the coincident segment, and the coordinates of this matching point are recorded. With values of $W(u)$, u, $h_0 - h$, and r^2/t thus determined, S and T can be obtained from Eqs. 4.32 and 4.33.*

Example of Theis Method. A well penetrating a confined aquifer is pumped at a uniform rate of 500 gpm. Drawdowns during the pumping period are measured in an observation well 200 ft away; observations of t and $h_0 - h$ are listed in Table 4.2. Values of r^2/t in ft^2/day are computed and appear in the right column of Table 4.2. Values of $h_0 - h$ and r^2/t are plotted on logarithmic paper. Values of $W(u)$ and u from Table 4.1 are plotted on another sheet of logarithmic paper and a curve is drawn through the points. The two sheets are superposed and shifted with coordinate axes parallel until the observational points coincide with the curve, shown in Fig. 4.9. A point selected along the

* Two useful devices for reducing computation time have been suggested by Walton.[57] The first avoids the computation of r^2/t values by plotting $h_0 - h$ versus t rather than r^2/t. In this case, the type curve must be turned over to obtain coincidence and a matching point, but results are identical. The second is the selection of a matching point not on the plotted curves but, instead, at the intersection of the major axes of the type curve; for example, where $W(u) = 1.0$ and $u = 0.01$. Two slide rule computations for S and T are thus eliminated.

TABLE 4.2 Pumping Test Data

(From U. S. Geological Survey)

(r = 200 ft)

Time Since Pumping Began, t		Drawdown in Observation Well, $h_0 - h$	r^2/t
Minutes	Days	Feet	Feet^2/Day
0	0	0.00	∞
1.0	6.96×10^{-4}	0.66	5.76×10^{7}
1.5	1.02×10^{-3}	0.87	3.84×10^{7}
2.0	1.39×10^{-3}	0.99	2.88×10^{7}
2.5	1.74×10^{-3}	1.11	2.30×10^{7}
3.0	2.09×10^{-3}	1.21	1.92×10^{7}
4	2.78×10^{-3}	1.36	1.44×10^{7}
5	3.48×10^{-3}	1.49	1.15×10^{7}
6	4.17×10^{-3}	1.59	9.6×10^{6}
8	5.57×10^{-3}	1.75	7.2×10^{6}
10	6.96×10^{-3}	1.86	5.76×10^{6}
12	8.33×10^{-3}	1.97	4.80×10^{6}
14	9.72×10^{-3}	2.08	4.1×10^{6}
18	1.25×10^{-2}	2.20	3.2×10^{6}
24	1.67×10^{-2}	2.36	2.4×10^{6}
30	2.09×10^{-2}	2.49	1.92×10^{6}
40	2.78×10^{-2}	2.65	1.44×10^{6}
50	3.48×10^{-2}	2.78	1.15×10^{6}
60	4.17×10^{-2}	2.88	9.6×10^{5}
80	5.57×10^{-2}	3.04	7.2×10^{5}
100	6.96×10^{-2}	3.16	5.76×10^{5}
120	8.33×10^{-2}	3.28	4.8×10^{5}
150	1.02×10^{-1}	3.42	3.84×10^{5}
180	1.25×10^{-1}	3.51	3.2×10^{5}
210	1.46×10^{-1}	3.61	2.74×10^{5}
240	1.67×10^{-1}	3.67	2.4×10^{5}

coincident segment gives the values $h_0 - h = 1.2$, $r^2/t = 1.95 \times 10^7$, $W(u) = 2.15$, and $u = 7.0 \times 10^{-2}$. Thus from Eq. 4.32,

$$T = \frac{114.6Q}{h_0 - h} W(u) = \frac{(114.6)(500)(2.15)}{1.2} = 103{,}000 \text{ gal/day/ft}$$

and from Eq. 4.33,

$$S = \frac{uT}{1.87r^2/t} = \frac{(7.0 \times 10^{-2})(103{,}000)}{(1.87)(1.95 \times 10^7)} = 0.000198$$

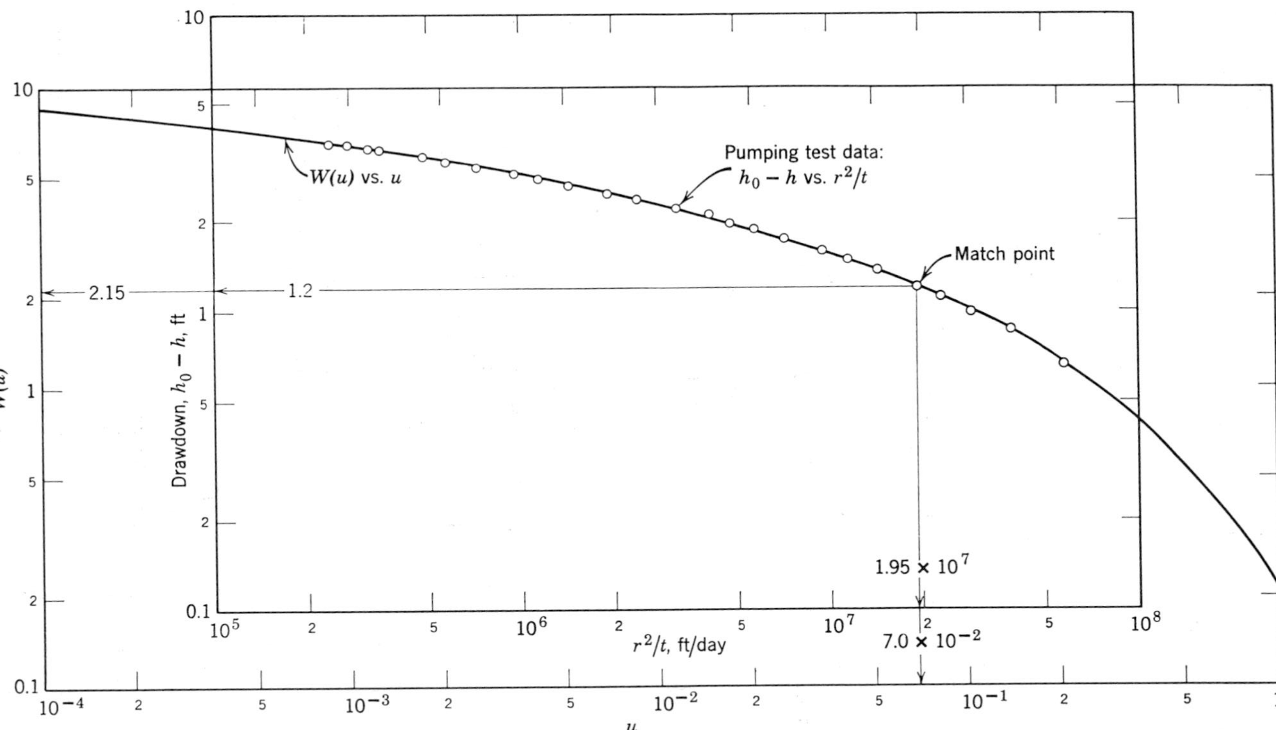

Fig. 4.9. Theis method of superposition for solution of the nonequilibrium equation.

Jacob Method of Solution. Jacob[10, 29] noted that for small values of r and large values of t, u is small, so that the series terms in Eq. 4.31 become negligible after the first two terms. As a result, the drawdown can be expressed by the asymptote

$$h_0 - h = \frac{Q}{4\pi T}\left(-0.5772 - \ln \frac{r^2 S}{4Tt}\right) \tag{4.34}$$

Rewriting as

$$h_0 - h = \frac{Q}{4\pi T}\left(\ln \frac{4Tt}{r^2 S} - 0.5772\right) \tag{4.35}$$

this reduces to

$$h_0 - h = \frac{2.30Q}{4\pi T} \log \frac{2.25Tt}{r^2 S} \tag{4.36}$$

Therefore, a plot of drawdown $h_0 - h$ versus the logarithm of t forms a straight line. From drawdown measurements in an observation well during a pumping period, $h_0 - h$ and t are known and can be plotted. The slope of the line fitting the data enables the formation constants to be computed. Rapid solutions are obtained from

$$T = \frac{264Q}{\Delta h} \tag{4.37}$$

and

$$S = \frac{0.3Tt_0}{r^2} \tag{4.38}$$

where Δh is the drawdown difference in feet per log cycle of time, t_0 is the time intercept on the zero-drawdown axis, and Q and T are expressed again in field units. The straight-line approximation for this method should be restricted to values of u less than about 0.01 to avoid large errors.

Example of Jacob Method. From the pumping test data of Table 4.2, $h_0 - h$ and t are plotted on semilogarithmic paper, as shown in Fig. 4.10. A straight line is fitted through the points, and $\Delta h = 1.30$ ft and $t_0 = 2.60 \times 10^{-4}$ day are read. Thus,

$$T = \frac{264Q}{\Delta h} = \frac{(264)(500)}{1.30} = 102{,}000 \quad \text{gal/day/ft}$$

and

$$S = \frac{0.3Tt_0}{r^2} = \frac{(0.3)(102{,}000)(2.60 \times 10^{-4})}{(200)^2} = 0.000199$$

Chow Method of Solution. Chow[9] developed a method of solution which has the advantages of avoiding curve fitting and being unrestricted in its application. Again, measurements of drawdown in an observation well near a pumped well are made. The observational

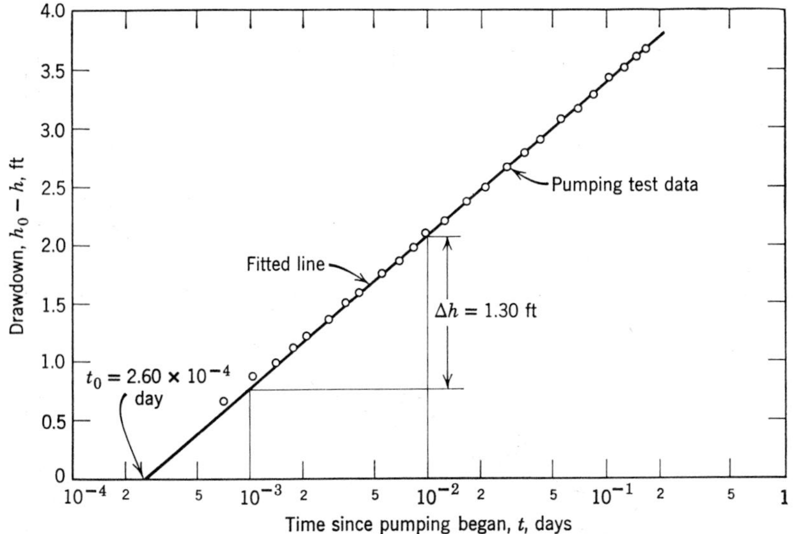

Fig. 4.10. Jacob method for solution of the nonequilibrium equation.

data are plotted on semilogarithmic paper in the same manner as for the Jacob method. On the plotted curve, choose an arbitrary point and note the coordinates, t and $h_0 - h$. Next, draw a tangent to the curve at the chosen point and determine the drawdown difference Δh, in feet, per log cycle of time. Compute $F(u)$ from

$$F(u) = \frac{h_0 - h}{\Delta h} \tag{4.39}$$

and find the corresponding values of $W(u)$ and u from Fig. 4.11.* Finally, compute the formation constants T by Eq. 4.32 and S by Eq. 4.33.

Example of Chow Method. In Fig. 4.12 data are plotted from Table 4.2, and point A is selected on the curve where $t = 4.0 \times 10^{-3}$ day and $h_0 - h =$ 1.55 ft. A tangent is constructed as shown; the drawdown difference per log cycle of time is $\Delta h = 1.26$ ft. Then $F(u) = 1.55/1.26 = 1.23$, and from Fig. 4.11, $W(u) = 2.72$ and $u = 0.038$. Hence

$$T = \frac{114.6Q}{h_0 - h} W(u) = \frac{(114.6)(500)(2.72)}{1.55} = 101{,}000 \text{ gal/day/ft}$$

and

$$S = \frac{uTt}{1.87r^2} = \frac{(0.038)(101{,}000)(4.0 \times 10^{-3})}{1.87(200)^2} = 0.000205$$

* For $F(u) > 2.0$, $W(u) = 2.30F(u)$, and u is obtained from Table 4.1.

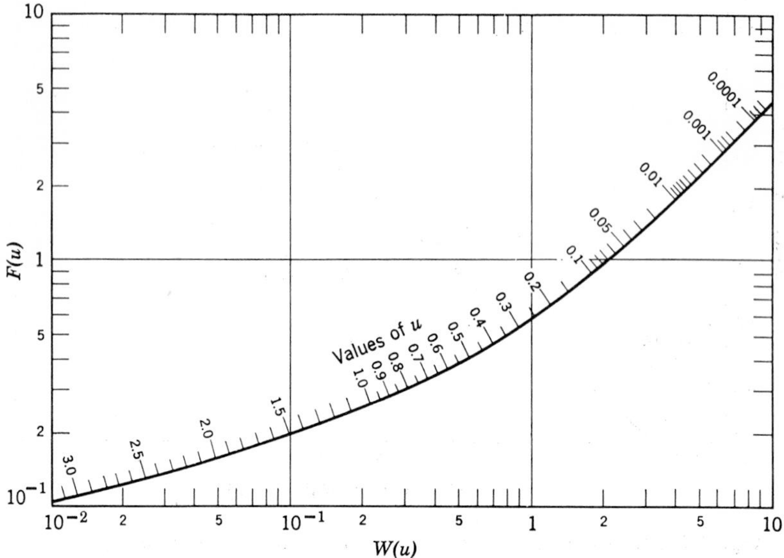

Fig. 4.11. Relation among $F(u)$, $W(u)$, and u (after Chow [9]).

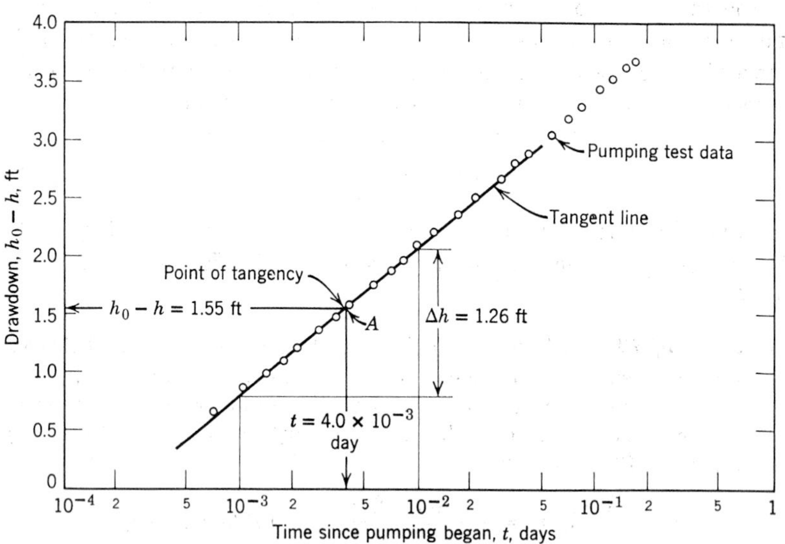

Fig. 4.12. Chow method for solution of the nonequilibrium equation.

The above examples refer to a confined aquifer, but the nonequilibrium equation can be applied also to unconfined aquifers when the drawdown is small compared to the total saturated thickness. In the derivation of the equation it was assumed that the water released from storage by lowering the head was released instantaneously. In unconfined aquifers, however, the storage coefficient is equivalent to the specific yield, a value which is attained only after the dewatered portion of the aquifer has drained for some time. Hence, to apply the nonequilibrium equation in unconfined aquifers, T is first determined and S is approximated by plotting values determined during the test period against log t and extrapolating the trend to an ultimate value. Jacob [29] suggested that more accurate values of T and S are obtained by subtracting $(h_0 - h)^2/2h_0$ from each drawdown.

The nonequilibrium equation is applicable for analysis of the recovery of a pumped well.[53] If a well is pumped for a known period of time and then shut down, the drawdown thereafter will be identically the same as if the discharge had been continued and a recharge well with the same flow were superposed on the discharged well at the instant the discharge is shut down.* The residual drawdown, $h_0 - h'$, where h' is the head during the recovery period, can be given as

$$h_0 - h' = \frac{Q}{4\pi T}\left[\int_{r^2S/4Tt}^{\infty} \frac{e^{-u}\,du}{u} - \int_{r^2S/4Tt'}^{\infty} \frac{e^{-u}\,du}{u}\right] \tag{4.40}$$

where t is the time since pumping started and t' is the time since pumping stopped. For r small and t' large, the exponential integrals can be approximated by the first two terms of Eq. 4.31 and the coefficient of transmissibility given by

$$T = \frac{2.30Q}{4\pi(h_0 - h')} \log \frac{t}{t'} \tag{4.41}$$

By measuring the rate of recovery of water level in a pumped well or a nearby observation well, T can be determined. For convenience in obtaining a solution, residual drawdowns $h_0 - h'$ should be plotted on a linear scale against t/t' on a logarithmic scale. Then T, similar to the Jacob method previously described, reduces to

$$T = \frac{264Q}{\Delta h'} \tag{4.42}$$

* An advantage of a recovery analysis of a pumped well is that it provides an easy check on pumping test results; also, it implies a constant discharge Q, which often is difficult to control accurately in the field.

where T is in gal/day/ft, Q in gal/min, and $\Delta h'$ is the change in residual drawdown, in feet, per log cycle of time. The value of S can be found from Eq. 4.38.

Solutions for Special Conditions. A variety of solutions to the nonequilibrium equation have been derived for special aquifer and pumping conditions. Inasmuch as these are of less general application than those outlined before and involve more extensive mathematical treatment, they will be omitted here. It is worth noting, however, that solutions have been obtained for pumping tests in which the drawdown is held constant and the discharge varies with time.[30] Problems of varying discharge in a prescribed manner also have been solved.[28,49] For example, if a well is pumped in a stepwise fashion, as sketched in Fig. 4.13, the nonequilibrium equation can be written to express the sum of the drawdowns at any time t for the incremental increases in Q up to that time. Similarly, cyclic or intermittent operation of a well can be treated.

Problems involving semiconfined aquifers, which may gain or lose water through adjacent semipermeable strata, have been solved by Jacob and others.[24,27] Rarely are confining beds completely impermeable; most of the time it is implicitly assumed that the flow is so slow as to be negligible. In many locations, however, this assumption fails; hence analyses of aquifer and well flows in these so-called "leaky" aquifers become important.

Well Flow Near Aquifer Boundaries

Even though aquifer boundaries in reality are not infinite, the error introduced in applying one of the above radial flow equations to a well located near an aquifer boundary may be insignificant. For

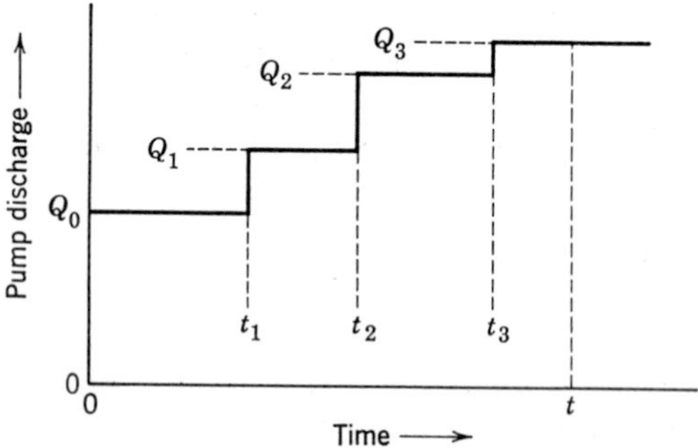

Fig. 4.13. Example of step-type pumping test.

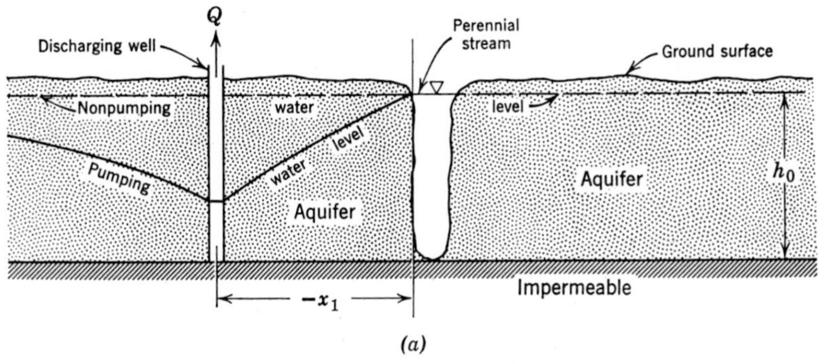

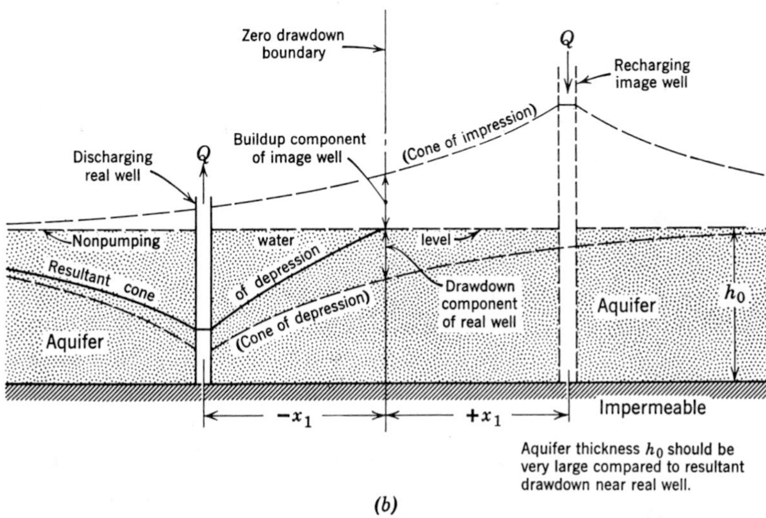

Fig. 4.14. Sectional views of (*a*) a discharging well near a perennial stream, and (*b*) the equivalent hydraulic system in an aquifer of infinite areal extent (after U. S. Geological Survey).

example, a comparison was made [40] between flow to a well located in the center of a circular boundary of radius r_0 (radial flow case) and flow to a well displaced a distance δ from the center. It was found that the discharges differed by less than 5 per cent when the eccentricity amounted to as much as $\delta/r_0 = 0.50$. Therefore, unless a well is located close to a boundary, the radial flow equations can be applied without appreciable error.

The solution of boundary problems in well flow often can be simpli-

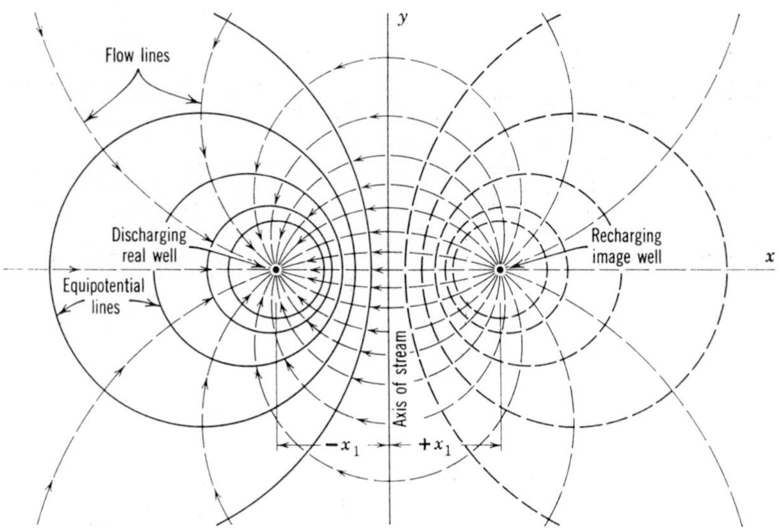

Fig. 4.15. Flow net for discharging real well and recharging image well (after U. S. Geological Survey).

fied by applying the method of images.[14, 29] An image is an imaginary well or stream introduced to create a hydraulic flow system which will be equivalent to the effects of a known physical boundary on the flow system. With images an aquifer of finite extent can be transformed to one of infinite extent, so that the radial flow equations can be applied to this substitute system.

Well Flow Near a Stream. An excellent example of the usefulness of the method of images is the situation of a well near a perennial stream.[14, 18, 29, 34, 55] It is desired to obtain the head at any point under the influence of pumping at a constant rate Q and to determine what fraction of the pumpage is derived from the stream. Sectional views are shown in Fig. 4.14 of the real system and an equivalent imaginary system. Note in Fig. 4.14*b* that an imaginary recharge well * has been placed directly opposite and at the same distance from the stream as the real well. This image well operates simultaneously and at the same rate as the real well so that the buildup (increase of head around a recharge well) and drawdown of head along the line of the stream exactly cancel. This furnishes a constant head along the

* A recharge well is a well through which water is added to an aquifer, hence it is the reverse of a pumping well.

stream, which is exactly equivalent to the constant elevation of the stream forming the aquifer boundary. Thus, in the plan view of the resulting flow net, illustrated by Fig. 4.15, is shown a single equipotential line coincident with the axis of the stream. The resultant asymmetrical drawdown of the real well is given at any point by the algebraic sum of the drawdown of the real well and the buildup of the recharge well, as if these wells were located in an infinite aquifer.

Solution of the hydraulically equivalent system under steady state conditions for the head anywhere on the pumping well side of the stream is given by

$$h_0 - h = \frac{Q}{4\pi T} \ln \frac{(x - x_1)^2 + y^2}{(x + x_1)^2 + y^2} \tag{4.43}$$

where $h_0 - h$ is the drawdown at any point (x, y), defined by the coordinates in Fig. 4.15. A pumping well is located at $(-x_1, 0)$ and a recharge well at $(+x_1, 0)$, both operating at a rate Q.

Further analysis of the flow distribution yields the fraction Q_s/Q of the well discharge which is obtained from the stream, Q_s being the flow from the stream. The result for nonequilibrium conditions can be expressed as a convergent series or in terms of a probability integral, but the dimensionless graphical solution presented in Fig. 4.16 simplifies computations. Here x_1 is the distance from the well to the stream, K is the permeability, b is the aquifer thickness, S is the storage coefficient, and t is the time from start of pumping. The same result applies to an unconfined aquifer by replacing S with specific yield, providing the drawdown is small compared to the saturated thickness.

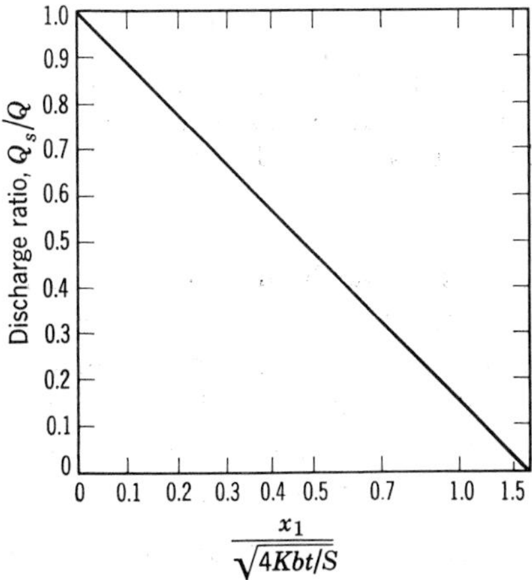

Fig. 4.16. Graph for determining the portion of well discharge furnished by a nearby stream (after Glover and Balmer [18]).

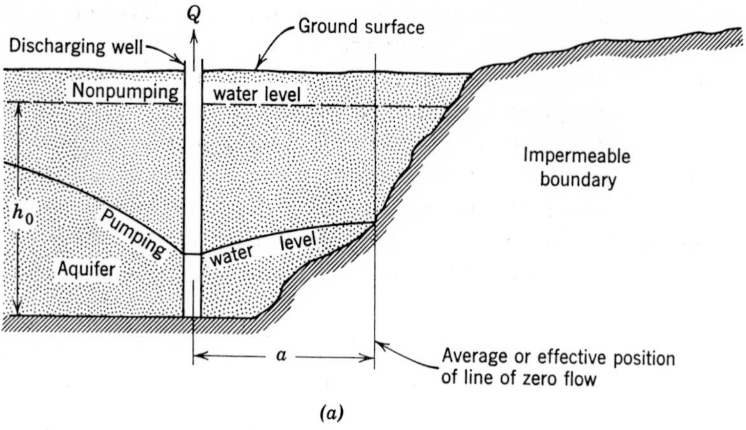

(a)

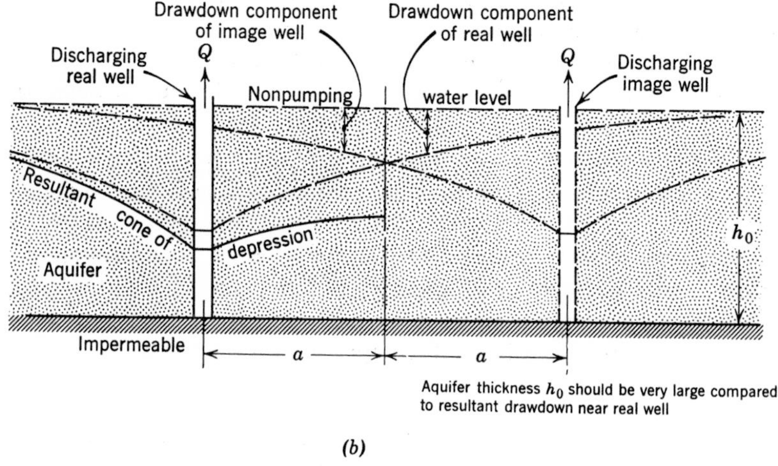

(b)

Fig. 4.17. Sectional views of (a) a discharging well near an impermeable boundary, and (b) the equivalent hydraulic system in an aquifer of infinite areal extent (after U. S. Geological Survey).

Well Flow Near Other Boundaries. In addition to the previous example, the method of images can be applied to a large number of ground water boundary problems. As before, actual boundaries are replaced by an equivalent hydraulic system, which includes imaginary wells and permits solutions to be obtained from equations applicable only to extensive aquifers.* Three boundary conditions to suggest

* The converse situation can also be solved. If a pumping test is conducted in an area where no prior geologic knowledge is available, the method of images can be applied to locate aquifer boundaries. Changes in slope of a drawdown-

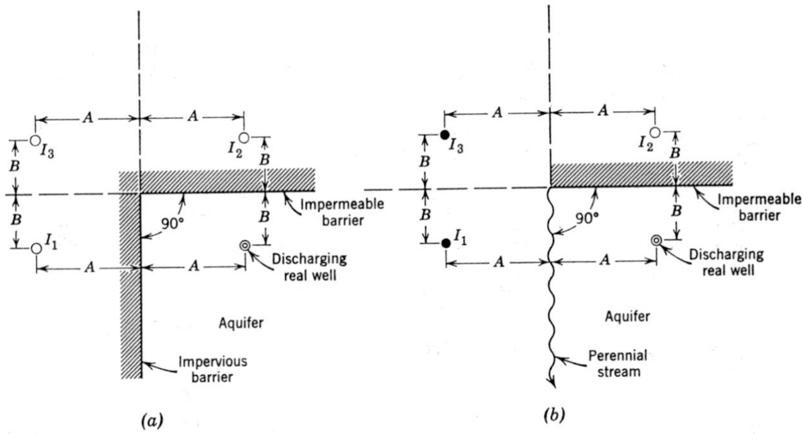

Fig. 4.18. Image well systems for a discharging well near aquifer boundaries: (*a*) aquifer bounded by two impermeable barriers intersecting at right angles, and (*b*) aquifer bounded by an impermeable barrier intersected at right angles by a perennial stream. Open circles are discharging image wells; filled circles are recharging image wells (after U. S. Geological Survey).

the adaptability of the method are shown in Figs. 4.17 and 4.18. Figure 4.17 shows a well pumping near an impermeable boundary. An image discharging well is placed opposite the pumping well with the same rate of discharge and at an equal distance from the boundary; therefore, along the boundary the wells offset one another, causing no flow across the boundary, which is the desired condition. Figure 4.18*a* shows a discharging well in an aquifer bounded on two sides by impermeable barriers. The image discharge wells I_1 and I_2 provide the required flow but, in addition, a third image well I_3 is necessary to balance drawdowns along the extensions of the boundaries. The resulting system of four discharging wells in an extensive aquifer represents hydraulically the flow system for the physical boundary conditions. Finally, Fig. 4.18*b* presents the situation of a well near an impermeable boundary and a perennial stream. The image wells required follow from the previous illustrations.

Multiple Well Systems

A common problem is to determine the interference produced by a group of pumping wells. For a given well field, the drawdown can be

time curve indicate the presence of boundaries. Analysis of such changes from multiple observation wells enables boundaries to be located.[14]

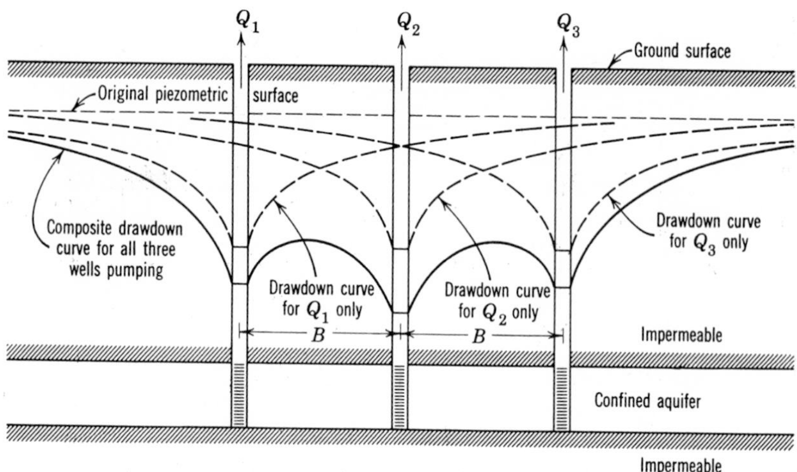

Fig. 4.19. Individual and composite drawdown curves for three wells in a line.

determined at any point if the well discharges are known, or vice versa. The drawdown at any point in the area of influence caused by the discharge of several wells is equal to the sum of the drawdowns caused by each well individually. Thus,

$$D_T = D_a + D_b + D_c + \cdots + D_n \tag{4.44}$$

where D_T is the total drawdown at a given point and $D_a, D_b, D_c, \cdots, D_n$ are the drawdowns at the point caused by the discharge of wells a, b, c, $\cdots$, n, respectively. The summation of drawdowns may be illustrated in a simple way by the well line of Fig. 4.19; the individual and composite drawdown curves are given for $Q_1 = Q_2 = Q_3$. Obviously the number of wells and the geometry of the well field are important in determining drawdowns. Solutions may be based on the equilibrium or nonequilibrium equation.

For a well field pumping from a confined aquifer, it follows that for n pumping wells

$$h_0 - h = \sum_i^n \frac{Q_i}{2\pi Kb} \ln \frac{R_i}{r_i} \tag{4.45}$$

where $h_0 - h$ is the drawdown at a given point in the area of influence, R_i is the distance from the ith well to a point at which the drawdown becomes negligible, and r_i is the distance from the ith well to the given point. The corresponding equation for an unconfined aquifer, valid only for relatively small drawdowns, is

$$h_0^2 - h^2 = \sum_i^n \frac{Q_i}{\pi K} \ln \frac{R_i}{r_i} \tag{4.46}$$

Equations of well discharge for particular well patterns can be stated from procedures developed by Muskat.[40] In the following equations it is assumed that all wells penetrate a confined aquifer, have the same diameter and drawdown, and discharge over the same period of time. Two wells a distance B apart (Fig. 4.20) have discharges Q_1 and Q_2 given by

$$Q_1 = Q_2 = \frac{2\pi Kb(h_0 - h_w)}{\ln (R^2/r_w B)} \tag{4.47}$$

where h_0 is the average piezometric head at the external boundary, h_w is that at the wells, R is the radius of the area of influence ($R \gg B$), and r_w is the well radius. Similarly, for three wells forming an equilateral triangle a distance B on a side,

$$Q_1 = Q_2 = Q_3 = \frac{2\pi Kb(h_0 - h_w)}{\ln (R^3/r_w B^2)} \tag{4.48}$$

With a line of three equally spaced wells a distance B apart, the outer wells discharge at

$$Q_1 = Q_3 = \frac{2\pi Kb(h_0 - h_w) \ln (B/r_w)}{2 \ln (R/B) \ln (B/r_w) + \ln (B/2r_w) \ln (R/r_w)} \tag{4.49}$$

whereas the middle well discharges at

$$Q_2 = \frac{2\pi Kb(h_0 - h_w) \ln (B/2r_w)}{2 \ln (R/B) \ln (B/r_w) + \ln (B/2r_w) \ln (R/r_w)} \tag{4.50}$$

The discharge of each of four wells forming a square of side B is

$$Q_1 = Q_2 = Q_3 = Q_4 = \frac{2\pi Kb(h_0 - h_w)}{\ln (R^4/\sqrt{2}\, r_w B^3)} \tag{4.51}$$

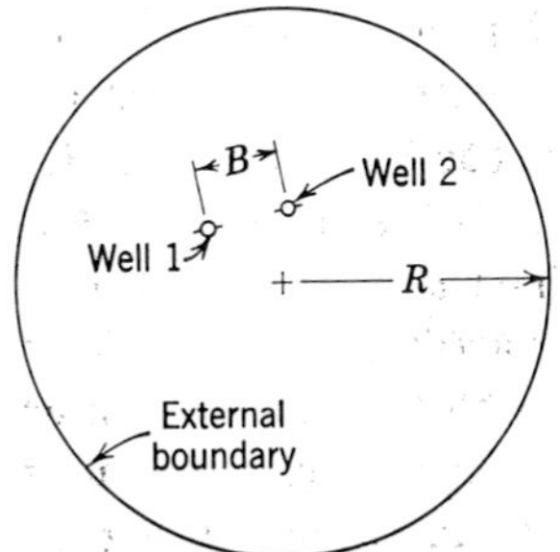

Fig. 4.20. Two interfering wells.

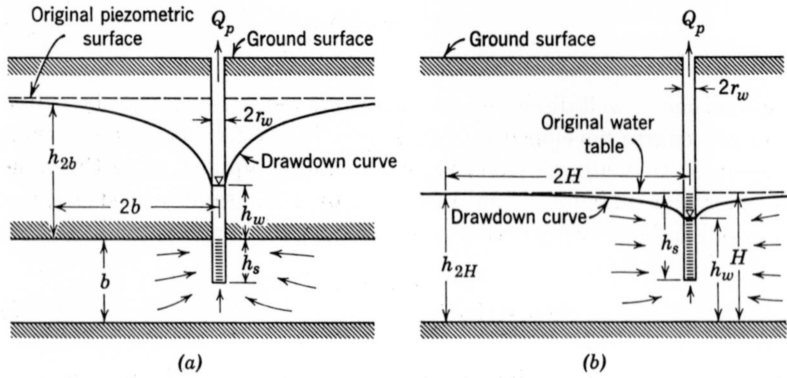

Fig. 4.21. Partially penetrating wells in (*a*) confined and (*b*) unconfined aquifers.

And finally, if a fifth well is pumped in the center of the previous square, the corner wells yield

$$Q_1 = Q_2 = Q_3 = Q_4$$
$$= \frac{2\pi Kb(h_0 - h_w)\ln(B/\sqrt{2}\,r_w)}{4\ln(\sqrt{2}R/B)\ln(B/\sqrt{2}\,r_w) + \ln(R/r_w)\ln(B/4\sqrt{2}\,r_w)} \qquad (4.52)$$

but the center well discharges only

$$Q_5 = \frac{2\pi Kb(h_0 - h_w)\ln(B/4\sqrt{2}\,r_w)}{4\ln(\sqrt{2}\,R/B)\ln(B/\sqrt{2}\,r_w) + \ln(R/r_w)\ln(B/4\sqrt{2}\,r_w)} \qquad (4.53)$$

The above equations (4.47 to 4.53) can be modified for application to unconfined aquifers by replacing h_0 by $h_0^2/2b$ and h_w by $h_w^2/2b$.

Partially Penetrating Wells

A well whose length of water entry is less than the aquifer which it penetrates is known as a partially penetrating well. Figure 4.21 illustrates situations of partially penetrating wells in confined and unconfined aquifers. Obviously the flow pattern to such wells differs from the radial flow assumed to exist around fully penetrating wells. The average length of a flow line into a partially penetrating well exceeds that into a fully penetrating well so that a greater resistance to flow is thus encountered. For practical purposes this results in the following relationships between two similar wells, one partially and one fully penetrating the same aquifer:

$$\text{If } Q_p = Q, \text{ then } (\Delta h)_p > \Delta h;$$
$$\text{and if } (\Delta h)_p = \Delta h, \text{ then } Q_p < Q.$$

Here Q is well discharge, Δh is drawdown at the well, and the subscript p refers to the partially penetrating well. Beyond a distance of twice the saturated thickness from the well, the effect of partial penetration is negligible on the flow pattern and the drawdown.

The analysis of partially penetrating wells is complicated except in the simplest cases. The problem has been investigated by Boreli,[4] Forchheimer,[16] de Glee,[17] Kozeny,[35] Muskat,[41] and Nahrgang,[42] among others. The most general solutions have been obtained by treating the well as a line of point sinks.[17,41] An infinite array of images along the well axis is necessary to satisfy the boundary conditions. Summing the potentials of the individual elements yields a potential distribution equivalent to a partially penetrating well.

For a well penetrating only the upper portion of a confined aquifer, the drawdown $h_{2b} - h_w$, as defined by Fig. 4.21a, can be expressed[17] for assumed steady state conditions as

$$h_{2b} - h_w = \frac{Q_p}{4\pi K}\left[\frac{2}{h_s}\ln\frac{\pi h_s}{2r_w} + \frac{0.20}{b}\right] \tag{4.54}$$

where K is permeability and other symbols are identified in Fig. 4.21a. The equation is valid for $1.3h_s \leq b$ and $h_s/2r_w \geq 5$. Because the drawdown curve beyond $2b$ can be closely approximated by the curve for a fully penetrating well (Eq. 4.11), the total drawdown of the partially penetrating well becomes

$$h_0 - h_w = \frac{Q_p}{2\pi K}\left[\frac{1}{h_s}\ln\frac{\pi h_s}{2r_w} + \frac{0.10}{b} + \frac{1}{b}\ln\frac{r_0}{2b}\right] \tag{4.55}$$

where h_0 is the head at the radius of influence r_0 from the well. Dividing Eq. 4.55 by the comparable expression for a fully penetrating well gives the discharge ratio

$$\frac{Q_p}{Q} = \frac{\ln (r_0/r_w)}{(b/h_s)\ln(\pi h_s/2r_w) + 0.10 + \ln(r_0/2b)} \tag{4.56}$$

where Q is the discharge of a similar fully penetrating well with the same total drawdown. Thus, a direct determination can be made of the effect of a partially penetrating well on its yield. In Fig. 4.22 appears a graph of Eq. 4.56 for estimating the discharge ratio from the penetration fraction h_s/b and the well slimness $h_s/2r_w$ with $r_0/r_w = 1000$. For example, if a 12-in. well penetrates only 20 ft into a 50-ft confined aquifer, then $h_s/b = 0.40$ and $h_s/2r_w = 20$. From Fig. 4.22, $Q_p/Q = 0.57$, in-

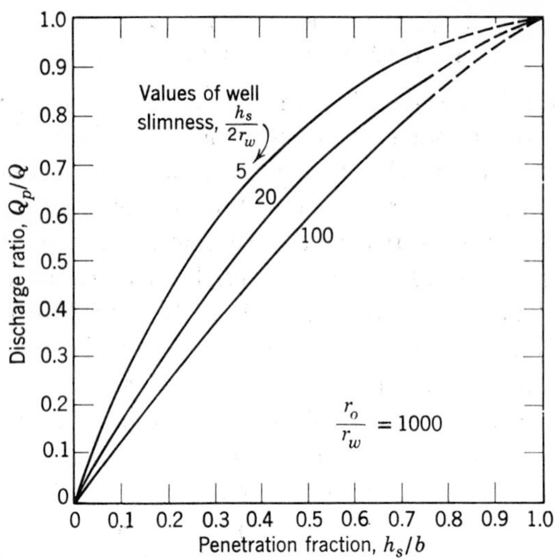

Fig. 4.22. Discharge of a partially penetrating well Q_p to that of a fully penetrating well Q for the same drawdown as a function of the penetration fraction and well slimness.

dicating that for a given drawdown the partially penetrating well yields only 57 per cent of what a similar fully penetrating well would yield for the same drawdown. Equations 4.54 to 4.56 apply equally to a well whose perforations begin at the bottom of the aquifer but do not extend to the top.

For partially penetrating wells in unconfined aquifers (Fig. 4.21*b*), the drawdown expression

$$h_{2H} - h_w = \frac{Q_p}{4\pi K}\left[\frac{2}{h_s}\ln\frac{\pi h_s}{2r_w} + \frac{0.20}{H}\right] \tag{4.57}$$

gives a good approximation where the drawdown is small in relation to the saturated thickness H. The similarity of Eqs. 4.57 and 4.54 make Eq. 4.56 and Fig. 4.22 valid for determining the discharge ratio Q_p/Q in unconfined aquifers by replacing b by H.

Partially penetrating wells in aquifers of anisotropic permeability have been treated by Muskat [41] and in semiconfined aquifers by de Glee.[17]

Characteristic Well Losses

The drawdown at a well includes not only that of the logarithmic drawdown curve at the well face, but also a well loss caused by flow through the well screen and flow inside of the well to the pump intake. Because the well loss is associated with turbulent flow, it may be indicated as being proportional to an nth power of the discharge, as Q^n, where n is a constant greater than one. Jacob [28] suggested that a value $n = 2$ might be reasonably assumed, but Rorabaugh [49] pointed out that n may deviate significantly from 2 and should be computed from step-drawdown pumping tests. An exact value for n cannot be stated because of differences of individual wells; detailed investigations of flows inside and outside of wells show that considerable variations occur from assumed flow distributions.[37,43]

Taking account of the well loss, the total drawdown D_w at the well may be written for the confined case

$$D_w = h_0 - h_w = \frac{Q}{2\pi Kb} \ln \frac{r_0}{r_w} + CQ^n \tag{4.58}$$

where C is a constant governed by the radius, construction, and condition of the well. For simplicity let

$$B = \frac{\ln (r_0/r_w)}{2\pi Kb} \tag{4.59}$$

so that

$$D_w = BQ + CQ^n \tag{4.60}$$

Therefore, as shown in Fig. 4.23, the total drawdown D_w consists of the aquifer loss BQ and the well loss CQ^n.

It is apparent that well losses can be minimized by keeping velocities into and within wells to a minimum. In this connection the relation between well discharge and well size should be noted. From Eqs. 4.10 and 4.15 it can be seen that Q is inversely proportional to $\ln (r_0/r_w)$, if all other variables are held constant. Study of this relation shows that discharge varies only a small amount with well radius. For example, increasing a well radius from 6 in. to 12 in. increases the discharge 10 per cent. However, when the comparison is extended to include well loss, the effect is significant. Doubling the well radius doubles the intake area, reduces entrance velocities to almost half, and (if $n = 2$) cuts the frictional loss to less than a third. For axial flow within the well, the area increases four times, reducing this loss an even greater extent.

For relatively low pumping rates well loss may be neglected, but for high pumping rates it can represent a sizable fraction of the total drawdown. Data from Rorabaugh [49] plotted in Fig. 4.24 illustrate the variation of well loss with discharge. For a screen size compatible

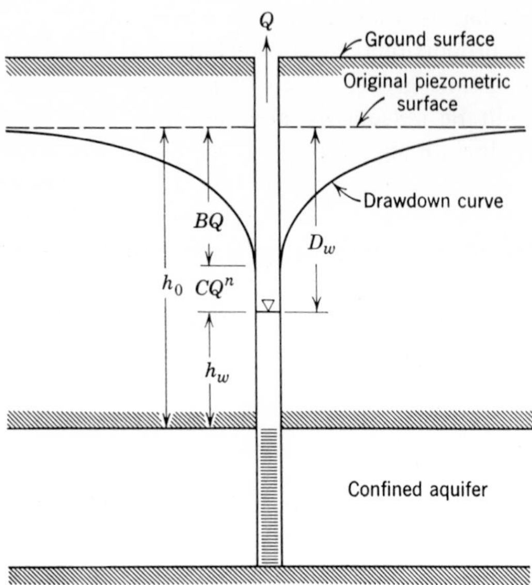

Fig. 4.23. Relation of well loss CQ^n to drawdown for a well penetrating a confined aquifer.

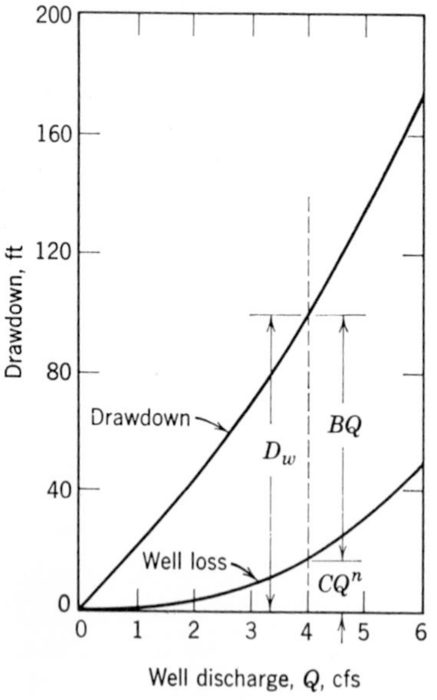

Fig. 4.24. Variation of total drawdown D_w, aquifer loss BQ, and well loss CQ^n with well discharge (after Rorabaugh[49]).

to the surrounding porous media and which is not clogged or encrusted, the portion of the well loss caused by water entering the well is small in comparison with the portion resulting from axial movement within the well.[37]

If the discharge is divided by the drawdown of the well, the specific capacity is obtained. This is a measure of the effectiveness of the well. Solving Eq. 4.60 for the specific capacity,

$$\frac{Q}{D_w} = \frac{1}{B + CQ^{n-1}} \tag{4.61}$$

which indicates, for approximately steady flow, that the specific capacity of a well is not constant, as is sometimes assumed; rather it decreases with increasing Q. An analogous situation can be demonstrated for the unconfined case.

Turning now to the nonequilibrium equation, it can be demonstrated that the specific capacity of a well varies not only with Q but also with the time t. Thus, from the approximate solution given by Eq. 4.36

$$D_w = \frac{2.30Q}{4\pi T} \log \frac{2.25Tt}{r_w{}^2S} + CQ^n \tag{4.62}$$

and

$$\frac{Q}{D_w} = \frac{1}{(2.30/4\pi T) \log (2.25Tt/r_w{}^2S) + CQ^{n-1}} \tag{4.63}$$

showing that the specific capacity decreases with Q and t. This effect is demonstrated by well data plotted in Fig. 4.25. Hence the practice of assuming that the discharge is directly proportional to drawdown, implying a constant specific capacity, can introduce sizable errors.

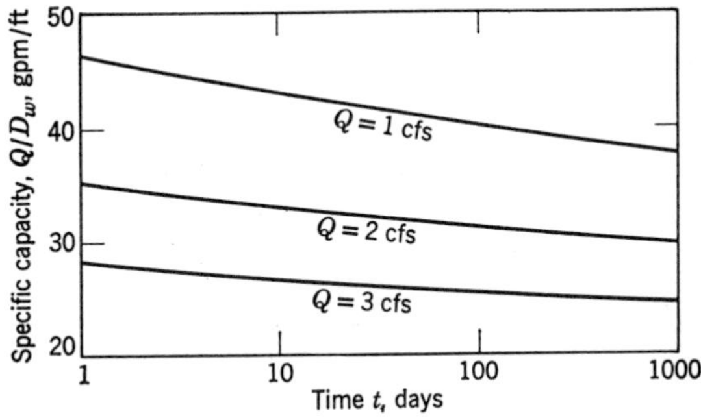

Fig. 4.25. Variation in specific capacity of a pumping well with discharge and time (after Jacob [28]).

References

1. Ahmad, N., Dynamics of ground water with special reference to tube wells, *Proc. Ankara Symposium on Arid Zone Hydrology,* UNESCO, Paris, pp. 77–98, 1953.
2. Avery, S. B., Analysis of ground-water lowering adjacent to open water, *Trans. Amer. Soc. Civil Engrs.,* vol. 118, pp. 178–208, 1953.
3. Babbitt, H. E., and D. H. Caldwell, The free surface around, and the interference between, gravity wells, *Univ. Illinois Eng. Exp. Sta. Bull.* 374, 60 pp., 1948.
4. Boreli, M., Free-surface flow toward partially penetrating wells, *Trans. Amer. Geophysical Union,* vol. 36, pp. 664–672, 1955.
5. Breitenoder, M., *Ebene Grundwasserströmungen mit freier Oberfläche,* Springer-Verlag, Berlin, 127 pp., 1942.
6. Brown, R. H., Selected procedure for analyzing aquifer test data, *Jour. Amer Water Works Assoc.,* vol. 45, pp. 844–866, 1953.
7. Bruin, J., and H. E. Hudson, Jr., Selected methods for pumping test analysis, *Rep. Investigation* 25, Illinois State Water Survey Div., Urbana, 54 pp., 1955.
8. Chow, V. T., Drawdown in artesian wells computed by nomograph, *Civil Eng.,* vol. 21, no. 10, pp. 48–49, 1951.
9. Chow, V. T., On the determination of transmissibility and storage coefficients from pumping test data, *Trans. Amer. Geophysical Union,* vol. 33, pp. 397–404, 1952.
10. Cooper, H. H., Jr., and C. E. Jacob, A generalized graphical method for evaluating formation constants and summarizing well-field history, *Trans. Amer. Geophysical Union,* vol. 27, pp. 526–534, 1946.
11. Dachler, R., *Grundwasserströmung,* J. Springer, Vienna, 141 pp., 1936.
12. Dupuit, J., *Études théoriques et pratiques sur la mouvement des eaux dans les canaux découverts et à travers les terrains perméables,* 2nd ed., Dunod, *Paris,* 304 pp., 1863.
13. Eliason, O. L., and W. Gardner, Computing the effective diameter of a well battery by means of Darcy's law, *Agric. Eng.,* vol. 14, pp. 53–54, 1933.
14. Ferris, J. G., Ground water, in *Hydrology* (by C. O. Wisler and E. F. Brater), John Wiley and Sons, New York, pp. 198–272, 1949.
15. Forchheimer, P., Über die Ergiebigkeit von Brunnen-Anlagen und Sickerschlitzen, *Zeitschrift des Architekten- und Ingenieurvereins zu Hannover,* vol. 32, pp. 539–564, 1886.
16. Forchheimer, P., Grundwasserbewegung, in *Hydraulik,* 3rd ed., B. G. Teubner, Leipzig, pp. 51–110, 1930.
17. de Glee, G. J., *Over grondwaterstroomingen bij wateronttrekking door middel van putten,* J. Waltman Jr., Delft, 175 pp., 1930.
18. Glover, R. E., and G. G. Balmer, River depletion resulting from pumping a well near a river, *Trans. Amer. Geophysical Union,* vol. 35, pp. 468–470, 1954.
19. Hall, H. P., A historical review of investigations of seepage toward wells, *Jour. Boston Soc. Civil Engrs.,* vol. 41, pp. 251–311, 1954.
20. Hall, H. P., An investigation of steady flow toward a gravity well, *La Houille Blanche,* vol. 10, pp. 8–35, 1955.

21. Hansen, V. E., Unconfined ground-water flow to multiple wells, *Trans. Amer. Soc. Civil Engrs.,* vol. 118, pp. 1098–1130, 1953.
22. Hantush, M. S., and C. E. Jacob, Plane potential flow of ground water with linear leakage, *Trans. Amer. Geophysical Union,* vol. 35, pp. 917–936, 1954.
23. Hantush, M. S., and C. E. Jacob, Non-steady Green's functions for an infinite strip of leaky aquifer, *Trans. Amer. Geophysical Union,* vol. 36, pp. 101–112, 1955.
24. Hantush, M. S., and C. E. Jacob, Non-steady radial flow in an infinite leaky aquifer, *Trans. Amer. Geophysical Union,* vol. 36, pp. 95–100, 1955.
25. Hantush, M. S., and C. E. Jacob, Steady three-dimensional flow to a well in a two-layered aquifer, *Trans. Amer. Geophysical Union,* vol. 36, pp. 286–292, 1955.
26. Jacob, C. E., On the flow of water in an elastic artesian aquifer, *Trans. Amer. Geophysical Union,* vol. 21, pp. 574–586, 1940.
27. Jacob, C. E., Radial flow in a leaky artesian aquifer, *Trans. Amer. Geophysical Union,* vol. 27, pp. 198–208, 1946.
28. Jacob, C. E., Drawdown test to determine effective radius of artesian well, *Trans. Amer. Soc. Civil Engrs.,* vol. 112, pp. 1047–1070, 1947.
29. Jacob, C. E., Flow of ground water, in *Engineering hydraulics* (H. Rouse, ed.), John Wiley and Sons, New York, pp. 321–386, 1950.
30. Jacob, C. E., and S. W. Lohman, Nonsteady flow to a well of constant drawdown in an extensive aquifer, *Trans. Amer. Geophysical Union,* vol. 33, pp. 559–569, 1952.
31. Jaeger, C., Die Grundwasserströmung, in *Technische Hydraulik,* Verlag Birkhauser, Basel, pp. 353–423, 1949.
32. Kashef, A. I., Y. S. Toulouklan, and R. E. Fadum, Numerical solutions of steady-state and transient flow problems—artesian and water-table wells, *Purdue Univ. Eng. Exp. Sta. Bull.* 117, Lafayette, Ind., 116 pp., 1952.
33. Kazmann, R. G., Notes on determining the effective distance to a line of recharge, *Trans. Amer. Geophysical Union,* vol. 27, pp. 854–859, 1946.
34. Kazmann, R. G., The induced infiltration of river water to wells, *Trans. Amer. Geophysical Union,* vol. 29, pp. 85–92, 1948.
35. Kozeny, J., Theorie und Berechnung der Brunnen, *Wasserkraft und Wasserwirtschaft,* vol. 28, pp. 88–92, 101–105, and 113–116, 1933.
36. Kozeny, J., Das Wasser in Boden, Grundwasserbewegung, in *Hydraulik,* Springer-Verlag, Vienna, pp. 380–445, 1953.
37. Li, W.-H., Interaction between well and aquifer, *Proc. Amer. Soc. Civil Engrs.,* vol. 80, sep. 578, 14 pp., 1954.
38. Meyer, R., A few recent theoretical results concerning ground-water flow, *La Houille Blanche,* vol. 10, pp. 86–108, 1955.
39. Mikels, F. C., and F. H. Klaer, Jr., Application of ground water hydraulics to the development of water supplies by induced infiltration, *Symposia Darcy,* Publ. 41, Assoc. Intl. d'Hydrologie Scientifique, pp. 232–242, 1956.
40. Muskat, M., *The flow of homogeneous fluids through porous media,* McGraw-Hill, New York, 763 pp., 1937.
41. Muskat, M., *Physical principles of oil production,* McGraw-Hill, New York, 922 pp., 1949.
42. Nahrgang, G., *Zur Theorie des vollkommen und unvollkommen Brunnens,* J. Springer, Berlin, 43 pp., 1954.

43. Petersen, J. S., C. Rohwer, and M. L. Albertson, Effect of well screens on flow into wells, *Trans. Amer. Soc. Civil Engrs.*, vol. 120, pp. 563–607, 1955.
44. Peterson, D. F., Jr., Hydraulics of wells, *Proc. Amer. Soc. Civil Engrs.*, vol. 81, sep. 708, 23 pp., 1955.
45. Peterson, D. F., Jr., O. W. Israelson, and V. E. Hansen, Hydraulics of wells, *Agric. Exp. Sta. Bull.* 351, Utah State Agric. College, Logan, 48 pp., 1952.
46. Polubarinova-Kochina, P. Y., *Theory of ground-water movement* (in Russian), Gostekhizdat, Moscow, 676 pp., 1952.
47. Remson, I., and S. M. Lang, A pumping-test method for the determination of specific yield, *Trans. Amer. Geophysical Union,* vol. 36, pp. 321–325, 1955.
48. Remson, I., and T. E. A. van Hylckama, Nomographs for the rapid analysis of aquifer tests, *Jour. Amer. Water Works Assoc.*, vol. 48, pp. 511–516, 1956.
49. Rorabaugh, M. I., Graphical and theoretical analysis of step-drawdown test of artesian well, *Proc. Amer. Soc. Civil Engrs.*, vol. 79, sep. 362, 23 pp., 1953.
50. Sichardt, W., *Das Fassungsvermögen von Rohrbrunnen und seine Bedeutung für die Grundwasserabsenkung, inbesondere für grössere Absenkstiefen,* J. Springer, Berlin, 89 pp., 1928.
51. Steggewentz, J. H., and B. A. Van Nes, Calculating the yield of a well taking account of replenishment of the ground water from above, *Water and Water Eng.*, vol. 41, pp. 561–563, 1939.
52. Theis, C. V., Equations for lines of flow in vicinity of discharging artesian well, *Trans. Amer. Geophysical Union,* vol. 13, pp. 317–320, 1932.
53. Theis, C. V., The relation between the lowering of the piezometric surface and the rate and duration of discharge of a well using ground-water storage, *Trans. Amer. Geophysical Union,* vol. 16, pp. 519–524, 1935.
54. Theis, C. V., The significance and nature of the cone of depression in ground-water bodies, *Econ. Geol.*, vol. 33, pp. 889–902, 1938
55. Theis, C. V., The effect of a well on the flow of a nearby stream, *Trans. Amer. Geophysical Union,* vol. 22, pp. 734–738, 1941.
56. Thiem, G., *Hydrologische Methoden,* Gebhardt, Leipzig, 56 pp., 1906.
57. Walton, W. C., The hydraulic properties of a dolomite aquifer underlying the village of Ada, Ohio, *Tech. Rep.* 1, Ohio Div. Water, Columbus, 31 pp., 1953.
58. Wenzel, L. K., Specific yield determined from a Thiem's pumping-test, *Trans. Amer. Geophysical Union,* vol. 14, pp. 475–477, 1933.
59. Wenzel, L. K., The Thiem method for determining permeability of water-bearing materials and its application to the determination of specific yield, *U. S. Geological Survey Water-Supply Paper* 679-A, Washington, D. C., 57 pp., 1936.
60. Wenzel, L. K., Methods for determining permeability of water-bearing materials with special reference to discharging-well methods, *U. S. Geological Survey Water-Supply Paper* 887, Washington, D. C., 192 pp., 1942.
61. Wenzel, L. K., and A. L. Greenlee, A method for determining transmissibility- and storage-coefficients by tests of multiple well-systems, *Trans. Amer. Geophysical Union,* vol. 24, pp. 547–564, 1943.
62. Yoshida, Y., *The summary of the studies on the collection wells and galleries as sources of water supplies,* Kumamoto, Japan, 96 pp., 1934.

Water Wells

CHAPTER 5

A water well is a hole or shaft, usually vertical, excavated in the earth for bringing ground water to the surface. Occasionally wells serve purposes, such as for subsurface exploration and observation, artificial recharge, and disposal of sewage or industrial wastes. Many methods exist for constructing wells; selection of a particular method depends upon the purpose of the water supply, the quantity of water required, depth to ground water, geologic conditions, and economic factors. Shallow wells are dug, bored, driven, or jetted, and deep wells are drilled by the cable tool, hydraulic rotary, or reverse rotary methods. After a deep well is drilled, it should be completed and developed for optimum yield and tested before installing a pump. For long life, wells should be sealed against entrance of surface contamination and given periodic maintenance. Wells of horizontal extent, including collector wells and infiltration galleries, are constructed where special ground water situations exist.

Test Holes and Well Logs

Before drilling a well in a new area it is common practice to put down a test hole. The purpose of a test hole is to determine depths to ground water, quality of water, and physical character and thickness of aquifers without the expense of a regular well which might prove to be unsuccessful. Diameters seldom exceed 8 to 10 in. Test holes may be put down by any method for well construction; however, the cable tool, hydraulic rotary, and jetting methods are commonly employed. If the test hole appears suitable as a site for a finished well, it can be reamed with hydraulic rotary equipment to convert it into a larger permanent well.

During drilling of a test hole a careful record, or log, is kept of the various formations and the depths at which they are encountered (see Chapter 10). A helpful method is to collect samples of cuttings in glass jars, labeling each with the depth where obtained. Later these can be studied and analyzed for grain size distribution. Many states require licensed well drillers to submit logs, recording depth, color, character, size of material, and structure of the strata penetrated, for wells which they drill. Proper identification of strata in the hydraulic rotary method requires careful analysis because drilling mud is mixed with each sample. A drilling-time log (see Chapter 10) is sometimes helpful in this respect.

Methods for Constructing Shallow Wells

Shallow wells, generally less than 50 feet in depth, are constructed by digging, boring, driving, or jetting. Each method is briefly described in the following paragraphs.

Dug Wells. Dating from Biblical times, dug wells have furnished countless water supplies throughout the world. Depths vary from about 10 to 40 feet, depending on the position of the water table, and diameters are usually several feet. Dug wells can yield relatively large quantities of water from shallow sources and are most extensively employed for individual water supplies in areas containing unconsolidated glacial and alluvial deposits. Their large diameters permit storage of considerable quantities of water.

In the past all dug wells were excavated by hand, and even today the same method is employed throughout much of the world. A pick and shovel are the basic implements. Loose material is hauled to the surface in a container by means of suitable pulleys and lines. Large dug wells can be constructed rapidly with portable excavating equipment such as clam-shell and orange-peel buckets. For safety and to prevent caving, lining (or cribbing) of wood or sheet piling should be placed in the hole to brace the walls. The well is permanently lined with a casing (often referred to as a "curb") of wood staves, brick, rock (Fig. 5.1), concrete, or metal.[11,14,29,36] Curbs should be perforated or contain openings for entry of water and must be firmly

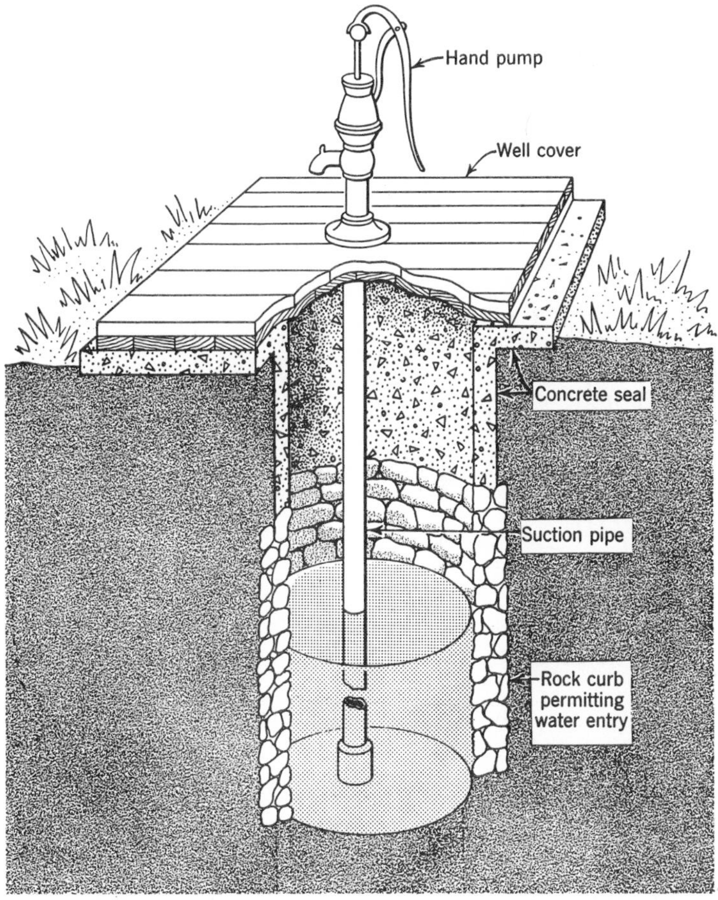

Fig. 5.1. A dug well.

seated at the bottom. Dug wells must be deep enough to extend a few feet (preferably 15 to 20) below the water table. Gravel should be backfilled around the curb and at the bottom of the well to control sand entry and possible caving. A properly constructed dug well penetrating a permeable aquifer can yield 500 to 1500 gpm, although most domestic dug wells yield less than 100 gpm.

Bored Wells. Where a water table exists at a shallow depth in an unconsolidated aquifer, bored wells can furnish small quantities of water at minimum cost.[11, 14, 29, 36] Bored wells are constructed with hand-operated or power-driven earth augers. Hand augers are available in several shapes and sizes, all operating with cutting blades at

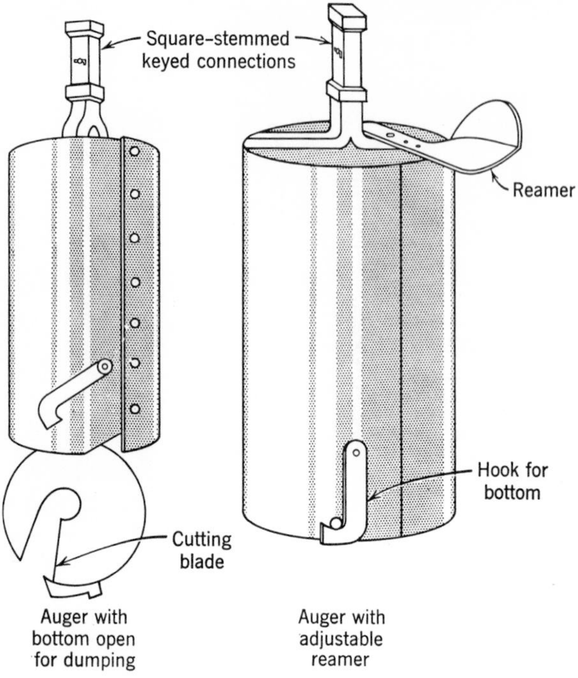

Fig. 5.2. Augers for boring wells.

the bottom which bore into the ground with a rotary motion. When the blades are full of loose earth the auger is removed from the hole and emptied, the operation being repeated until the desired hole depth is reached. Hand-bored wells seldom exceed 6 or 8 in. in diameter and 50 ft in depth. Power-driven augers will bore holes up to 36 in. in diameter and, under favorable conditions, to depths exceeding 100 ft. The auger consists of a cylindrical steel bucket (Fig. 5.2) with a cutting edge projecting from a slot in the bottom. The bucket is filled by rotating it in the hole by a drive shaft of adjustable length. When full, the auger is hoisted to the surface and the excavated material is removed through hinged openings on the side or bottom of the bucket. Reamers, attached to the top of the bucket, can enlarge holes to diameters exceeding the auger size.

Augers work best in formations which do not cave. Where loose sand and gravel are encountered, or the boring reaches the water table, it is necessary to lower a casing to the bottom of the hole and continue boring inside. Casings may be made of concrete, tile, or metal. Augers sometimes supplement other well drilling methods where sticky clay

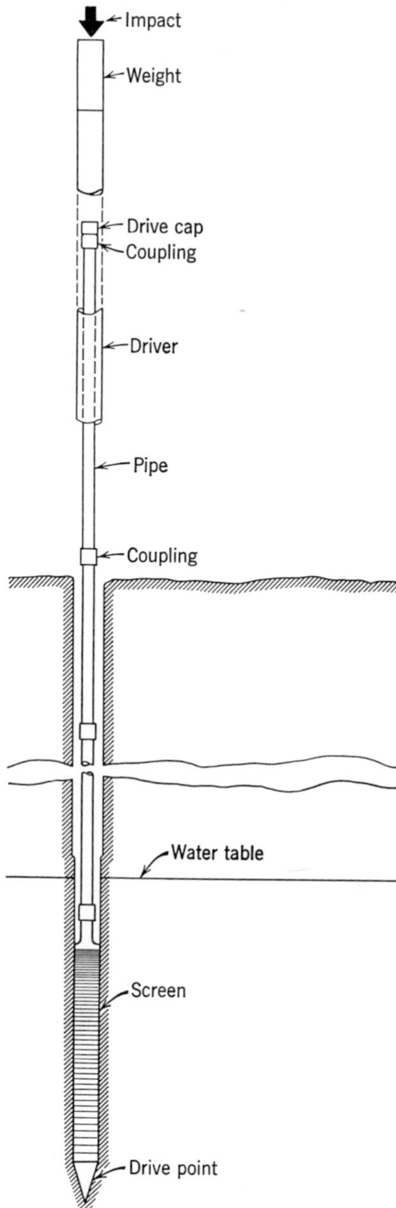

Fig. 5.3. A driven well with driving mechanism.

formations are encountered; here augers are more effective than any other penetrating device.

Driven Wells. A driven well consists of a series of connected lengths of pipe driven by repeated impacts into the ground to below the water table.[11, 14, 29, 36] Water enters the well through a drive (or sand) point at the lower end of the well (Fig. 5.3). This consists of a screened cylindrical section protected during driving by a steel cone at the bottom. Diameters of driven wells are small, most falling in the range of 1¼ to 4 in. Standard-weight water pipe having threaded couplings serves for casing. Most depths are less than 50 ft although a few exceed 100 feet. As suction-type pumps extract water from driven wells, the water table must be near the ground surface if a continuous water supply is to be obtained. For best results the water table should be within 10 to 15 ft of ground surface in order to provide adequate drawdown without exceeding the suction limit. Yields from driven wells are small, discharges of 20 to 50 gpm being representative.

Driven wells are best suited for domestic supplies, for temporary water supplies, and for exploratory purposes. Batteries of driven

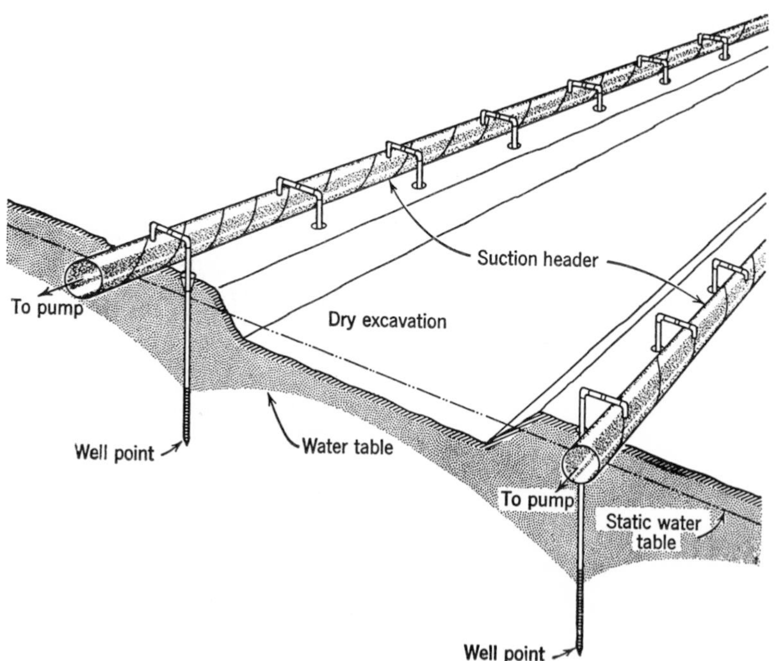

Fig. 5.4. A well-point system to dewater an excavation site.

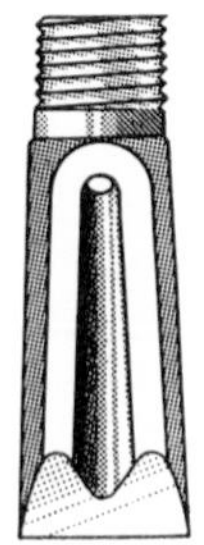
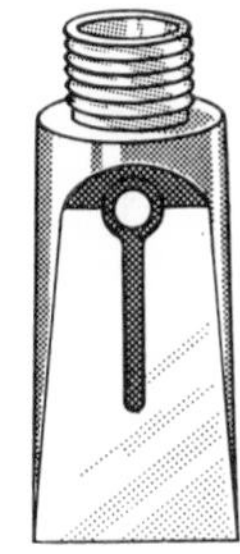
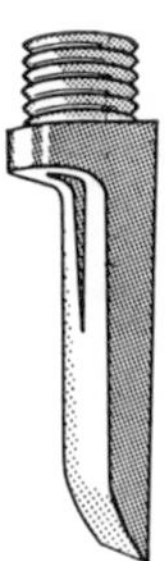

Fig. 5.5. Jetting drill bits.

wells connected by a suction header to a single pump are effective for localized lowering of the water table. Such installations, known as well-point systems, are particularly advantageous for dewatering excavations for foundations and other subsurface construction operations. Figure 5.4 illustrates how a well-point installation reduces the ground water level to furnish a dry excavation.

Driven wells are limited to unconsolidated formations containing no large gravel or rocks which might damage the drive point. To drive a well, the pipe casing and threads should be protected at the top with a drive cap (see Fig. 5.3). Driving can be done with a maul, sledge, drop hammer, or air hammer. Another procedure features a driving bar connected by a rope to the surface which delivers blows inside the well directly on the tapered steel drive point. Screens are available in a variety of opening sizes, the choice depending upon the size of particles in the water-bearing stratum.

Important advantages of driven wells are that they can be constructed in a short time, at minimum cost, and by one man.

Jetted Wells. Jetted wells are constructed by the cutting action of a downward-directed stream of water. The high-velocity stream washes the earth away while the casing, which is lowered into the deepening hole, conducts the water and cuttings up and out of the well. Small diameter holes of 1½ to 3 in. are formed in this manner (although the method is capable of producing diameters up to 12-in. or more) to depths greater than 50 feet. Jetted wells have only small yields and are best adapted to unconsolidated formations. Because of the speed of jetting a well and the portability of the equipment, jetted wells are useful for exploratory test holes and for well-point systems.[5, 27]

Various types of jetting drill bits are shown in Fig. 5.5. In penetrating clays and hardpans, the drill pipe is raised and lowered sharply,

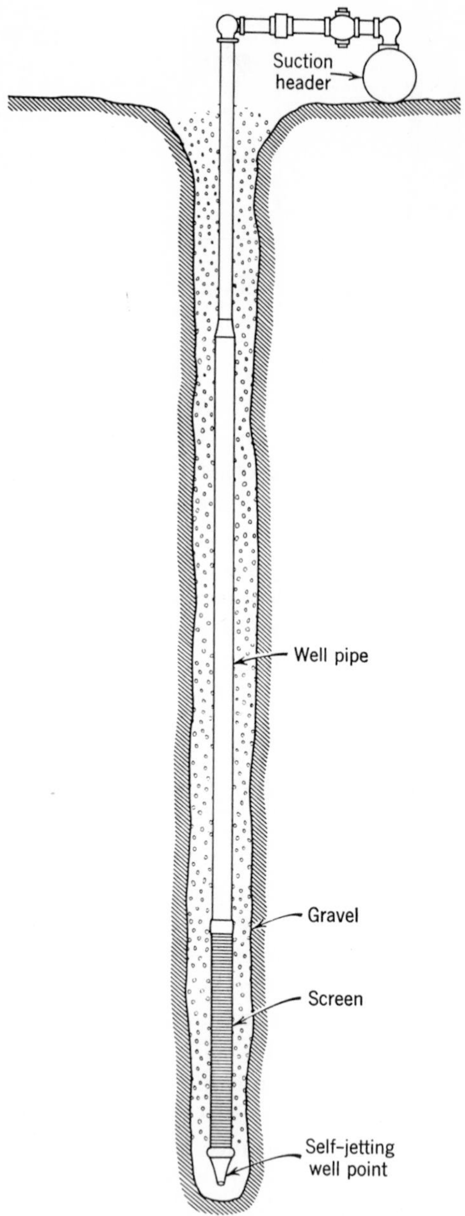

Fig. 5.6. Jetted well with self-jetting well point.

causing the bit to shatter the formation. During the jetting operation, the drill pipe is turned slowly to insure a straight hole. To complete a shallow jetted well after the casing extends to below the ground water table, the well pipe with screen attached is lowered to the bottom of the hole inside the casing. The outer casing is then pulled and the well is ready for pumping.

A simplification of the above procedure can be obtained using a self-jetting well point.[36] This consists of a tube of brass screen ending in a jetting nozzle, which is screwed to the well pipe (Fig. 5.6). As soon as the well point has been jetted to the required depth, the well is completed and ready for pumping. Gravel may be added around the drill pipe for permanent installations.

Methods for Drilling Deep Wells

Most large, deep, high-capacity wells are constructed by drilling. Three basic methods of construction are employed: cable tool (also known as percussion or standard), hydraulic rotary, and reverse rotary. Each method is particularly suited for drilling in certain formations and not in others.[22] Recognizing this fact, many experienced drillers arrange their drilling rigs to be able to switch methods as required for drilling in formations of a variable nature.

Examples of the construction of deep wells in unconsolidated and consolidated formations are shown in Figs. 5.7 and 5.8, respectively, taken from standard specifications for deep wells prepared by the American Water Works Association.[1] The construction procedure of a successful well is dependent upon local conditions encountered in drilling; hence, each well should be treated as an individual project. Construction methods differ regionally within the United States and also from one driller to another. General construction methods are described in the following sections.

Cable Tool Method. Wells drilled by the cable tool method are constructed with a standard well drilling rig, percussion tools, and a bailer.[13,14,29,36] The method is adapted to drilling deep holes of 3 to 24 in. in diameter through consolidated rock materials. In unconsolidated sand and gravel, especially quicksand, it is least effective as the loose material slumps and caves around the bit. Drilling is accomplished by regular lifting and dropping of a string of tools. On the lower end, a bit with a relatively sharp chisel edge breaks the rock by impact.

From top to bottom, a string of tools consists of a rope socket, a set of jars, a drill stem, and a drilling bit (Fig. 5.9). The total weight

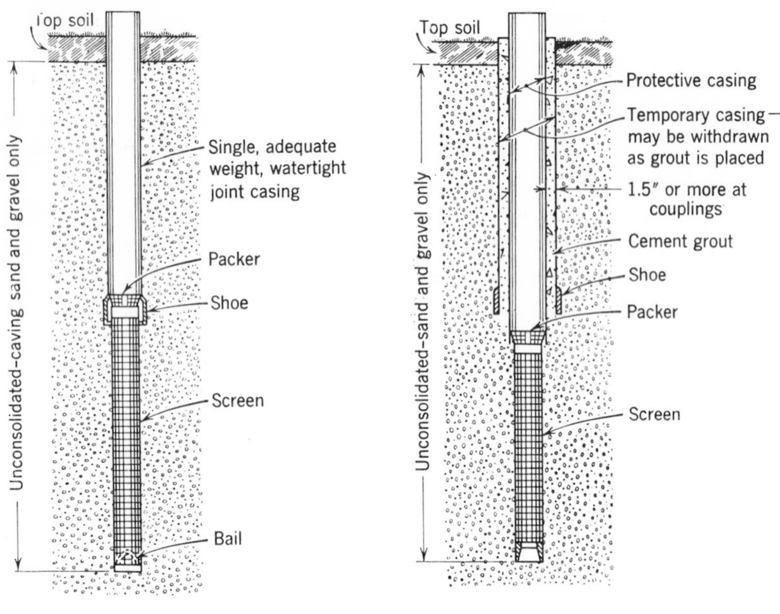

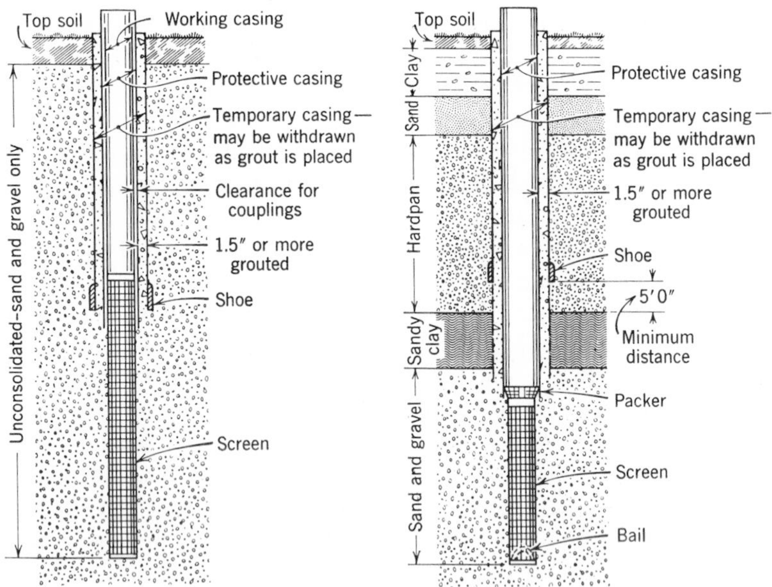

Fig. 5.7. Examples of well construction in unconsolidated formations (reproduced by permission from Amer. Water Works Assoc.[1]).

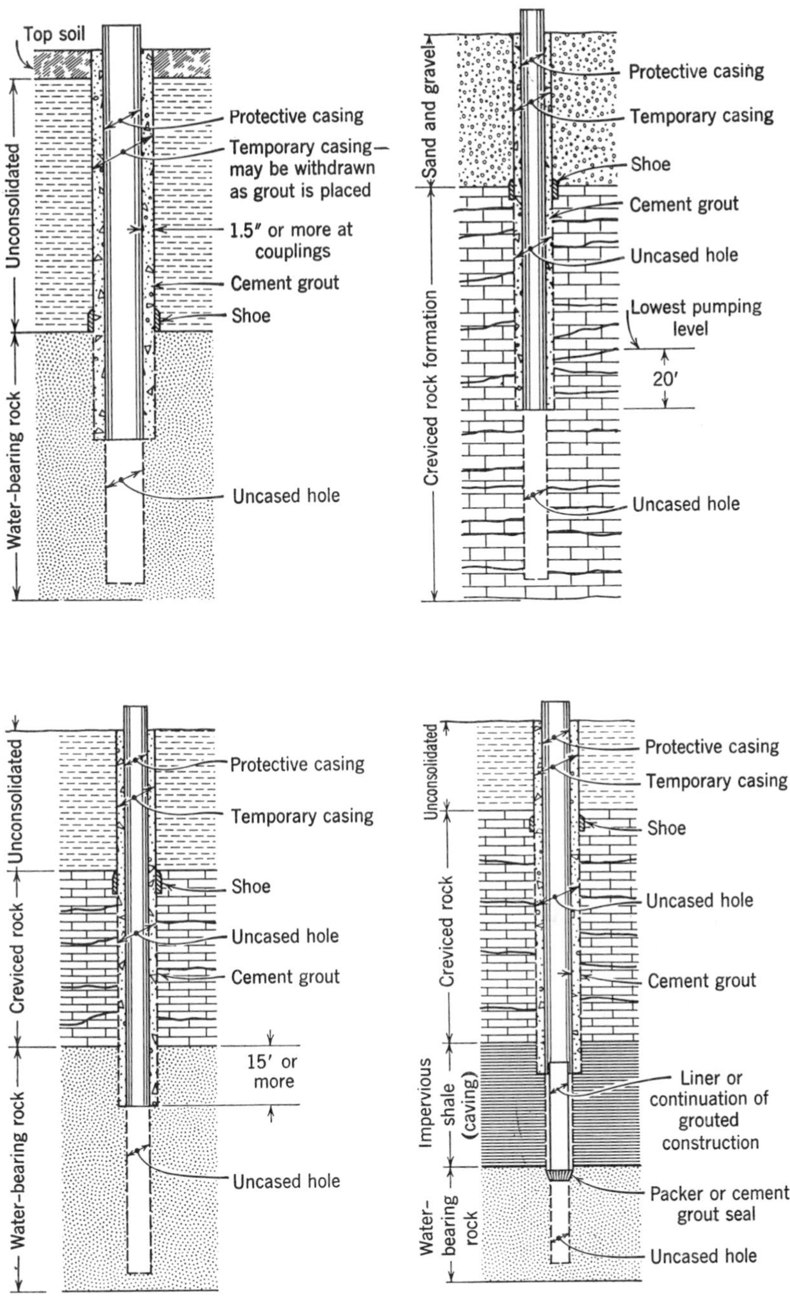

Fig. 5.8. Examples of well construction in consolidated formations (reproduced by permission from Amer. Water Works Assoc.[1]).

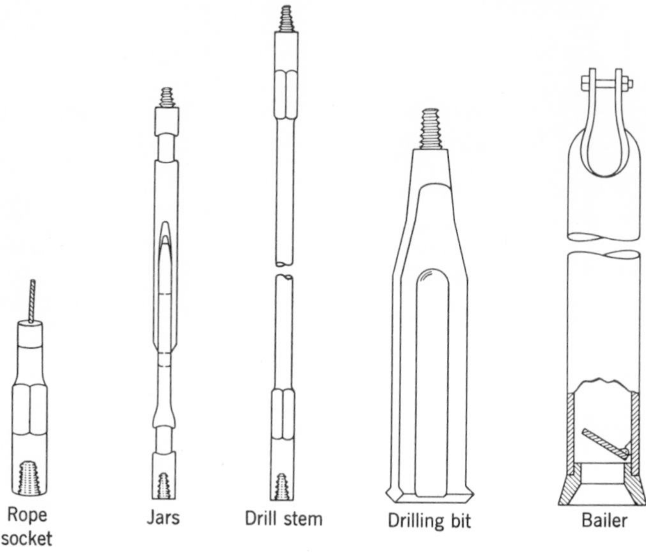

Fig. 5.9. Basic well drilling tools for the cable tool method.

may amount to several thousand pounds. Tools are made of steel and are joined with tapered box-and-pin screw joints. The most important part of the string of tools is the bit, which does the actual drilling. Bits are manufactured in lengths of 3 to 10 ft and weigh up to 3000 lb. Variously shaped bits are made for drilling in different rock formations. The drill stem is a long steel bar which adds weight and length to the drill so that it will cut rapidly and vertically. Drill stems vary from 6 to 30 ft in length and from 2½ to 6 in. in diameter, and weigh 100 to 3000 lb. A set of jars consists of a pair of narrow connecting links. They have no direct effect on the drilling, their purpose being only to loosen the tools, should these stick in the hole. Under normal tension on the drilling line the jars remain fully extended. When tools become stuck, the line is slackened to allow the links to open to their full length, usually less than 6 in., whereupon an upstroke of the line will cause the upper section of the jars to impart an upward blow to the tools. The rope socket attaches the drilling rope or cable to the string of tools.

Drill cuttings are removed from the well by a bailer (Fig. 5.9). Although several models are manufactured, a bailer consists essentially of a section of pipe with a valve at the bottom and a ring at the top for attachment to the bailer line. When lowered into the well, the valve permits cuttings to enter the bailer but prevents them from escaping. After filling, the bailer is hoisted to the surface and emptied. Bailers are available in a range of diameters, lengths of 10 to 30 ft, and capacities of 2 to 90 gal.

The drilling rig for the cable tool method consists of a mast, a multiline hoist, a walking beam, and an engine. In most present-day designs the entire assembly is truck-mounted (Fig. 5.10) for ready portability. The mast must be sufficiently high to allow the longest string of tools or section of pipe to be hoisted out of the hole; 30 to 50 ft is typical. The drilling line is fixed to a reel so that the walking beam, which has a variable length of stroke, causes the other end of the drilling line to rise and fall.

During drilling the tools make 40 to 60 strokes per minute, ranging from 16 to 40 in. in length. The drilling line is rotated so that the bit will form a round hole, and additional line is let out as needed so that the bit will always strike the bottom of the hole. Water should be added to the hole if none is encountered to form a paste with the cuttings, thereby reducing friction on the falling bit. After the bit has cut 4 or 5 ft through a formation, the string of tools is lifted out and the hole is bailed. In unconsolidated formations, casing should be maintained to near the bottom of the hole to avoid caving. Casing is driven down by means of drive clamps fastened to the drill stem; the up and down motion of the tools striking the top of the casing, protected by a drive head, sinks the casing. On the bottom of the first section of casing, a drive shoe (see Fig. 5.7), with a beveled cutting edge is fastened to protect the casing as it is being driven.

Casing may be constructed from standard pipe or from well casing of corrosion-resistant steel with individual sections connected by threaded or welded joints. In the Western United States, where large diameter irrigation wells to depths of several hundred feet are common in alluvial formations, a double-wall casing is sometimes selected to provide greater strength during the heavy driving.[22] This casing, often referred to as stovepipe, is formed by telescoping short cylindrical sections halfway through one another. A continuous double-wall pipe with staggered joints is created, as shown in Fig. 5.11. Sections are fastened in place by denting, riveting, or welding. In the Eastern United States, single-wall casing formed of long individual sections is usually satisfactory.

In drilling any deep well it is important that proper alignment be maintained so as not to interfere with pump installation and operation. A common specification allows deviations up to 6 in. per 100 feet from the vertical. The problem is greatest in drilling through

Fig. 5.10. Well drilling by the cable tool method with a truck-mounted portable drilling rig. The entire string of tools is visible to the right of the mast. A section of casing is being lowered into the well; additional sections appear in the foreground. The bailer, supported by a cable from the mast, stands to the right of the well (courtesy Bucyrus-Erie Co.).

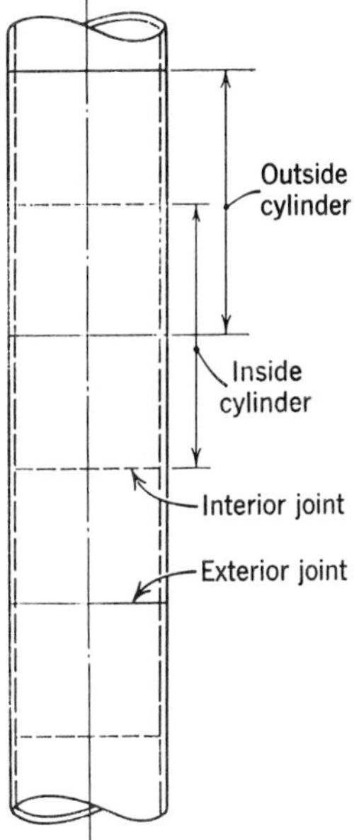

Fig. 5.11. Detail showing assembly of double-wall, or stovepipe, casing.

rock formations. Some drillers have found that holes tending to bend can be corrected by detonating explosives at the bottom. This shatters the surrounding rock and permits drilling to progress vertically.

Hydraulic Rotary Method. The fastest method for drilling in unconsolidated strata is the hydraulic rotary method.[14,29,36] Deep wells up to 18 in. in diameter, and even larger with a reamer, can be constructed. The method operates continuously with a hollow rotating bit through which a mixture of clay and water, or drilling mud, is forced. Material loosened by the bit is carried upward in the hole by the rising mud. No casing is ordinarily required during drilling because the mud forms a clay lining on the wall of the well which prevents caving.

Drilling bits come in various designs. All have hollow shanks and one or more centrally located orifices for jetting the mud into the bottom of the hole. The bit is attached to a drill rod of heavy pipe which is screwed to the end of the kelly—a square section of drill rod. The drill is turned by a rotating table which fits closely around the kelly and allows the drill rod to slide downward as the hole deepens. The drilling rig for a hydraulic rotary outfit (Fig. 5.12) consists of a derrick, or mast, a rotating table, a pump for the drilling mud, a hoist, and the engine.

Drilling mud emerging from the hole is conducted by pipe or ditch to a slush pit or tank. Cuttings settle out so that the mud can be pumped back into the hole for another circuit. Water and clay are added to the mud as needed to maintain quantity and consistency.

Fig. 5.12. A truck-mounted hydraulic rotary well drilling rig (courtesy Bucyrus-Erie Co.).

Following drilling, casing is lowered into the hole with perforated sections inserted or created opposite aquifers. To remove clay deposits on the wall of the hole, the well is washed by lowering the drill to the bottom of the well. Water, often containing Calgon * (sodium hexametaphosphate), is forced down through the drill rod. A collar, or swab, the size of the casing is attached to the drill rod above the bit so that the water is forced out through perforations in the casing, causing a washing action on the clay wall. At the same time, the bit is plunged up and down, creating a surging action. When the washing at one level is completed, the bit is raised and the operation repeated. After the washing, gravel is fed into the annular space surrounding the casing if a gravel-packed well is desired.

Reverse Rotary Method. A variation of the hydraulic rotary method, known as the reverse rotary method, is common in Europe and becoming increasingly popular in the United States. It is capable of drilling wells up to 48 in. in diameter through unconsolidated formations. The procedure is essentially a suction dredging method in which the cuttings are removed by a suction pipe. The drilling rig is similar to that for the hydraulic rotary method, except that it includes a large-capacity centrifugal pump, a 6-in. diameter drill pipe, and a bit somewhat like the cutterhead of a dredge. The walls of the hole during drilling are supported by hydrostatic pressure acting against a film of fine-grained material deposited on the walls by the drilling water. Cuttings are removed by water, not drilling mud, flowing up through the pipe. The mixture is circulated through a sump in which sand settles out, but fine-grained particles are recirculated back into the hole where they aid in stabilizing the walls. The water table should be several feet below ground surface to obtain an effective head differential between well and aquifer.

Casing and cleaning of the well correspond to methods for the hydraulic rotary method.

Well Completion

After a deep well has been drilled it must be completed. Well completion provides for ready entrance of ground water into the well with minimum resistance in and around the casing.

Perforations and Screens. In consolidated formations, where the material surrounding the well is stable, ground water enters directly

* Calgon acts as a dispersing agent for clays, silts, and calcium carbonate and iron deposits.[19] As such it is helpful in the washing, developing, and cleaning of wells.

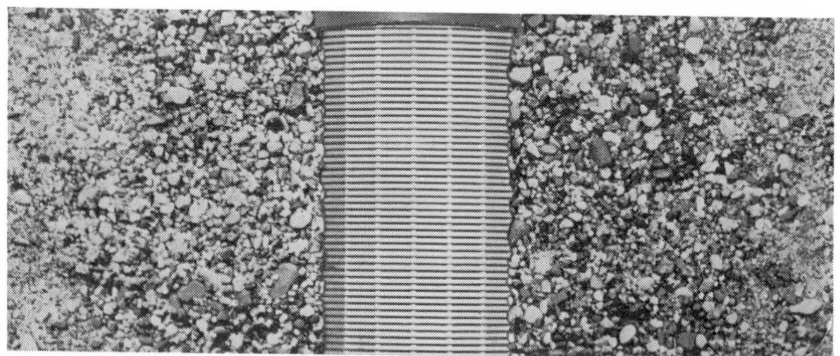

Fig. 5.13. Grain size distribution around the well screen of a properly developed well in an unconsolidated formation (courtesy Edward E. Johnson, Inc.).

into the uncased well (Fig. 5.8). In unconsolidated formations, however, a casing is necessary which must serve the dual purposes of freely admitting water into the well and supporting the outside material. The casing must either contain perforations or be replaced by a well screen. Water should be allowed to enter along all portions of a well penetrating permeable aquifers assuming that the water quality (see Chapter 7) is suitable for the planned water use. Other sections of the well should contain blank casing and be sealed by puddled clay or cement grout, as shown in Fig. 5.7, to prevent vertical water movement along the exterior of the casing.

Perforations can be made in the field, otherwise machine-perforated casing is available. Field perforating can be done before placement by punching or by cutting with an acetylene torch. In-place perforations can be made with a well knife or well perforator. Generally, a horizontal louvered opening gives a better control of unconsolidated materials than does a vertical slot.[22] Openings should be large enough to allow 50 to 80 per cent of the surrounding grains to pass into the well.

In the Eastern United States, well screens are often inserted as casing sections to provide water entry. These are available in various designs, diameters, slot sizes, and corrosion-resistant metals. A spiral-wound screen is illustrated by Fig. 5.13. Slots are tapered with the widest space at the inner surface to prevent particles from accumulating within the openings and blocking flow. Plastic screens are a recent innovation. Well screens are particularly advantageous in sandy aquifers as here the screen opening can be selected to filter a specified fraction of the sand. A slot size which passes 50 to 80 per cent of the aquifer material should be selected as the coarse remaining fraction forms a highly permeable zone around the well. Screen manufacturers will recommend the most satisfactory slot size based on a grain size analysis of a given aquifer. Well screens are also used with gravel packs. Connections between blank casing and well screen are welded or sealed by packers (Fig. 5.7).

Gravel Packing. A gravel-packed well is one containing a gravel screen or envelope surrounding the perforated portions of the casing (see Fig. 5.14). The gravel increases the effective well diameter, acts as a strainer to keep fine material out of the well, and protects the casing from caving of surrounding formations. A gravel-packed well properly constructed in an unconsolidated formation usually will have a greater specific capacity than one of the same diameter not surrounded by gravel. In aquifers containing a large proportion of fine sand, a

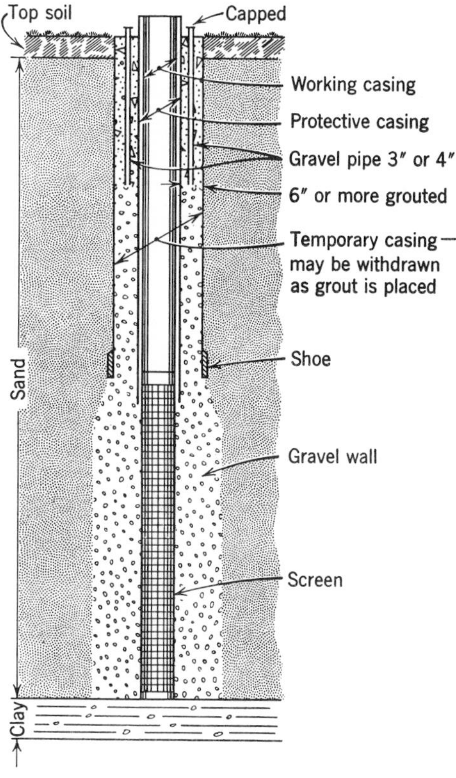

Fig. 5.14. A gravel-packed well (reproduced by permission from Amer. Water Works Assoc.[1]).

gravel screen is a necessity to avoid a sand-pumping well. Most successful recharge wells in unconsolidated aquifers are gravel packed.

The thickness of the gravel layer will vary with the type of formation and method of drilling; however, a minimum of 6 in. is usually required to be entirely effective. Careful selection of the gravel size is important if sand is to be held back at the outer edge of the pack, where the entrance velocity is lowest, but at the same time furnishing a highly permeable zone around the well. Experience favors a gravel pack consisting of a range of grain sizes, usually from sand up to ¼-in. gravel.[22] The proper grain size distribution for a gravel pack should be related to (1) the mechanical analysis of the aquifer and (2) the perforation or screen slot size. Often local availability of material is also an important factor in selecting a gravel.

In sandy aquifers, where a gravel pack is most essential, deep wells should be constructed by the hydraulic rotary or reverse rotary method. Gravel is added after washing by shoveling it around the casing at the surface and adding more as the gravel sinks into place. It is sometimes placed through small pipes or pilot holes around the casing which feed the gravel down into position.[36] This procedure avoids the common difficulty of gravel catching on narrow sections of the hole and failing to form a continuous uniform pack. A further refinement is the use of bladeless pumps for pumping the gravel into place.

Gravel can also be placed around relatively shallow cable tool wells. The procedure involves placing a large blank casing during drilling after which a smaller casing containing perforated sections or screens is set inside. The annular space is filled with gravel and the outer casing is pulled out of the well.

Well Development

Following completion, a new deep well is developed to increase its specific capacity, prevent sanding, and obtain maximum economic well life.[4,7,36] These results are accomplished by removing the finer material from the natural formations surrounding the perforated sections of the casing. Figure 5.13 shows the grain size distribution resulting around a properly developed well in an unconsolidated aquifer. Of course, where a well has been gravel packed much of the same purpose has been accomplished, although development is still beneficial. The importance of developing wells cannot be underestimated; all too often development is not carried out adequately to produce full potential yields.

Development procedures by pumping, surging, injection of compressed air, backwashing, and addition of solid carbon dioxide are described in subsequent paragraphs. Detonation of explosives also is sometimes effective in rock wells as the blast increases the fractures and joints of the surrounding rock.[21, 23]

Developing by pumping requires a pump with a suction pipe extending to near the center of the perforations or screens. The pump should be operated at a low discharge * until the water clears, following which the process should be repeated in a step-wise manner at successively higher discharges until the maximum pump or well capacity is reached. After the water clears at the maximum discharge, the pump should be shut down and the water level in the well allowed to return to normal; then the entire process should be repeated. This irregular and noncontinuous pumping agitates the fine material surrounding the well so that it can be carried into the well and pumped out. The coarse fraction entering the well is removed by a bailer or sand pump from the bottom.†

A more effective method for developing a well is surging, created by the rapid up-and-down motion of a plunger. The plunger is operated above the perforations or screens in wells tapping unconsolidated aquifers and in the casing above open holes of wells in rock aquifers. Calgon is often added to the well water. As the plunger rises, it draws water into the well, while lowering forces water out into the aquifer. This flow reversal overcomes sand bridging and brings fine material into the well. Surging may be performed with a bailer or a circular surge block. The so-called hollow surge block is attached to a string of pipe through which water is pumped out of the well as the surge block moves up and down. In this manner, sand and mud are continuously removed rather than forced back into the formation on each down stroke of a solid surge block. Surging should be continued until no more sand and mud enter the well.

To develop wells by compressed air an air compressor is connected to an air pipe into the well. Around the air pipe a discharge pipe is fitted, as shown in Fig. 5.15. Both pipes should be capable of being shifted vertically by clamps. Initially, the pipes extend to near the bottom of the screened section; for efficient operation, the water depth in the discharge pipe should exceed two-thirds the length of the pipe. To begin the development the air pipe is closed and the air pressure

* If a high discharge occurs initially, "bridging" (a wedging of sand grains around individual perforations formed by the sudden pull on the sand toward the well) can prevent fine material from being removed and reduce the effectiveness of the development process.

† This applies to all development methods.

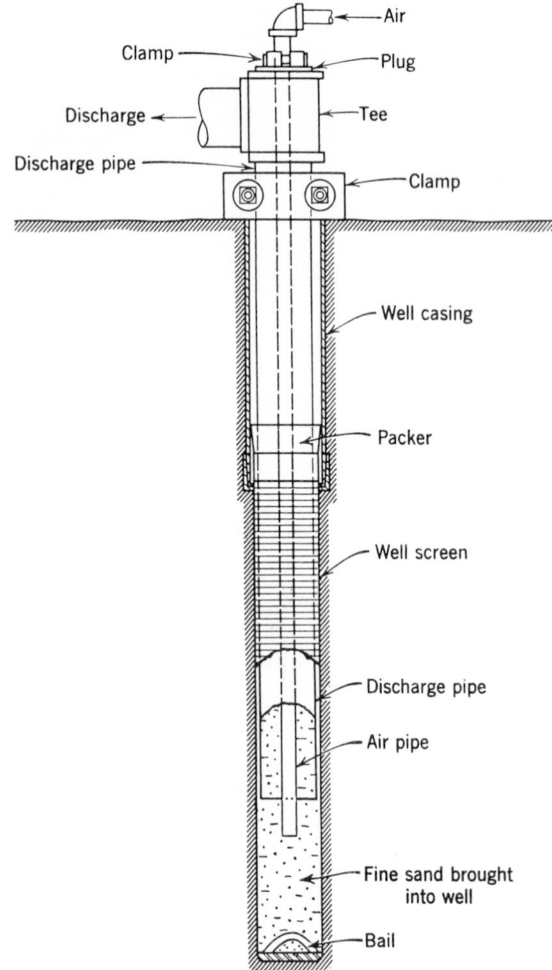

Fig. 5.15. Installation for well development with compressed air.

is allowed to build up to 100 to 150 psi, whereupon it is released suddenly into the well by means of a quick-opening valve. The inrush of air creates a powerful surge within the well, first increasing then decreasing the pressure as water is forced up the discharge pipe. The process loosens the fine material surrounding the perforations which may then be brought into the well by continuous air injection creating an air lift pump. The operation is repeated at intervals along the screened section until sand accretion becomes negligible.

In the backwashing method the top of the well is fitted with an airtight cover. Discharge and air pipes are installed similar to the previous method, together with a separate short air pipe and a three-way valve, as shown in Fig. 5.16. Air is released through the long air pipe, forcing air and water (often containing Calgon) out of the well through the discharge pipe. After the water clears, the air supply is shut off and the water is allowed to return to its static level. The three-way valve is then turned to admit air into the top of the well through the short air

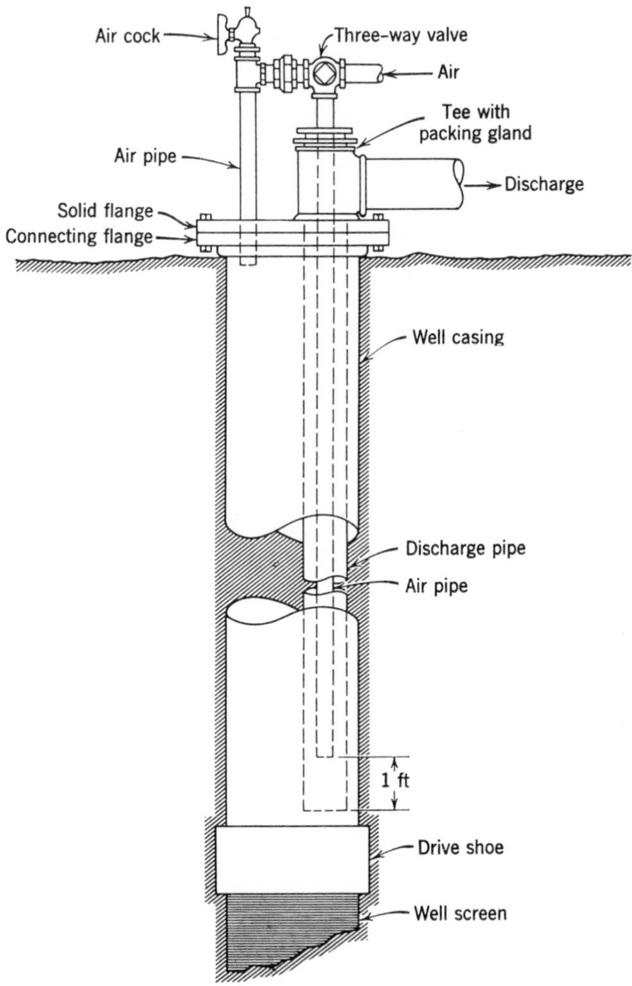

Fig. 5.16. Installation for well development by backwashing.

pipe. This backwashes the water from the well through the discharge pipe and at the same time agitates the sand grains surrounding the well. Air is forced into the well until it begins escaping from the discharge pipe, after which the three-way valve is turned and the air supply is again directed down the long air pipe to pump the well. Backwashing is repeated until the well is fully developed.

Fig. 5.17. Explosion of mud and water extending 125 feet into the air from a well in Utah after development with dry ice (courtesy H. S. Snyder).

A novel method for well development is based on the surge produced by adding solid carbon dioxide (dry ice) to a well. First, in order to loosen clay impregnating and reducing the flow from the aquifer, hydrochloric (muriatic) acid is poured into the well. The casing is capped at the top and compressed air is forced into the well, the pressure forcing the chemical into the clogged strata. Finally, the cap is removed and blocks of dry ice are dropped into the well. The accumulation of gaseous carbon dioxide released by sublimation builds up a pressure within the well which upon release causes a burst of muddy water (Fig. 5.17) from the well.

Testing Wells for Yield

Following development of a new well, it should be tested to determine its yield and drawdown. This information provides a basis for determining the water supply available from the well, for selecting the type of pump, and for estimating the cost of pumping. A test is accomplished by measuring the static water level, after which the well is pumped at a maximum rate until the water level in the well stabilizes. The depth to water is then noted. The difference in depths is the drawdown, and the discharge-drawdown ratio is an estimate of the specific capacity of the well. The discharge can be determined by any of several measuring devices connected to the discharge pipe. Well water depths are measured by a chalked tape, an electric sounding wire, or an air line and pressure gage.

Pumping Equipment

For shallow wells where only small discharges are needed, hand-operated pitcher pumps, turbine pumps, gear pumps, and centrifugal pumps may be installed. Discharges range from a few to about 100 gpm depending upon the pump type and size of intake and discharge pipes. Suction lifts should not exceed 20 to 25 ft for efficient and continuous operation.

For deep wells requiring lifts greater than about 25 ft, large-capacity pumps serving irrigation, municipal, or industrial water requirements are installed. The selection of a proper pump is important for continued satisfactory well yields. Factors to be considered include diameter and depth of well, depth to water table, drawdown, seasonal variability of ground water level, duration of pumping, capacity, initial and maintenance costs, power required, and water quality. Several types of pumps are suitable for deep-well operation: plunger, deep-well turbine, displacement, air lift, submersible, and jet. In large deep wells yielding flows of several hundred or more gallons per minute, the deep-well turbine pump has been most widely adopted.[2] Upon request pump manufacturers will furnish advice as to size and type of pump best suited to a particular well.

Sanitary Protection of Wells

Wherever ground water pumped from a well is intended for human consumption, proper sanitary measures must be taken to protect the purity of the water.[15, 25] Contamination sources may exist either above or below ground surface. Precautions apply equally to supplies obtained from springs. Figure 5.18 shows, for example, a typical method for protecting a spring water supply.

Subsurface sources of contamination can result from privies, septic tanks, sewers, cesspools, barnyards, and livestock areas. Ordinarily, wells should be located at least 50 to 100 ft away and not on the downhill side of such sources. Local health department regulations should be ascertained and observed. Rock aquifers, such as limestone, require particular attention as they are capable of transmitting pollutants much greater distances than unconsolidated formations.

Surface contamination can enter wells either through the annular space outside of the casing or through the top of the well itself. To close avenues of access for undesirable water outside of the casing, the annular space should be filled with cement grout, as shown for deep wells in Figs. 5.7 and 5.8 and for a shallow well in Fig. 5.19. Entry through the top of the well can be avoided by providing a watertight cover to seal the top of the casing. Some pumps are available with closed metal bases which provide the necessary closure. For pumps having an open-type base, or where the pump is not placed directly over the well, a seal is required for the annular opening between the discharge pipe and casing. Seals may be made of metal or lead packing; asphaltic and mastic compounds are also satisfactory. Covers around the well should be made of concrete, should be elevated above the adjacent land level, and should slope away from the well (Fig. 5.19).

Whenever a new well is completed or an old well repaired, contamination from equipment, well materials, or surface water may be introduced into the well. Addition of a chlorine compound will disinfect the well. Following disinfection, the well should be pumped to waste until all traces of chlorine are removed. As a final check on the purity of the

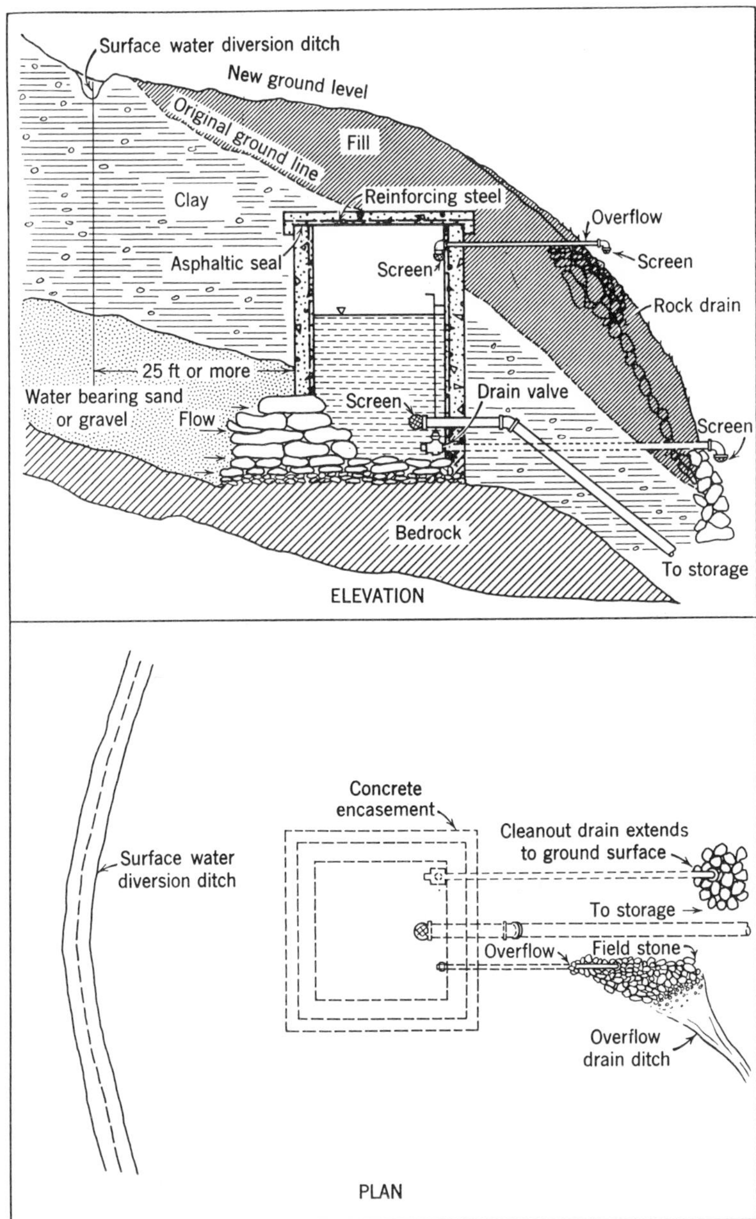

Fig. 5.18. Typical method of sanitary protection for a spring (after Joint Committee on Rural Sanitation [15]).

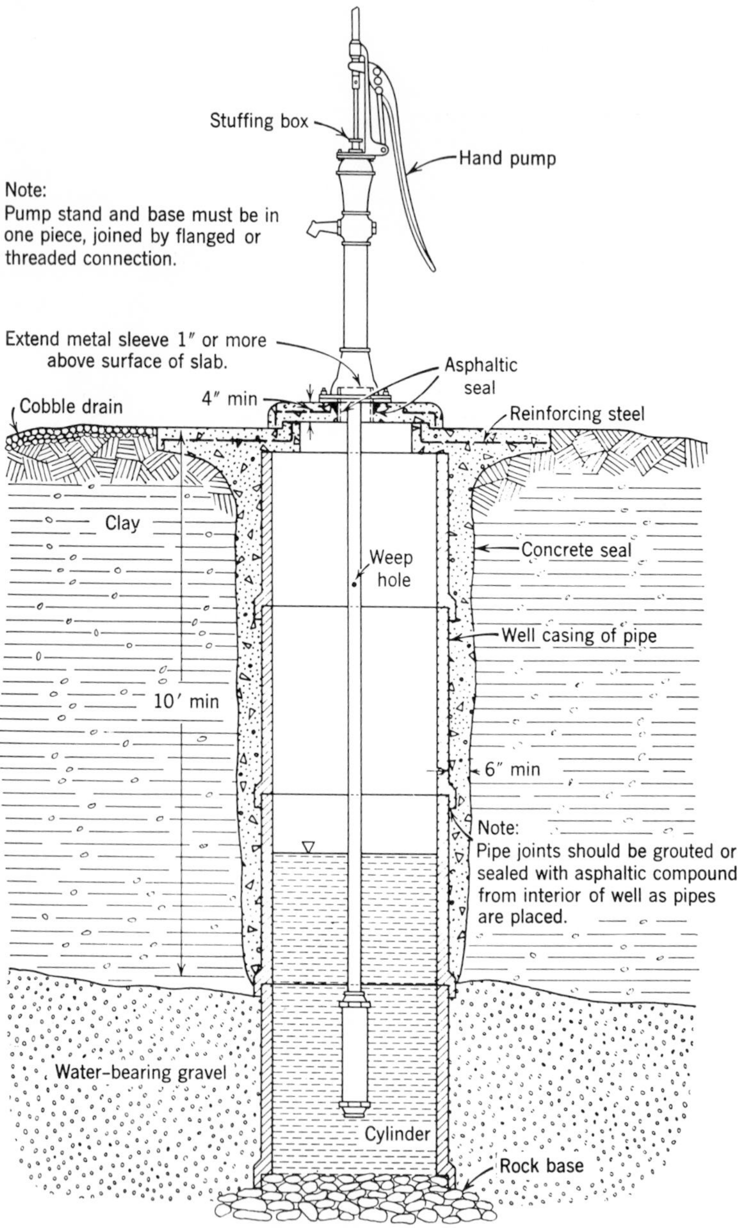

Fig. 5.19. Dug well sealed for sanitary protection (after Joint Committee on Rural Sanitation[15]).

water for drinking, a sample should be collected and sent to a laboratory for bacteriological examination.

Whenever a well is abandoned, for whatever reason, it should be sealed by filling it with clay, concrete, or earth. Not only is surface contamination then unable to enter the well, but sealing serves other useful purposes: prevents accidents, avoids possible movement of inferior water from one aquifer to another, and conserves water in flowing wells.

Maintenance and Repair of Wells

A new well, properly drilled, cased, and developed, will give years of satisfactory service with little or no attention. However, many wells fail; that is, they yield decreasing quantities of water with time.* One cause of failure is depletion of the ground water supply. Not a fault of the well, this trouble can sometimes be remedied by decreasing pumping drafts, resetting the pump, or deepening the well. A second cause of well trouble results from faulty well construction. Such items as poor casing connections, improper perforations or screens, incomplete placement of gravel packs, and poorly seated wells are typical of difficulties encountered. Depending upon the particular situation, the well can be repaired,[20] but sudden failures involving entrance of sand or collapse of a casing often require replacement of the entire well.

The third and most prevalent cause of well failure results from corrosion or incrustation of perforated sections of casing.[6,10] Corrosion may result from direct chemical action of the ground water or from electrolytic action caused by the presence of two different metals in the well. The effects of corrosion can be minimized by selecting well screens of corrosion-resistant metal (such as nickel, copper, or stainless steel), and by providing cathodic protection.† Incrustation is caused by precipitation on or near perforated well casings of materials carried in solution by ground water. The sudden pressure drop associated with water entering a well under heavy pumping releases carbon dioxide and causes precipitation of calcium carbonate. The presence of oxygen in a well can change soluble ferrous iron to insoluble ferric hydroxide. Perforations can be cleaned by adding hydrochloric acid [12] or Calgon [19] to the well, followed by agitation and surging. Development methods with compressed air and dry ice are also sometimes effective.

* Frequently the pump rather than the well is at fault, hence it should be checked before beginning any extensive well repair.

† One method of providing cathodic protection for a well is to introduce a metal low on the electrochemical scale, which will be corroded instead of the well casing. Rods of magnesium suspended in the well water are excellent for this purpose.

Particularly in recharge wells, perforations may become plugged with algae or bacterial growths. The addition of chlorine in the recharge water inhibits such growths. Pumping wells having the problem have been improved by pumping chlorinated water into them, followed by redevelopment.[37]

Collector Wells

For cities and industries located near rivers, the problem of obtaining a high quality, low temperature water at reasonable cost has become increasingly difficult. In many places in Europe and the United States, ground water pumped from collector wells has proved to be a successful solution.[16,17,18] If located adjacent to a surface water supply, a collector well lowers the water table and thereby induces infiltration of surface water through the bed of the water body to the well (see Chapter 11). In this manner greater supplies of water can be obtained than would be available at the same location from ground water alone. The method is best adapted to permeable alluvial aquifers.

Plan and elevation views of a collector well are shown in Fig. 5.20. Patents for this type of well were obtained by L. Ranney and H. Fehlmann for Ranney Method Water Supplies, Inc., Columbus, Ohio, and Grundwasserbauten A. G., Berne, Switzerland, respectively. The central cylinder consists of a monolithic concrete caisson about 15 ft in diameter. This cylinder is sunk down into the aquifer by excavating the inside earth material. After the requisite depth is reached, a thick concrete plug is poured to seal the bottom. To collect the water lengths of 6 or 8 in. diameter casings are jacked hydraulically into the water-bearing formation through precast portholes in the caisson to form a radial pattern of horizontal pipes. In the Ranney well, slotted pipe is placed directly, whereas in the Fehlmann well a blank casing is installed after which a perforated pipe is placed inside and the blank casing removed. Both types of construction provide for washing of silt and fine sand into the casing during construction so that natural gravel packs are formed around the perforations (Fig. 5.20). The number, length, and radial pattern of the collector pipes can be varied to obtain the maximum capacity; usually more pipes are extended toward than away from the surface water source.

The large area of exposed perforations in a collector well causes low inflow velocities which minimize incrustation, clogging, and sand transport. Polluted river water is filtered by its passage through the unconsolidated aquifer to the well. The initial cost of a collector well exceeds that of a vertical well; however, advantages of large yields, reduced pumping heads, and low maintenance costs are factors to be

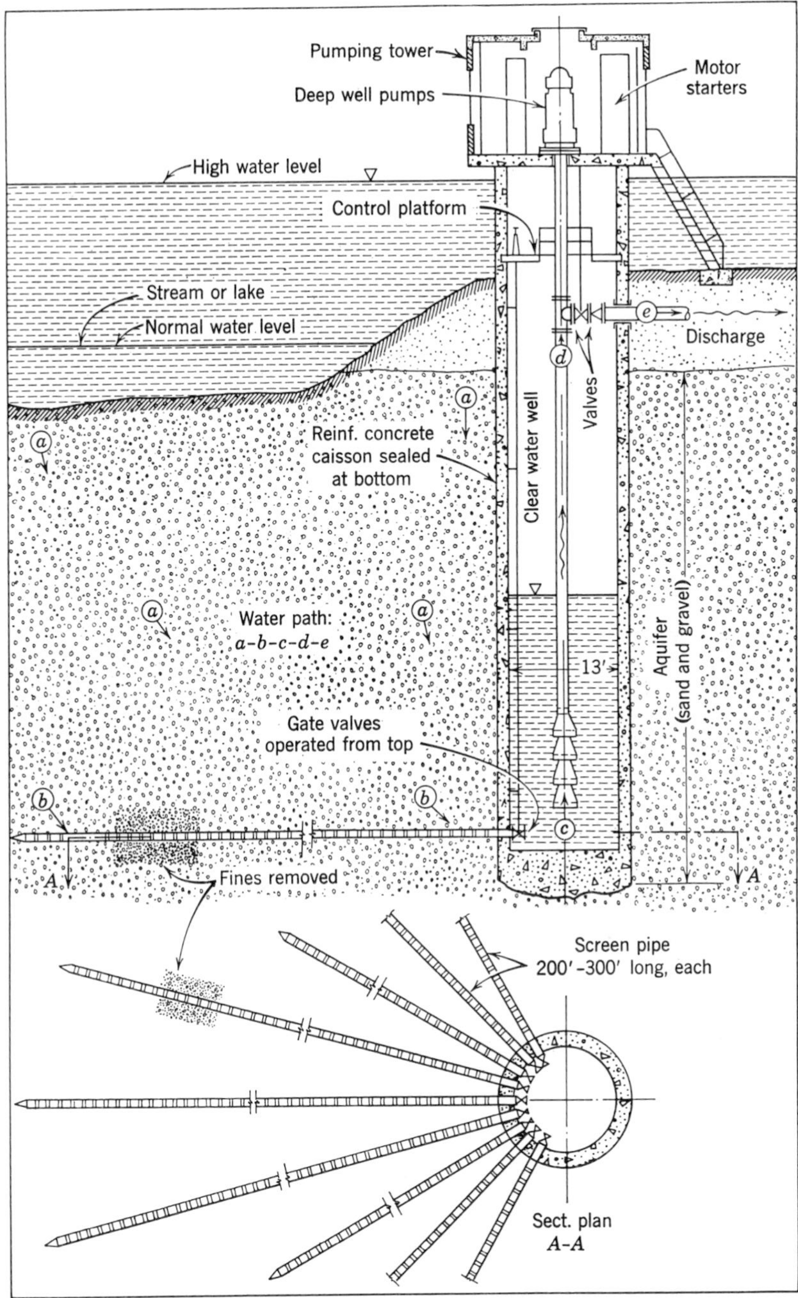

Fig. 5.20. A collector well located near a surface water body (courtesy Ranney Method Water Supplies, Inc.).

considered. Yields vary with local conditions; the average for a large number of such wells approximated 5000 gpm.

Collector wells also function successfully in permeable aquifers removed from surface water supplies. Several such installations gave an average yield of about 2800 gpm.

Infiltration Galleries

An infiltration gallery is a horizontal permeable conduit for intercepting and collecting ground water by gravity flow. Galleries date from ancient times as an economic means of collecting ground water supplies, and over the past century have been widely installed in Europe and the United States. On oceanic islands they have the particular advantage of enabling fresh water to be collected with little or no disturbance of underlying salt water [34,35] (see Chapter 12). To be successful, a gallery must be located in a permeable aquifer with a high water table and fed by an adequate nearby water source of suitable chemical quality. Many infiltration galleries are laid parallel to river beds, where with induced infiltration an adequate perennial water supply is assured.* Depths of 10 to 20 ft are common, greater depths usually being unnecessary and more costly to construct.

Galleries function in the same manner as drainage tile. Construction materials giving longest life include vitrified clay, brick, concrete, and cast iron. The cylinders are perforated or are placed so that openings at joints allow low entrance velocities for collected water. Diameters of 2 to 5 ft and manholes at intervals of a few hundred feet facilitate inspection and maintenance. Design velocities seldom exceed 2 ft/sec. Water entering a gallery flows to a collection sump where it is pumped for use. Yields from infiltration galleries vary widely depending upon local conditions; however, infiltration rates of 700 to 3500 gpm per 1000 ft of gallery length are not unusual.

An open drainage ditch will serve the same purpose as an infiltration gallery. However, because a ditch is subject to problems of algae, erosion, clogging by vegetation, and surface contamination, a gallery is, in general, a preferable means for collecting ground water.

* An unusual form of infiltration gallery is found in the chalk aquifers of southeastern England. A typical well consists of a vertical shaft sunk down into the chalk and connecting with unlined horizontal tunnels, or adits, roughly 6 ft in diameter and extending for distances of 100 to 7500 ft. The permeability of solid chalk is quite low (about 0.002 darcy), hence the long tunnels are constructed to intersect a maximum number of fissures, from which most of the water is obtained.

References

1. Amer. Water Works Assoc., *AWWA standard for deep wells,* New York, 51 pp., 1958.
2. Amer. Water Works Assoc., American standard specifications for deep well vertical turbine pumps, *Jour. Amer. Water Works Assoc.,* vol. 47, pp. 703–729, 1955.
3. Anderson, K. E., *Water well handbook,* Missouri Water Well Drillers Assoc., Rolla, 199 pp., 1951.
4. Anon., The principles and practical methods of developing water wells, *Bull.* 1033, Edward E. Johnson, St. Paul, Minn., 34 pp., 1941.
5. Anon., Now they're jetting relief wells, *Western Const. News,* vol. 30, no. 9, pp. 57–58, 1955.
6. Anon., The corrosion and incrustation of well screens, *Bull.* 834, Edward E. Johnson, St. Paul, Minn., 12 pp., 1955.
7. Bennison, E. W., *Ground water—its development, uses, and conservation,* Edward E. Johnson, St. Paul, Minn., 509 pp., 1947.
8. Bennison, E. W., Fundamentals of water well operation and maintenance, *Jour. Amer. Water Works Assoc.,* vol. 45, pp. 252–258, 1953.
9. Bieske, E., *Bohrbrunnen,* 5th ed., R. Oldenbourg, Munich, 359 pp., 1953.
10. Blakeley, L. E., The rehabilitation, cleaning, and sterilization of water wells, *Jour. Amer. Water Works Assoc.,* vol. 37, pp. 101–114, 1945.
11. Bowman, I., Well-drilling methods, *U. S. Geological Survey Water-Supply Paper* 257, Washington, D. C., 139 pp., 1911.
12. DeWitt, M. M., How to acidize water wells, *The American City,* vol. 62, no. 10, pp. 92–93, 1947.
13. Gordon, R. W., *Water well drilling with cable tools,* Bucyrus-Erie Co., South Milwaukee, Wis., 230 pp., 1958.
14. Johnston, C. N., Irrigation wells and well drilling, *Agric. Exp. Sta. Circ.* 404, Univ. Calif., Berkeley, 32 pp., 1951.
15. Joint Committee on Rural Sanitation, Individual water supply systems, *Publ.* 24, U. S. Public Health Service, Washington, D. C., 61 pp., 1950.
16. Kazmann, R. G., River infiltration as a source of ground water supply, *Trans. Amer. Soc. Civil Engrs.,* vol. 113, pp. 404–424, 1948.
17. Kazmann, R. G., The utilization of induced stream infiltration and natural aquifer storage at Canton, Ohio, *Econ. Geol.,* vol. 44, pp. 514–524, 1949.
18. Klaer, F. H., Jr., Providing large industrial water supplies by induced infiltration, *Min. Eng.,* vol. 5, pp. 620–624, 1953.
19. Kleber, J. P., Well cleaning with Calgon, *Jour. Amer. Water Works Assoc.,* vol. 42, pp. 481–484, 1950.
20. McCombs, J., and A. G. Fiedler, Methods of exploring and repairing leaky artesian wells, *U. S. Geological Survey Water-Supply Paper* 596, Washington, D. C., pp. 1–32, 1928.
21. Milaeger, R. E., Development of deep wells by dynamiting, *Jour. Amer. Water Works Assoc.,* vol. 34, pp. 684–690, 1942.
22. Moss, R., Jr., Water well construction in formations characteristic of the Southwest, *Jour. Amer. Water Works Assoc.,* vol. 50, pp. 777–788, 1958.

23. Mylander, H. A., Well improvement by use of vibratory explosives, *Jour. Amer. Water Works Assoc.,* vol. 44, pp. 39–48, 1952.
24. Nebolsine, R., New trends in ground-water development, *Jour. New England Water Works Assoc.,* vol. 57, pp. 186–200, 1943.
25. Ongerth, H. J., Sanitary construction and protection of wells, *Jour. Amer. Water Works Assoc.,* vol. 34, pp. 671–677, 1942.
26. Petersen, J. S., C. Rohwer, and M. L. Albertson, Jr., Effect of well screens on flow into wells, *Proc. Amer. Soc. Civil Engrs.,* vol. 79, sep. 365, 24 pp., 1953.
27. Pillsbury, A. F., and J. E. Christiansen, Installing ground-water piezometers by jetting for drainage investigations, *Agric. Eng.,* vol. 28, pp. 409–410, 1947.
28. Plumb, C. E., and J. L. Welsh, Abstract of laws and recommendations concerning water well construction and sealing in the United States, *Water Quality Investigations Rep.* 9, Calif. Div. Water Resources, Sacramento, 391 pp., 1955.
29. Rohwer, C., Putting down and developing wells for irrigation, *U. S. Dept. Agric. Circ.* 546, Washington, D. C., 85 pp., 1940.
30. Rorabaugh, M. I., Stream-bed percolation in development of water supplies, *Assemblée Générale de Bruxelles, Assoc. Intl. d'Hydrologie Scientifique,* vol. 2, pp. 165–174, 1951.
31. Schoff, S. L., Geology and water well construction, *Jour. Amer. Water Works Assoc.,* vol. 42, pp. 475–478, 1950.
32. Schwalen, H. C., The stovepipe or California method of well drilling as practiced in Arizona, *Bull.* 112, Univ. Arizona Agric. Exp. Sta., Tucson, pp. 103–154, 1925.
33. Smith, L. A., Deep wells in sandstone rock, Water Works Eng., vol. 94, pp. 710–712, 1941.
34. Stone, R., Infiltration galleries, *Proc. Amer. Soc. Civil Engrs.,* vol. 80, sep. 472, 12 pp., 1954.
35. Todd, D. K., Discussion of Infiltration galleries, *Proc. Amer. Soc. Civil Engrs.,* vol. 81, sep. 647, pp. 7–9, 1955.
36. War Dept., Well drilling, *Tech. Manual* 5-297, Washington, D. C., 276 pp., 1943.
37. White, H. L., Rejuvenating wells with chlorine, *Civil Eng.,* vol. 12, pp. 263–265, 1942.

Ground Water Levels and Fluctuations

CHAPTER 6

A ground water level, whether it be the water table of an unconfined aquifer or the piezometric surface of a confined aquifer, indicates the elevation of atmospheric pressure of the aquifer. Any phenomenon which produces a change in pressure on the ground water will cause the ground water level to change.[58] Changes in storage, resulting from differences between supply and withdrawal of water, cause levels to vary in time from a few minutes to many years. Effects of pumping on ground water levels were described in Chapter 4. Other localized storage changes are produced by variations of stream stages and evapotranspiration. External loads such as tides, trains, atmospheric pressure, and earthquakes are borne in part by the ground water of confined aquifers, hence they affect piezometric levels. Where necessary, man can control ground water levels to suit his purpose; regulation of seepage through earth dams and land drainage are examples of such controls.

Secular and Seasonal Variations

Secular variations of ground water levels are those extending over periods of several years or more. Alternating series of wet and dry years in which the rainfall is above or below the mean, will produce long-period fluctuations of levels.[12,14,30] The long records of rainfall and ground water levels from San Bernardino Valley, Calif., shown in

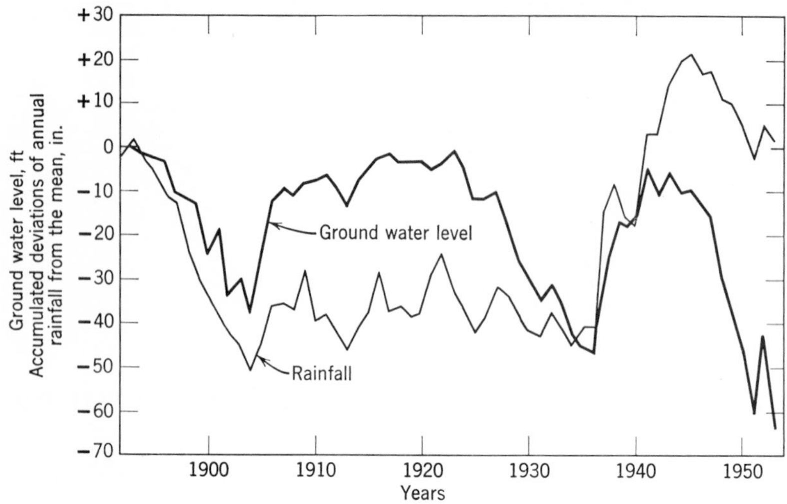

Fig. 6.1. Secular variations of maximum annual ground water level and annual rainfall in San Bernardino Valley, Calif.

Fig. 6.1, illustrate this point. Rainfall is not an accurate indicator of ground water level changes. Recharge is the governing factor (assuming annual withdrawals are constant), which depends upon rainfall intensity and distribution and amount of surface runoff.

In other instances pronounced trends may be noted. Thus, in overdeveloped basins where draft exceeds recharge, a downward trend of ground water levels may continue for many years. Figure 6.2 provides a good example.

Many ground water levels show a seasonal pattern of fluctuation. These result from influences such as recharge from rainfall and irrigation and discharge from pumping which follow well-defined seasonal cycles.[46] The magnitude of the fluctuations, of course, depends upon the quantities of water recharged and discharged; a fully developed aquifer will have a greater range than one only partially developed. The seasonal fluctuations apparent in Fig. 6.2 result from heavy pumpage for irrigation during the summer months. Highest levels occur about April and lowest about September, marking the beginning and the end of the irrigation season.

In several areas, land subsidence has been observed to accompany extensive drawdowns by excessive pumping from confined aquifers.*

* This subsidence should not be confused with that occurring in peat lands where lowering of the water table by drainage produces oxidation and wind erosion of surface organic matter.[65]

Areas affected include, among others, the Houston-Galveston area of Texas[66] and the San Joaquin[40] and Santa Clara valleys[52] of California. Figure 6.2 shows lowering of the piezometric surface and land subsidence at one location in the San Joaquin Valley. Here, over a 20-year period (1931–1951), the average subsidence ratio equalled 1:23, indicating that the land subsided 1 ft for every 23 ft of lowering of the piezometric surface. The cause of the phenomenon is as yet incompletely understood; however, it is believed that reduction of hydrostatic pressure in the aquifer increases the stress on confining clay layers, resulting in their being compressed. An intensive investigation of the problem is underway in California.[40]

Streamflow and Ground Water Levels

Where a stream channel is in direct contact with an unconfined aquifer, the stream may recharge the ground water or receive discharge from the ground water, depending on the relative water levels. An influent stream is one supplying ground water; an effluent stream is one receiving ground water discharge. Various situations are illustrated by the water level contours in Fig. 6.3. Often an influent stream may become an effluent one, and conversely, as the stream stage changes.

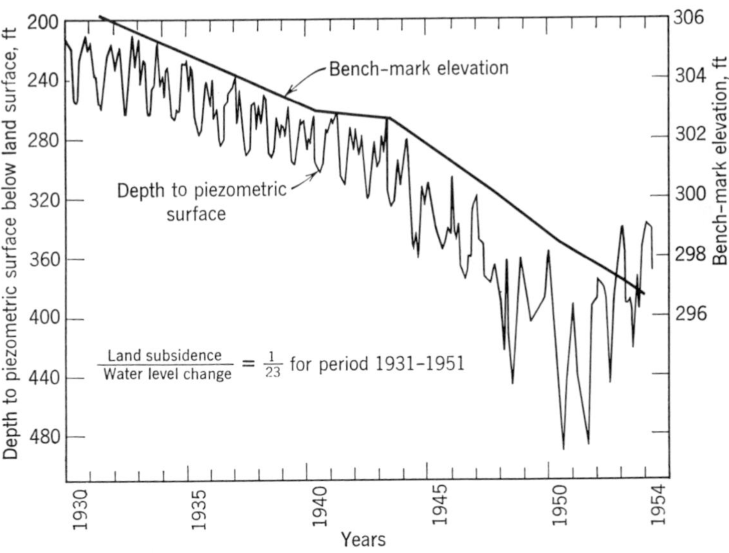

Fig. 6.2. Changes in ground surface and piezometric surface elevations near Delano, Calif. Annual fluctuations result from seasonal pumping for irrigation (after Poland and Davis[40]).

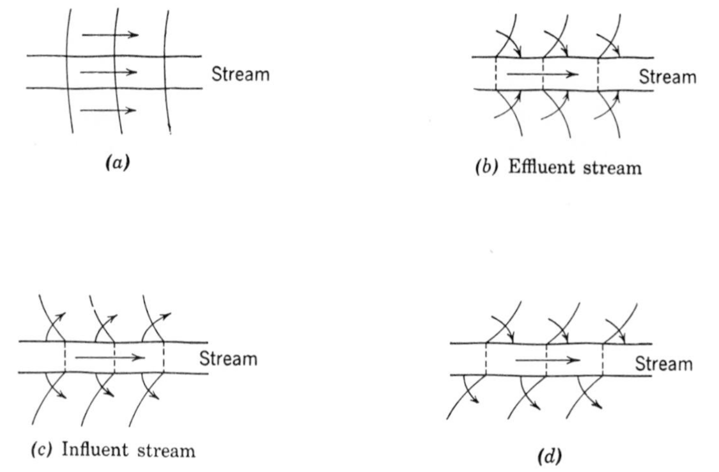

Fig. 6.3. Ground water contours and flow directions in relation to stream stages.

During a flood period of a stream, ground water levels are temporarily raised near the channel by inflow from the stream. The water so stored and released after the flood is referred to as bank storage. For certain boundary conditions the bank storage and its rate of inflow and outflow can be computed; for others model investigations (see Chapter 14) are helpful.[51]

Figure 6.4 illustrates ground water conditions adjacent to a flooding stream based on a model study of an idealized situation. A flood hydrograph of sinusoidal form (Fig. 6.4*a*) was superimposed on the aquifer and stream situation sketched in Fig. 6.4*b*. As a result of the flood the bank storage increased and then decreased, the variation of the volume of water in storage being depicted in Fig. 6.4*c*. The derivative of the volume curve yields the ground water flow curve (Fig. 6.4*d*). From this it can be seen that a stream fluctuation produces large variations in magnitude and direction of ground water flow.

That portion of streamflow coming from ground water discharge is base flow. It may vary from a negligible fraction of the total flow during periods of high surface runoff to the total flow during drought periods. Base flow is not subject to the wide fluctuations which streamflow coming from surface runoff often displays. Empirical methods have been developed for estimating base flow; [1] however, most of these are for the purpose of segregating surface runoff from total flow and give at best only crude estimates of the actual ground water contribution.

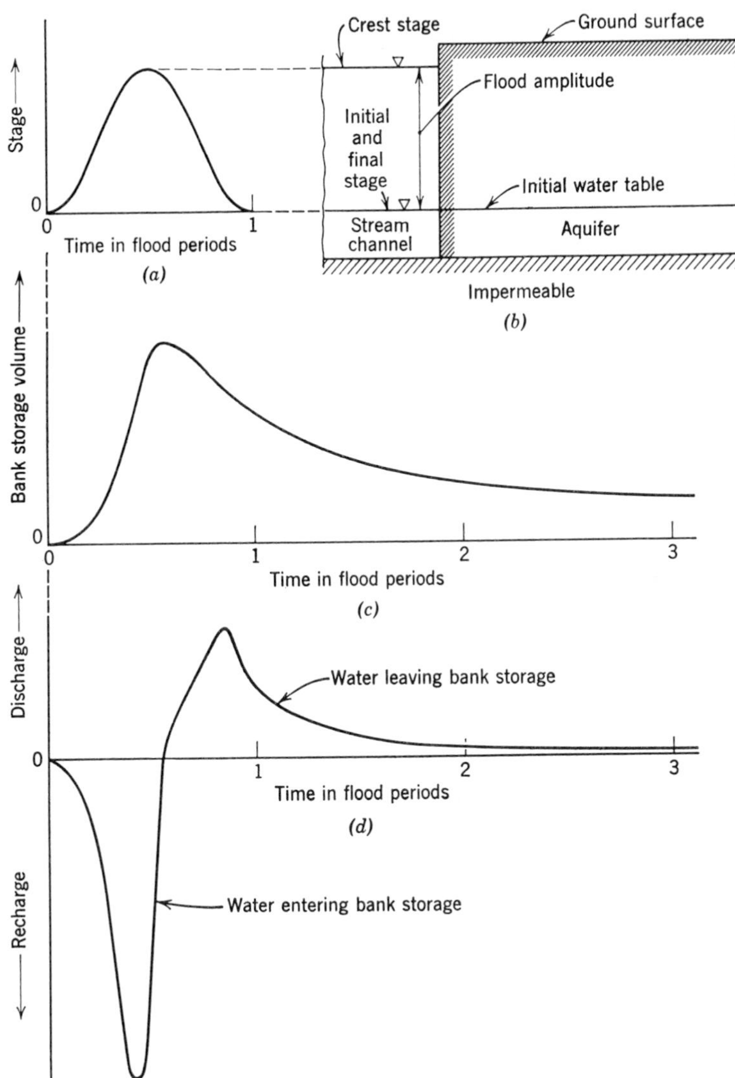

Fig. 6.4. Ground water flow in relation to a flooding stream determined by a laboratory model investigation for an idealized situation. (*a*) Flood hydrograph; (*b*) vertical cross-section of field conditions simulated by model; (*c*) volume of bank storage as a function of time; (*d*) ground water flow to and from bank storage (after Todd [51]).

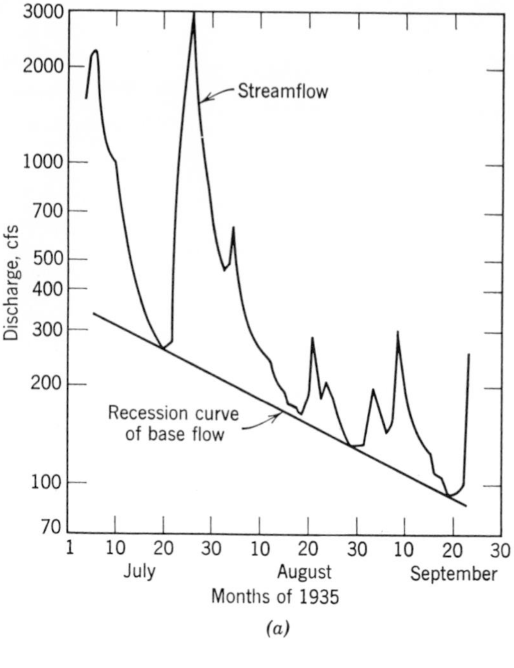

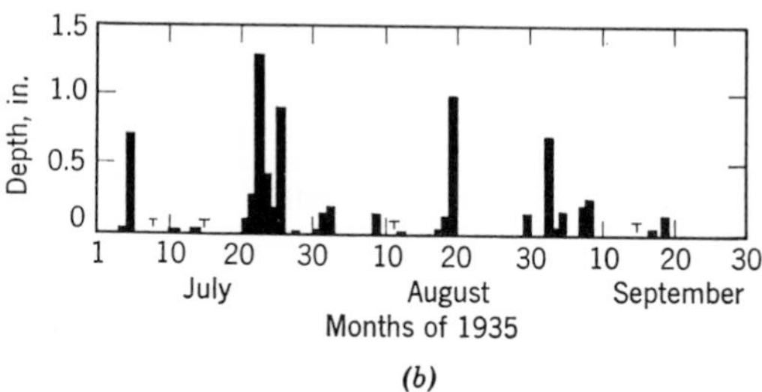

Fig. 6.5. Ground water recession curve of base flow during one summer for the Iowa River at Marshalltown, Iowa; (*a*) streamflow, and (*b*) daily rainfall (after Barnes [3]).

A ground water recession curve shows the variation of base flow with time during periods of little or no rainfall over a river basin. It is a measure of the drainage rate of ground water storage from the basin. If large, highly permeable aquifers are contained within a drainage area, the base flow will be sustained even through prolonged droughts; but if the aquifers are small and of low permeability, the base flow will decrease relatively rapidly and may even cease altogether. Knowledge of the shape of a recession curve enables estimates of streamflow to be made during drought periods.[6,34,35] Analyses of hydrographs by various investigators [3,15,42,55] have shown that the empirical equation

$$Q = Q_0 e^{-at} \tag{6.1}$$

gives a good approximation to the recession curve. The river discharge is Q at time t after a given discharge Q_0; a is a constant governed by characteristics of the basin. The value of a can be determined from the slope of a straight line fitted to a series of consecutive discharges plotted on semilogarithmic paper. As an example, the recession curve is sketched for the low-flow portion of the hydrograph in Fig. 6.5. A theoretical derivation of recession curves from confined and unconfined aquifers has been presented by Werner and Sundquist.[63]

Fluctuations Due to Evapotranspiration

Unconfined aquifers with water tables near ground surface frequently exhibit diurnal fluctuations which can be ascribed to evaporation and/or transpiration.[54,64] Both processes cause a discharge of ground water into the atmosphere and have nearly the same diurnal variation because of their high correlation with temperature.

Evaporation from ground water is negligible unless the water table is near the ground surface. Rates depend upon the position of the capillary zone relative to ground surface. Measurements of ground water evaporation in tanks filled with soils ranging from clays to loams were made by White.[64] Tanks were set in the ground and water levels were controlled through small central wells. Results, expressed as a percentage of evaporation from a 12-ft evaporation pan on the ground surface, are shown in Fig. 6.6 Each point represents comparative measurements for one month between a tank and the pan. The scatter of points can be attributed to the several soils tested. From the dashed line fitting the points it can be seen that evaporation is comparatively high for water tables within one foot of ground surface, and further that it decreases to an almost negligible rate for water tables three or more feet below ground surface.

Where the root zone of vegetation reaches the saturated stratum, the uptake of water by roots equals for practical purposes the transpiration rate. Figure 6.7 shows water level variations obtained from a well in a thicket of willows near Milford, Utah. Rapid foliage growth during August (Fig. 6.7*a*) caused daily fluctuations averaging about 3.75 in. with the water table between 5 and 6 ft below ground sur-

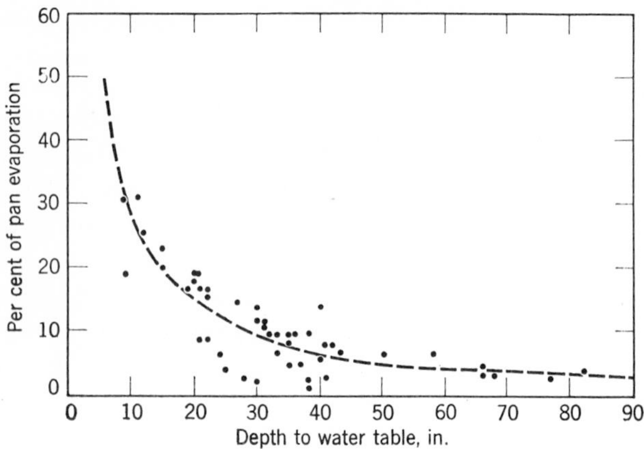

Fig. 6.6. Ground water evaporation, expressed as a percentage of pan evaporation, as a function of the depth to the water table (after White [64]).

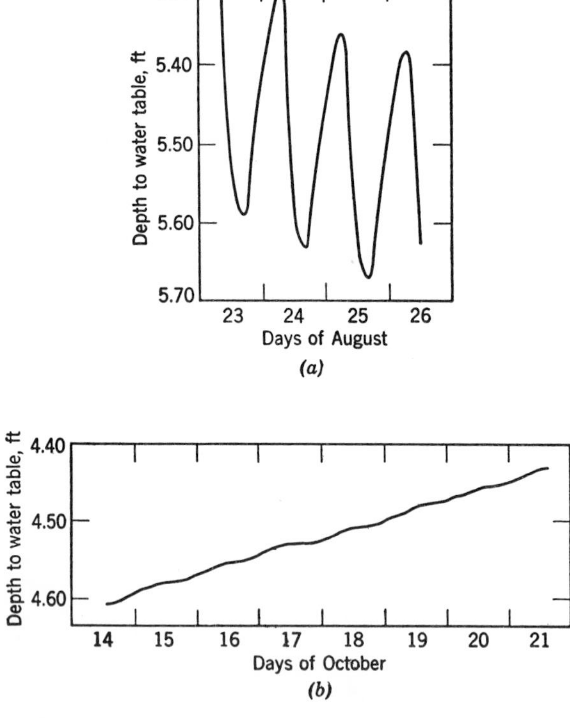

Fig. 6.7. Effect of transpiration discharge on ground water levels in (*a*) summer and (*b*) after frost, near Milford, Utah (after White [64]).

face. Heavy frosts occurred in early October so that most leaves had fallen by mid-October; thereafter, diurnal fluctuations were negligible (Fig. 6.7*b*) with the vegetation dormant.

Magnitudes of transpiration fluctuations depend upon the type of vegetation, season, and weather. Hot windy days produce maximum drawdowns, whereas cool cloudy days show only small variations. Fluctuations begin with the appearance of foliage and cease after killing frosts. Cutting of plants eliminates or materially reduces amplitudes.[64] Transpiration discharge does not occur in nonvegetated areas, such as plowed fields, nor in areas where the ground water table is far below ground surface. After rain on high water table vegetated land, the water table rises sharply as the increased soil moisture meets the transpiration demand and reduces the ground water discharge; but on cleared land or when vegetation is dormant, little or no rise is evident.

The pattern of diurnal fluctuation resulting from discharge of ground water is nearly identical for evaporation, transpiration, or their combined effect. The maximum water table level occurs in midmorning (see Fig. 6.8) and represents a temporary equilibrium between discharge and recharge from surrounding ground water. From then until early evening losses exceed recharge and the level falls. The steep slope near midday indicates maximum discharge associated with highest temperatures. The evening minimum again represents an equilibrium point, while the rise during the night hours is recharge in excess of discharge.

White [64] suggested a method for computing the total quantity of ground water withdrawn by evapotranspiration during a day. If it is assumed that evapotranspiration is negligible from midnight to 4 A.M. and, further, that the water table level during this interval approximates the mean for the day, then the hourly recharge from midnight to 4 A.M. may be taken as the average rate for the day. Letting h equal the hourly rate of rise of the water table from midnight to 4 A.M., as shown by the upper curve in Fig. 6.8, and s the net fall or rise of the water table during the 24-hour period, then as a good approximation the total ground water discharge

$$Q_{ET} = S_y(24h \pm s) \tag{6.2}$$

where S_y is the specific yield near the water table. Actually, as pointed out by Troxell,[54] the rate of ground water recharge to the vegetated area varies inversely with the water table level. The difference between the recharge rate and the slope of the ground water level curve

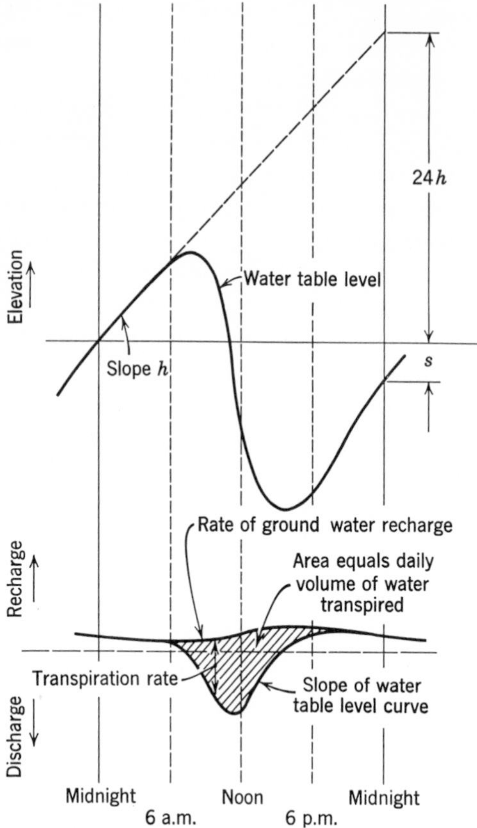

Fig. 6.8. Interrelations of water table level, recharge, and transpiration fluctuations (after Troxell[54]).

gives the transpiration discharge. The lower portion of Fig. 6.8 illustrates this; the area between the two curves is a measure of the daily volume of water transpired.

Fluctuations Due to Meteorological Phenomena

Atmospheric Pressure. Changes in atmospheric pressure have no effect on water tables but do produce sizable fluctuations in wells penetrating confined aquifers.[19,33,38,56] The relationship is inverse, that is, increases in atmospheric pressure produce decreases in water levels, and conversely. When atmospheric pressure changes are expressed in terms of a column of water, the ratio of water level change to pressure change expresses the barometric efficiency of an aquifer. Most observations yield values in the range of 20 to 75 per cent.

The effect is apparent in data shown in Fig. 6.9. The upper curve indicates observed water levels in a well at Iowa City, Iowa, penetrating a confined aquifer. The lower curve shows atmospheric pressure inverted, expressed in feet of water, and multiplied by 0.75. A close correspondence of major fluctuations exists in the two curves; the equality of amplitudes indicates that the barometric efficiency of the aquifer is about 75 per cent.

The explanation of the phenomenon can be given by recognizing that aquifers are elastic bodies.[19, 31, 56] If Δp_a is the change in atmospheric pressure and Δp_w is the resulting change in hydrostatic pressure at the top of a confined aquifer, then

$$\Delta p_a = \Delta p_w + \Delta s_c \tag{6.3}$$

where Δs_c is the increased compressive stress on the aquifer (Fig. 6.10). At a well penetrating the confined aquifer, the relation

$$p_w = p_a + \gamma h \tag{6.4}$$

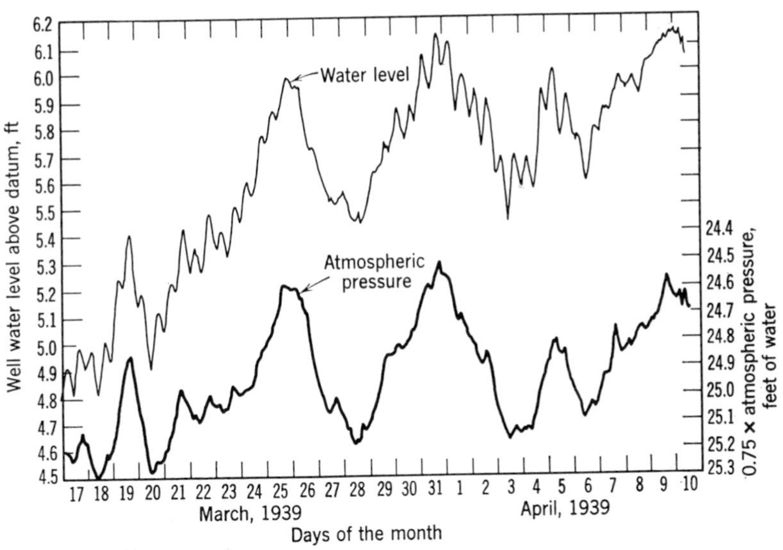

Fig. 6.9. Response of water level in a well penetrating a confined aquifer to atmospheric pressure changes, showing a barometric efficiency of 75 per cent (after Robinson [44]).

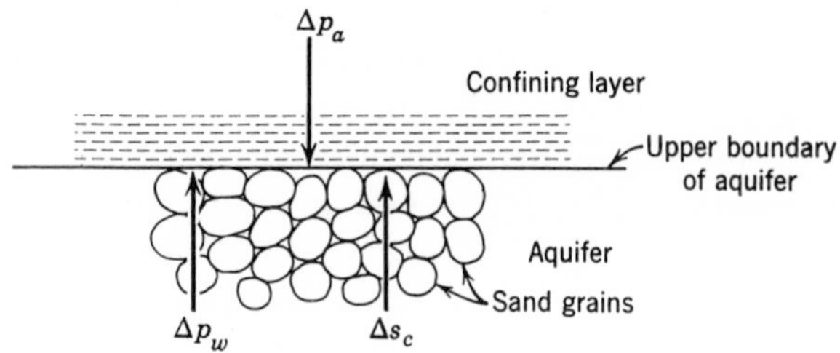

Fig. 6.10. Idealized distribution of forces at the upper boundary of a confined aquifer resulting from a change in atmospheric pressure.

exists as shown in Fig. 6.11*a*, where γ is the specific weight of water. Let the atmospheric pressure increase by Δp_a, then

$$p_w + \Delta p_w = p_a + \Delta p_a + \gamma h' \tag{6.5}$$

as shown in Fig. 6.11*b*. Substituting for p_w from Eq. 6.4 yields

$$\Delta p_w = \Delta p_a + \gamma(h' - h) \tag{6.6}$$

But from Eq. 6.3 it is apparent that $\Delta p_w < \Delta p_a$, indicating that $h' < h$. Generally, therefore, the water level in a well falls with an increase in atmospheric pressure. It follows that the converse is also true. For an unconfined aquifer atmospheric pressure changes are transmitted directly to the water table, both in the aquifer and a well, hence no fluctuation results.

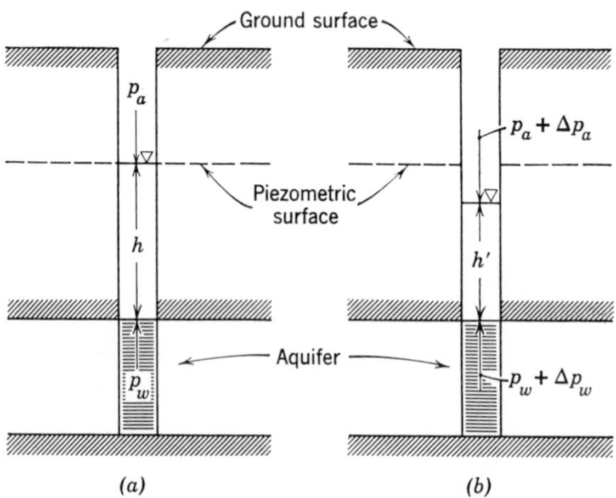

Fig. 6.11. Effect of an increase in atmospheric pressure on the water level of a well penetrating a confined aquifer.

Jacob[19] obtained an expression relating the barometric efficiency to aquifer and water properties. If a column of unit volume extends through a confined aquifer, then an increase in atmospheric pressure Δp_a will change the column water volume V_w by

$$\Delta V_w = -\frac{\Delta p_w}{E_w}\alpha \tag{6.7}$$

where E_w is the bulk modulus of compression of water (equaling approximately 300,000 psi) and α is porosity. Similarly, the aquifer volume V_s within the column will be compressed (neglecting compression of the solid particles forming the aquifer) by an amount

$$\Delta V_s = -\frac{\Delta s_c}{E_s} \tag{6.8}$$

where E_s is the modulus of elasticity of the structure of the aquifer. The change in water volume can be assumed to balance the aquifer compression, so that $\Delta V_w = \Delta V_s$. These relations, together with those of Eqs. 6.3 and 6.6, can now be substituted in the barometric efficiency equation

$$B = \frac{\gamma\,\Delta h}{\Delta p_a} \tag{6.9}$$

to yield

$$B = \frac{\alpha E_s}{\alpha E_s + E_w} \tag{6.10}$$

The right side of Eq. 6.10 is constant for a given aquifer. The barometric efficiency can be interpreted as a measure of the competence of overlying confining beds to resist pressure changes; thick impermeable confining strata are associated with high barometric efficiencies, whereas thinly confined aquifers will display low values.

Carrying the analysis one step further, it can be shown that barometric efficiency is related to the storage coefficient of an aquifer. The compressibility β of an aquifer can be expressed from Eq. 3.36 as

$$\beta = -\left(\frac{\Delta V_w}{\Delta p_w} + \frac{\Delta V_s}{\Delta s_c}\right) \tag{6.11}$$

Substituting from Eqs. 6.7 and 6.8

$$\beta = \frac{\alpha}{E_w} + \frac{1}{E_s} \tag{6.12}$$

and from Eq. 6.10

$$\beta = \frac{\alpha}{E_w B} \tag{6.13}$$

Rewriting from Eq. 3.37, the storage coefficient

$$S = \beta \gamma b \tag{6.14}$$

where b is the aquifer thickness. Then, inserting β from Eq. 6.13,

$$S = \frac{\alpha \gamma b}{E_w B} \tag{6.15}$$

Thus, from the barometric efficiency of a confined aquifer, an estimate of its storage coefficient can be obtained.

Wind. Minor fluctuations of water levels are caused by wind blowing over the tops of wells.[38] The effect is identical to the action of a vacuum pump. As a gust of wind blows across the top of a casing, the air pressure within the well is suddenly lowered and, as a consequence, the water level quickly rises. After the gust passes, the air pressure in the well rises and the water level falls. The effect is illustrated by Fig. 6.12, which shows a well record at Miami, Fla., during the passage of a hurricane. The storm center passed north of Miami

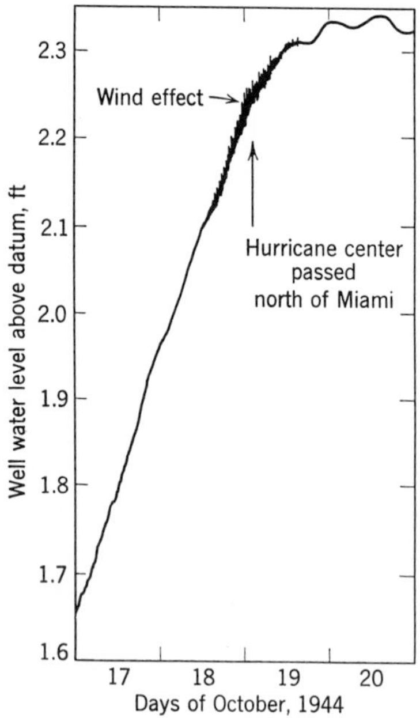

Fig. 6.12. Wind-induced water level fluctuations in a well at Miami, Fla., during passage of a hurricane (after Parker and Stringfield [38]).

during the night of Oct. 18, 1944. Wind velocities reached 54 mph on October 18 and 65 mph on October 19; rapid fluctuations accompanying these winds are apparent on the well record.

Rainfall. As previously mentioned, annual ground water level fluctuations result from seasonal variations of recharge from rainfall. For a sinusoidal recharge pattern the computation of water level fluctuations is analogous to that for ocean tides, described below.[21, 22, 37, 62]

Fluctuations Due to Tides, External Loads, and Earthquakes

Ocean Tides. In coastal aquifers in contact with the ocean, sinusoidal fluctuations of ground water levels occur in response to tides. If the sea level varies with a simple harmonic motion, a train of sinusoidal waves is propagated inland from the submarine outcrop of the aquifer. With distance, inland amplitudes of the waves decrease and the time lag of a given maximum increases. The problem has been solved by analogy to heat conduction in a semi-infinite solid subject to periodic temperature variations normal to the infinite dimension.[11, 23, 62]

For simplicity consider the one-directional flow in a confined aquifer as shown in Fig. 6.13a. From Eq. 3.43 the applicable differential equation governing the flow is

$$\frac{\partial^2 h}{\partial x^2} = \frac{S}{T}\frac{\partial h}{\partial t} \tag{6.16}$$

where h is the net rise or fall of the piezometric surface with reference to the mean level, x is the distance inland from the outcrop, S is the storage coefficient of the aquifer, and T is the coefficient of transmissibility (equal to Kb), and t is time. Letting the amplitude, or half range, of the tide be h_0 (see Fig. 6.13a), the applicable boundary conditions include $h = h_0 \sin \omega t$ at $x = 0$ and $h = 0$ at $x = \infty$. The angular velocity is ω; for a tidal period t_0,

$$\omega = \frac{2\pi}{t_0} \tag{6.17}$$

The solution of Eq. 6.16 with these boundary conditions is

$$h = h_0 e^{-x\sqrt{\pi S/t_0 T}} \sin\left(\frac{2\pi t}{t_0} - x\sqrt{\pi S/t_0 T}\right) \tag{6.18}$$

From this it follows that the amplitude h_x of ground water fluctuations at a distance x from the shore equals

$$h_x = h_0 e^{-x\sqrt{\pi S/t_0 T}} \tag{6.19}$$

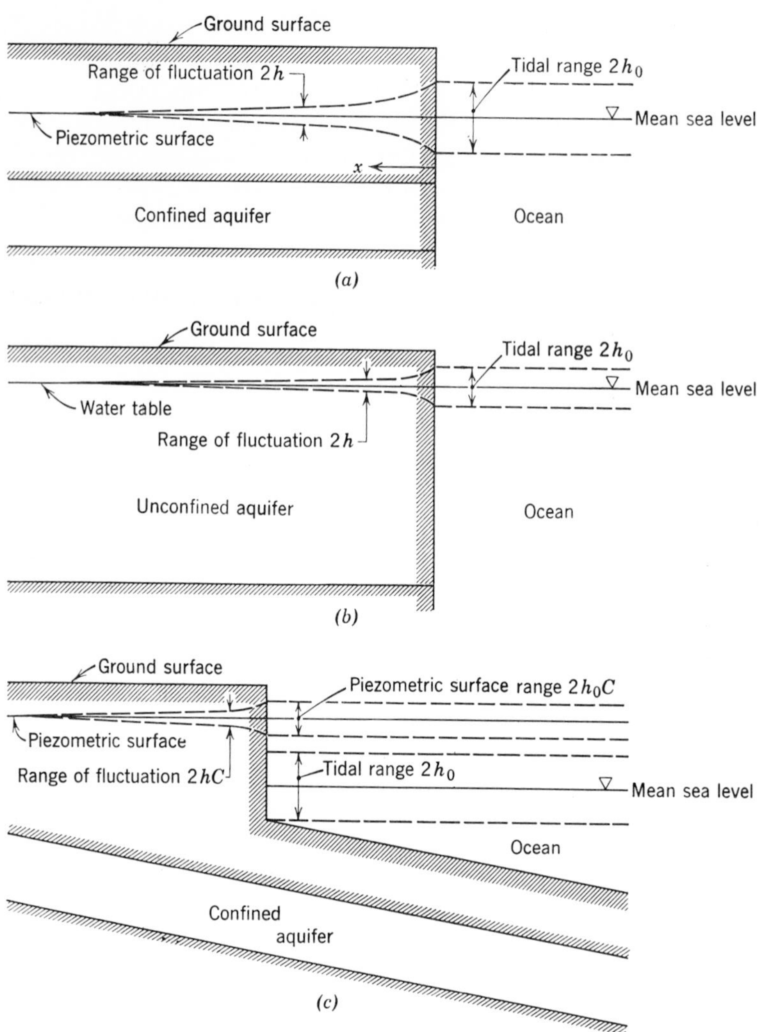

Fig. 6.13. Ground water level fluctuations produced by ocean tides: (*a*) confined aquifer, (*b*) unconfined aquifer, and (*c*) loading of a confined aquifer.

The time lag t_L of a given maximum or minimum after it occurs in the ocean can be obtained by solving the quantity within the parentheses of Eq. 6.18 for t, so that

$$t_L = x\sqrt{t_0S/4\pi T} \qquad (6.20)$$

The waves travel with a velocity

$$v_w = \frac{x}{t_L} = \sqrt{4\pi T/t_0 S} \tag{6.21}$$

and the wavelength is given by

$$L_w = v_w t_0 = \sqrt{4\pi t_0 T/S} \tag{6.22}$$

Substituting the wavelength for x in Eq. 6.19 shows that the amplitude decreases by a factor $e^{-2\pi}$, or $1/535$, for each wavelength. Water flows into the aquifer during half of each cycle and out during the other half. By Darcy's law the quantity of flow V per half-cycle per foot of coast is

$$V = \int_{-t_0/8}^{3t_0/8} q\,dt = T\int_{-t_0/8}^{3t_0/8} \left(\frac{\partial h}{\partial x}\right)_{x=0} dt \tag{6.23}$$

where q is the flow per foot of coast. Differentiating Eq. 6.18 to obtain $\partial h/\partial x$ and integrating yields [11]

$$V = h_0\sqrt{2t_0\,ST/\pi} \tag{6.24}$$

The above analysis is also applicable as a good approximation to water table fluctuations of an unconfined aquifer if the range of fluctuation is small in comparison to the saturated thickness (Fig. 6.13*b*). In Fig. 6.14 are shown fluctuations in wells penetrating an unconfined aquifer at various distances from a surface water level varying approximately with a sinusoidal pattern.

Just as atmospheric pressure changes produce variations of piezometric levels, so do tidal fluctuations vary the load on confined aquifers extending under the ocean floor (Fig. 6.13*c*). Contrary to the atmospheric pressure effect, tidal fluctuations are direct; that is, as the sea level increases, the ground water level does also. Figure 6.15 illustrates the effect for a well only 100 ft from shore. The ratio of piezometric level amplitude to tidal amplitude is known as the tidal efficiency of the aquifer. Jacob [19] showed that tidal efficiency C is related to barometric efficiency B by

$$C = 1 - B \tag{6.25}$$

Thus, tidal efficiency is a measure of the incompetence of overlying confining beds to resist pressure changes. Aquifer response to loading rather than head change at the outcrop requires that the amplitude given by Eq. 6.18 be multiplied by C. From Eqs. 6.10 and 6.25,

$$C = \frac{E_w}{\alpha E_s + E_w} \tag{6.26}$$

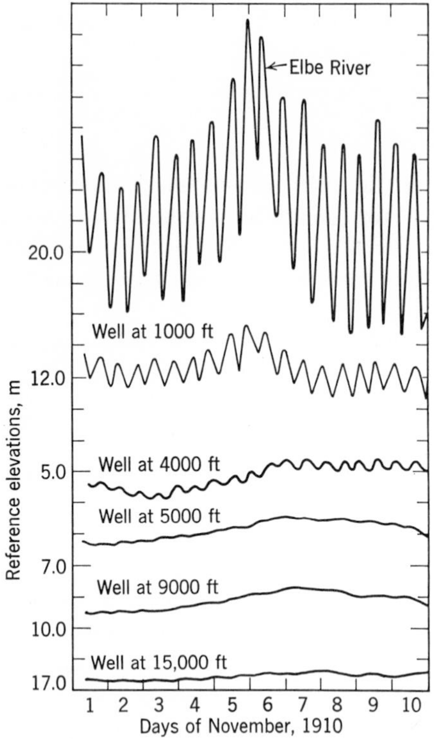

Fig. 6.14. Fluctuations of the Elbe River and water table levels in wells at various distances from the river (after Werner and Noren [62]).

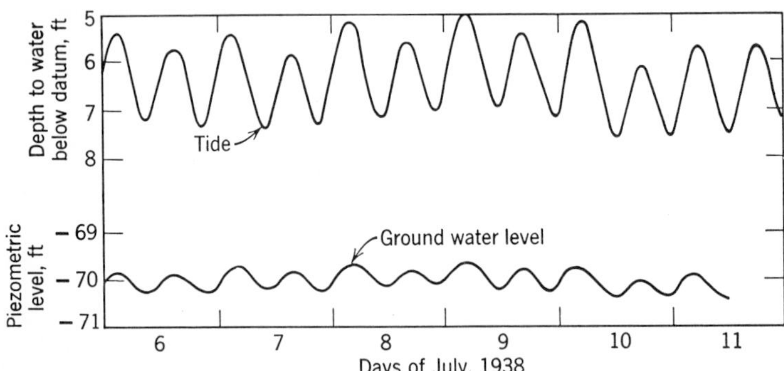

Fig. 6.15. Tidal fluctuations and induced piezometric surface fluctuations observed in a well 100 feet from shore at Mattawoman Creek, Md. (after Meinzer [32]).

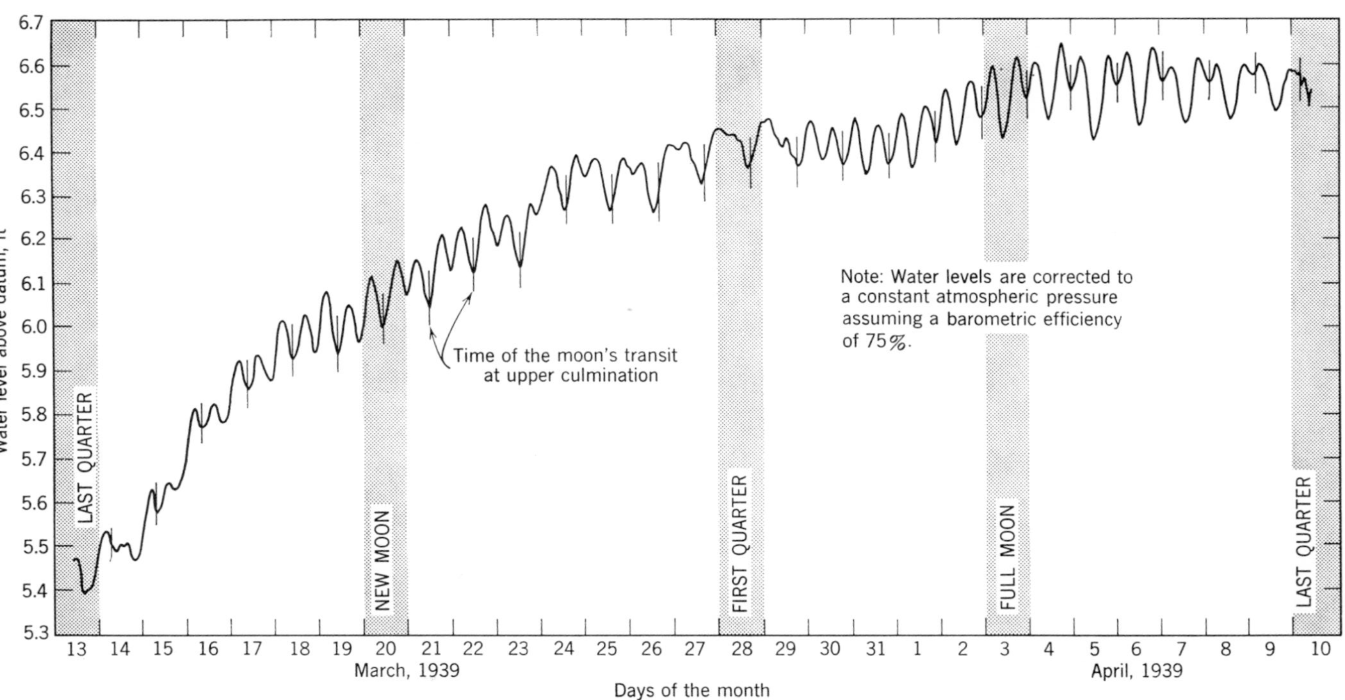

Fig. 6.16. Water level fluctuations in a confined aquifer produced by earth tides (after Robinson[44]).

The storage coefficient of an aquifer can be computed from observations of the tidal efficiency[19,20] by replacing B by $1 - C$ in Eq. 6.15.

Earth Tides. Regular semidiurnal fluctuations of small magnitude have been observed in piezometric surfaces of confined aquifers located at great distances from the ocean. For example, wells located in the inland states of Iowa, New Mexico, and Tennessee[41,44] display the phenomenon. After correcting well levels for atmospheric pressure changes, these fluctuations appear quite distinctly in certain wells where the phenomenon has been investigated. Figure 6.16 shows fluctuations over a lunar cycle from an 840-ft well tapping a confined aquifer in Iowa City, Iowa.

These fluctuations have been attributed to earth tides, resulting from the attraction exerted on the earth's crust by the moon and, to a lesser extent, the sun. Robinson's observations[44] supporting this hypothesis, based on analyses of well records, make convincing evidence: (*a*) two daily cycles of fluctuations occur about 50 min later each day, as does the moon; (*b*) the average daily retardation of cycles agrees closely with that of the moon's transit; (*c*) the daily troughs of the water level coincide with the transits of the moon at upper and lower culmination; and (*d*) periods of large regular fluctuations coincide with periods of new and full moon, whereas periods of small irregular fluctuations coincide with periods of first and third quarters of the moon. All of these facts may be noted in the data of Fig. 6.16.

At times of new and full moon the tide-producing forces of the moon and sun act in the same direction, then ocean tides display a greater than average range. But when the moon is in the first and third quarters, tide-producing forces of the sun and moon act per-

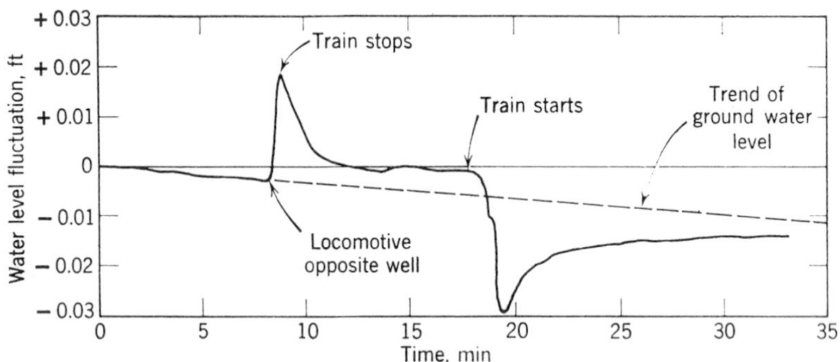

Fig. 6.17. Water level fluctuations in a confined aquifer produced by a train stopping and starting near the observation well (after Jacob[18]).

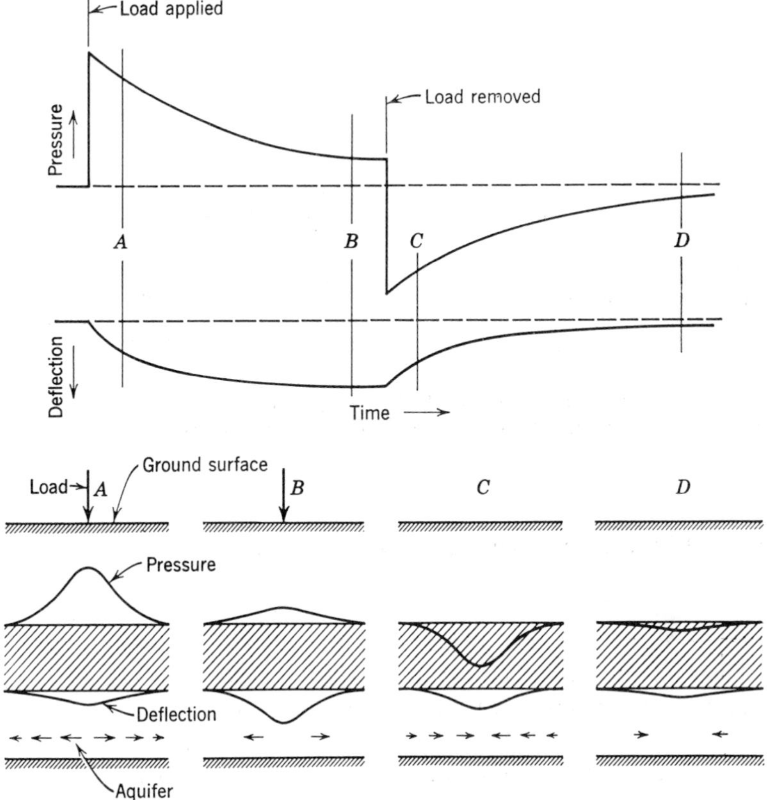

Fig. 6.18. Hydrostatic pressure variations and aquifer deflections resulting from a point load applied and later removed from the ground surface above a confined aquifer (after Jacob [18]).

pendicular to one another, causing ocean tides of smaller than average range. The coincidence of the time of low water with that of the moon's transit can be explained by reasoning that at this time tidal attraction is maximum; therefore, the overburden load on the aquifer is reduced, allowing the aquifer to expand slightly.

External Loads. The elastic property of confined aquifers results in changes in hydrostatic pressure when changes in loading occur. Some of the best examples are exhibited by wells located near railroads where passing trains produce measurable fluctuations of the piezometric surface. The phenomenon has been reported by several investigators.[18, 38, 43] Figure 6.17 illustrates changes in water level

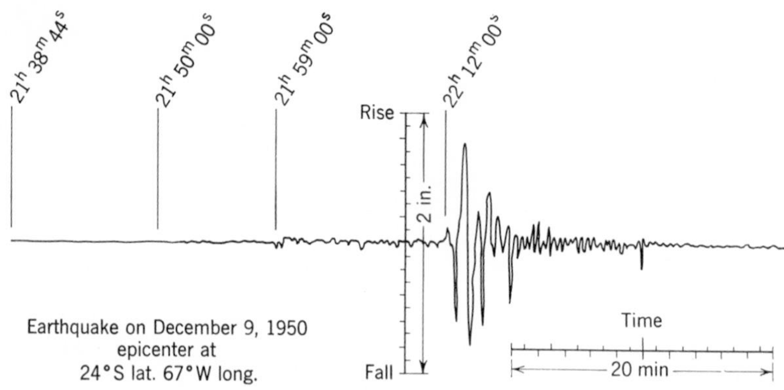

Fig. 6.19. Earthquake water level fluctuations in a well at Milwaukee, Wis., resulting from an earthquake centered on the Argentina-Chile border (after Vorhis [59]).

produced by a train stopping and starting near a well at Smithtown, N. Y.

The application of a load compresses the aquifer and increases the hydrostatic pressure. Thereafter the pressure decreases and approaches its original value asymptotically as water flows radially away from the point where the load is applied. Thus, initially the load is shared by the confined water and the solid material of the aquifer; however, as the water flows radially outward, an increasing proportion of the load is borne by the structure of the aquifer. The schematic diagram after Jacob [18] in Fig. 6.18 shows this effect. Here a point load instantaneously applied is represented. The lower surface of the aquifer is assumed fixed; lengths of arrows indicate the relative magnitudes of flow velocities at various distances from the load. During the interval from A to B the hydrostatic pressure decreases and the deflection of the upper surface of the aquifer increases. Subsequently, when the load is removed, the pressure drops to a minimum and then recovers toward its initial value as shown by times C and D.

Earthquakes. Observations reveal that earthquakes have a variety of effects on ground water.[25, 38, 39, 50, 59] Most spectacular are sudden rises or falls of water levels in wells, changes in discharge of springs, appearance of new springs, and eruptions of water and mud out of the ground.[16] More commonly, however, earthquake shocks produce small fluctuations in wells penetrating confined aquifers. A good example is furnished by the water level record on an expanded time scale shown in Fig. 6.19. This earthquake was centered on the Argentina-Chile border, nearly 5000 miles from the recording well in Milwaukee, Wis. Although little is known of the quantitative effects of earthquakes on ground water, these fluctuations are presumed to result from compression and expansion of elastic confined aquifers by the passage of earthquake waves. These waves travel at speeds of approximately 125 miles per minute [38] so that fluctuations appear after little more than one hour even from the most distant earthquake centers.

Control by Drains and Wells

Water tables near ground surface can be controlled by construction of drains or wells to maintain levels at or below specified depths.

Drains are designed in several ways. Some are composed of coarse sand or gravel so that their permeability is higher than the surrounding porous media. Water flows readily through them so that they serve as outlets for draining surrounding ground water. Horizontal lines of open-jointed tile or perforated pipe are widely employed for drains. Other drains are simply open ditches which intercept ground water whenever the water table rises above the bottom of the ditch.

Drains have many applications, only a few of which can be mentioned here. An earth dam usually contains drains near its toe to prevent saturation of the downstream face.[4,7] Figure 6.20 illustrates the effect. Most foundations of structures contain drains around their perimeters to reduce hydrostatic pressure or water entrance. Modern highways often contain subdrains to avoid saturation of the highway grade. On agricultural lands, adequate drainage systems are essential for stabilizing water tables below the root zone.[17,45,48] High water tables may result naturally in flat lands bordering rivers, lakes, or the ocean, or may be produced artificially by percolation from excess irrigation water. To regulate water levels within narrow limits over a large area, drains are laid in parallel lines at depths and spacings governed by local crop and soil conditions.[9,10] A typical configuration

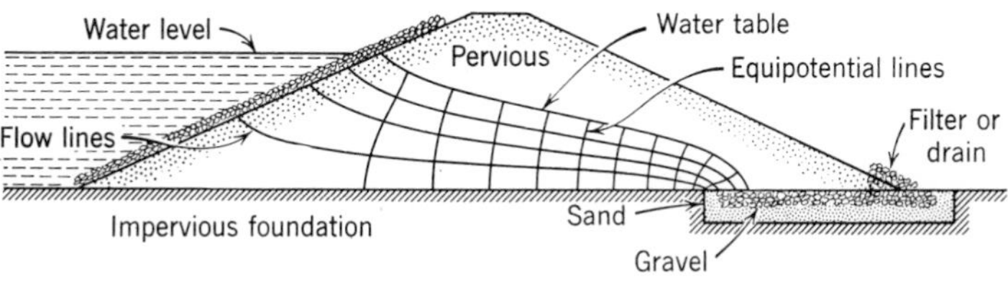

Fig. 6.20. Effect of a drain in an earth dam to prevent saturation of the downstream face (after Creager, Justin, and Hinds [7]).

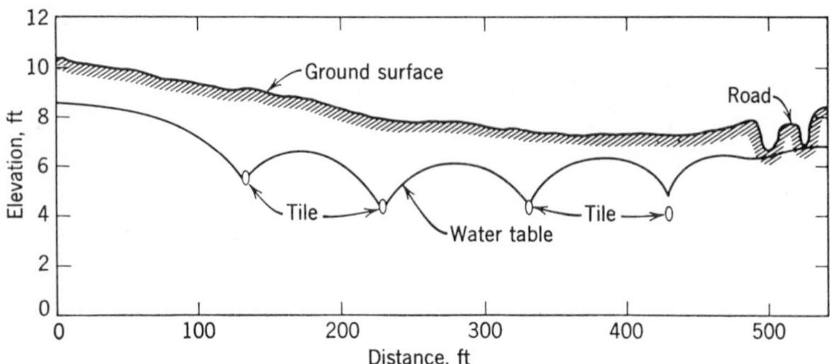

Fig. 6.21. Water table controlled by a system of tile drains in flat agricultural land (after *Eng. Exp. Sta. Bull.* 52, Iowa State College).

of the water table in a field containing tile drains is shown by the profile in Fig. 6.21.

Pumping wells also may control water levels, the process being identical to wells providing water supplies.[27] Where drainage wells are employed on agricultural lands, the extracted water may be reapplied to the land for irrigation or may be wasted depending on the salinity of the water (see Chapter 7). Well points, mentioned in Chapter 5, are lines of small-diameter wells most often installed for dewatering subsurface construction sites. Relief wells are placed near the toes of dams and levees to lower water tables and thereby reduce uplift pressures produced by seepage under the structures.[2, 24, 36, 57]

The design and construction of drains for controlling ground water levels is beyond the scope of this text. Basic principles involved, however, are the same as those described in preceding chapters. The subject has been extensively treated, particularly in civil and agricultural engineering literature, and by several texts.[7, 28, 45]

References

1. Amer. Soc. Civil Engrs., Hydrology handbook, *Manual of Eng. Practice* 28, New York, 184 pp., 1949.
2. Anon., Vertical relief wells reduce uplift on Sardis and Fort Peck Dams, *Eng. News-Record,* vol. 139, pp. 246–250, 1947.
3. Barnes, B. S., The structure of discharge-recession curves, *Trans. Amer. Geophysical Union,* vol. 20, pp. 721–725, 1939.
4. Casagrande, A., Seepage through dams, *Jour. New England Water Works Assoc.,* vol. 51, pp. 131–172, 1937.

5. Christiansen, J. E., Ground-water studies in relation to drainage, *Agric. Eng.*, vol. 24, pp. 339–342, 1943.
6. Clark, W. E., Forecasting the dry-weather flow of Pond Creek, Oklahoma; a progress report, *Trans. Amer. Geophysical Union,* vol. 37, pp. 442–450, 1956.
7. Creager, W. P., J. D. Justin, and J. Hinds, *Engineering for dams,* vol. 3, John Wiley and Sons, New York, pp. 655–714, 1945.
8. Cross, W. P., The relation of geology to dry-weather stream flow in Ohio, *Trans. Amer. Geophysical Union,* vol. 30, pp. 563–566, 1949.
9. Donnan, W. W., and G. B. Bradshaw, Drainage investigation methods for irrigated areas in Western United States, *U. S. Dept. Agric. Tech. Bull.* 1065, Washington, D. C., 45 pp., 1952.
10. Ferris, J. G., A quantitative method for determining ground-water characteristics for drainage design, *Agric. Eng.,* vol. 31, pp. 285–289, 1950.
11. Ferris, J. G., Cyclic fluctuations of water level as a basis for determining aquifer transmissibility, *Assemblée Générale de Bruxelles, Assoc. Intl. d'Hydrologie Scientifique,* vol. 2, pp. 148–155, 1951.
12. Fishel, V. C., Long-term trends of ground-water levels in the United States, *Trans. Amer. Geophysical Union,* vol. 37, pp. 429–435, 1956.
13. George, W. O., and F. E. Romberg, Tide-producing forces and artesian pressures, *Trans. Amer. Geophysical Union,* vol. 32, pp. 369–371, 1951.
14. Gleason, G. B., Changes in ground-water elevations of the South Coastal Basin during the past quarter-century in comparison to long-time mean precipitation and runoff, *Trans. Amer. Geophysical Union,* vol. 23, pp. 108–124, 1942.
15. Grundy, F., The ground-water depletion curve, its construction and uses, *Assemblée Générale de Bruxelles, Assoc. Intl. d'Hydrologie Scientifique,* vol. 2, pp. 213–217, 1951.
16. Heck, N. H., Relation of seismology to hydrology, *Trans. Amer. Geophysical Union,* vol. 14, pp. 34–36, 1933.
17. Hooghoudt, S. B., Tile drainage and subirrigation, *Soil Sci.,* vol. 74, pp. 35–49, 1952.
18. Jacob, C. E., Fluctuations in artesian pressure produced by passing railroad-trains as shown in a well on Long Island, New York, *Trans. Amer. Geophysical Union,* vol. 20, pp. 666–674, 1939.
19. Jacob, C. E., On the flow of water in an elastic artesian aquifer, *Trans. Amer. Geophysical Union,* vol. 21, pp. 574–586, 1940.
20. Jacob, C. E., Notes on the elasticity of the Lloyd Sand on Long Island, New York, *Trans. Amer. Geophysical Union,* vol. 22, pp. 783–787, 1941.
21. Jacob, C. E., Correlation of ground-water levels and precipitation on Long Island, New York, *Trans. Amer. Geophysical Union,* vol. 24, pp. 564–573, 1943.
22. Jacob, C. E., Correlation of ground-water levels and precipitation on Long Island, New York, *Trans. Amer. Geophysical Union,* vol. 25, pp. 928–939, 1944.
23. Jacob, C. E., Flow of ground water, in *Engineering hydraulics* (H. Rouse, ed.), John Wiley and Sons, New York, pp. 321–386, 1950.
24. Jones, W. R., Easy-to-install drain wells placed behind leaking levee, *Eng. News-Record,* vol. 146, p. 37, May 17, 1951.
25. La Rocque, G. A., Jr., Fluctuations of water-level in wells in the Los Angeles

Basin, California, during five strong earthquakes, 1933–1940, *Trans. Amer. Geophysical Union,* vol. 22, pp. 374–386, 1941.
26. Lee, C. H., The interpretation of water-levels in wells and test-holes, *Trans. Amer. Geophysical Union,* vol. 15, pp. 540–554, 1934.
27. Lewis, M. R., Flow of ground-water as applied to drainage wells, *Trans. Amer. Soc. Civil Engrs.,* vol. 96, pp. 1194–1211, 1932.
28. Luthin, J. N. (ed.), *Drainage of agricultural lands,* Amer. Soc. Agronomy, Madison, Wis., 620 pp., 1957.
29. Mansur, C. I., and R. I. Kaufman, Control of underseepage, Mississippi River levees, St. Louis District, *Proc. Amer. Soc. Civil Engrs.,* vol. 82, no. SM1, 31 pp., 1956.
30. McGuinness, C. L., Recharge and depletion of ground-water supplies, *Proc. Amer. Soc. Civil Engrs.,* vol. 72, pp. 963–984, 1946.
31. Meinzer, O. E., Compressibility and elasticity of artesian aquifers, *Econ. Geol.,* vol. 23, pp. 263–291, 1928.
32. Meinzer, O. E., Ground water in the United States, *U. S. Geological Survey Water-Supply Paper* 836-D, Washington, D. C., pp. 157–232, 1939.
33. Meissner, R., Der Einfluss von Luftdruckschwankungen auf den Grundwasserstand, *Zeitschrift für Geophysik,* vol. 19, pp. 161–180, 1953.
34. Merriam, C. F., Ground-water records in river-flow forecasting, *Trans. Amer. Geophysical Union,* vol. 29, pp. 384–386, 1948.
35. Merriam, C. F., Evaluation of two elements affecting the characteristics of the recession curve, *Trans. Amer. Geophysical Union,* vol. 32, pp. 597–600, 1951.
36. Middlebrooks, T. A., and W. H. Jervis, Relief wells for dams and levees, *Trans. Amer. Soc. Civil Engrs.,* vol. 112, pp. 1321–1402, 1947.
37. Netherlands State Institute for Water Supply, The effect of the yearly fluctuations in rainfall on the flow of ground water from an extended area of recharge, *Assemblée Générale d'Oslo, Assoc. Intl. d'Hydrologie Scientifique,* vol. 3, pp. 47–56, 1948.
38. Parker, G. G., and V. T. Stringfield, Effects of earthquakes, trains, tides, winds, and atmospheric pressure changes on water in the geologic formations of Southern Florida, *Econ. Geol.,* vol. 45, pp. 441–460, 1950.
39. Piper, A. M., Fluctuations of water-surface in observation-wells and at stream gaging-stations in the Mokelumne Area, California, during the earthquake of December 20, 1932, *Trans. Amer. Geophysical Union,* vol. 14, pp. 471–475, 1933.
40. Poland, J. F., and G. H. Davis, Subsidence of the land surface in the Tulare-Wasco (Delano) and Los Banos-Kettleman City Area, San Joaquin Valley, California, *Trans. Amer. Geophysical Union,* vol. 37, pp. 287–296, 1956.
41. Richardson, R. M., Tidal fluctuations of water level observed in wells in East Tennessee, *Trans. Amer. Geophysical Union,* vol. 37, pp. 461–462, 1956.
42. Riggs, H. C., A method of forecasting low flow of streams, *Trans. Amer. Geophysical Union,* vol. 34, pp. 427–434, 1953.
43. Roberts, W. J., and H. E. Romine, Effect of train loading on the water level in a deep glacial-drift well in Central Illinois, *Trans. Amer. Geophysical Union,* vol. 28, pp. 912–917, 1947.
44. Robinson, T. W., Earth-tides shown by fluctuations of water-levels in wells in New Mexico and Iowa, *Trans. Amer. Geophysical Union,* vol. 20, pp. 656–666, 1939.

45. Roe, H. B., and Q. C. Ayres, *Engineering for agricultural drainage,* McGraw-Hill, New York, 501 pp., 1954.
46. Rorabaugh, M. I., Prediction of ground-water levels on basis of rainfall and temperature correlations, *Trans. Amer. Geophysical Union,* vol. 37, pp. 436–441, 1956.
47. Rose, N. A., and W. H. Alexander, Jr., Relation of phenomenal rise of water levels to a defective gas well, Harris County, Texas, *Bull. Amer. Assoc. Pet. Geol.,* vol. 29, pp. 253–279, 1945.
48. Schilfgaarde, J. van, D. Kirkham, and R. K. Frevert, Physical and mathematical theories of tile and ditch drainage and their usefulness in design, *Research Bull.* 436, Agric. Exp. Sta., Iowa State College, Ames, pp. 667–706, 1956.
49. Snyder, F. F., A conception of runoff-phenomena, *Trans. Amer. Geophysical Union,* vol. 20, pp. 725–738, 1939.
50. Thomas, H. E., Fluctuations of ground-water levels during the earthquakes of November 10, 1938 and January 24, 1939, *Bull. Seismological Soc. Amer.,* vol. 30, pp. 93–97, 1940.
51. Todd, D. K., Ground-water flow in relation to a flooding stream, *Proc. Amer. Soc. Civil Engrs.,* vol. 81, sep. 628, 20 pp., 1955.
52. Tolman, C. F., and J. F. Poland, Ground-water, salt-water infiltration, and ground-surface recession in Santa Clara Valley, Santa Clara County, California, *Trans. Amer. Geophysical Union,* vol. 21, pp. 23–35, 1940.
53. Trousdell, K. B., and M. D. Hoover, A change in ground-water level after clearcutting of Loblolly pine in the Coastal Plain, *Jour. Forestry,* vol. 53, pp. 493–498, 1955.
54. Troxell, H. C., The diurnal fluctuation in the ground-water and flow of the Santa Ana River and its meaning, *Trans. Amer. Geophysical Union,* vol. 17, pp. 496–504, 1936.
55. Troxell, H. C., The influence of ground-water storage on the runoff in the San Bernardino and Eastern San Gabriel Mountains of Southern California, *Trans. Amer. Geophysical Union,* vol. 34, pp. 552–562, 1953.
56. Tuinzaad, H., Influence of the atmospheric pressure on the head of artesian water and phreatic water, *Assemblée Générale de Rome, Assoc. Intl. d'Hydrologie Scientifique,* vol. 2, pp. 32–37, 1954.
57. Turnbull, W. J., and C. I. Mansur, Relief well systems for dams and levees, *Trans. Amer. Soc. Civil Engrs.,* vol. 119, pp. 842–878, 1954.
58. Veatch, A. C., Fluctuations of the water level in wells, with special reference to Long Island, New York, *U. S. Geological Survey Water-Supply Paper* 155, Washington, D. C., 83 pp., 1906.
59. Vorhis, R. C., Interpretation of hydrologic data resulting from earthquakes, *Geologische Rundschau,* vol. 43, pp. 47–52, 1955.
60. Wenzel, L. K., Several methods of studying fluctuations of ground-water levels, *Trans. Amer. Geophysical Union,* vol. 17, pp. 400–405, 1936.
61. Werner, P. W., Notes on flow-time effects in the great artesian aquifers of the earth, *Trans. Amer. Geophysical Union,* vol. 27, pp. 687–708, 1946.
62. Werner, P. W., and D. Noren, Progressive waves in non-artesian aquifers, *Trans. Amer. Geophysical Union,* vol. 32, pp. 238–244, 1951.
63. Werner, P. W., and K. J. Sundquist, On the ground-water recession curve for large watersheds, *Assemblée Générale de Bruxelles, Assoc. Intl. d'Hydrologie Scientifique,* vol. 2, pp. 202–212, 1951.

64. White, W. N., A method of estimating ground-water supplies based on discharge by plants and evaporation from soil, *U. S. Geological Survey Water-Supply Paper* 659, Washington, D. C., pp. 1–105, 1932.
65. Wier, W. W., Subsidence of peat lands of the Sacramento-San Joaquin Delta, California, *Hilgardia,* vol. 20, pp. 37–56, 1950.
66. Winslow, A. G., and W. W. Doyel, Land-surface subsidence and its relation to the withdrawal of ground water in the Houston-Galveston region, Texas, *Econ. Geol.,* vol. 49, pp. 413–422, 1954.

Quality of Ground Water

CHAPTER 7

In recent years it has been recognized that the quality of ground water is of nearly equal importance to quantity. As greater development and use of ground water continues, combined with the reuse of water, quality suffers unless consideration is given to protecting it. Invariably, encroachment by man increases opportunities for pollution. The quality required of a ground water supply depends upon its purpose; thus, the needs for drinking water, industrial water, and irrigation water vary widely. To establish quality criteria, measures of chemical, physical, and bacterial constituents must be specified, as well as standard methods for reporting results of water analyses. Recommended limits of water quality can then be determined, serving as guides for proper protection and development of ground water basins.

Sources of Salinity

All ground waters contain salts carried in solution. The kinds and concentration of salts depend upon the environment, movement, and source of the ground water. Ordinarily, higher proportions of dissolved constituents are found in ground waters than in surface waters because of the greater exposure to soluble materials in geologic strata. Soluble salts found in ground water originate primarily from solution of rock materials.[24] In areas recharging large volumes of water underground such as alluvial streams or artificial recharge areas, the quality of the infiltrating surface water can have a marked effect on that of the ground water. Locally, absorbed gases of magmatic origin contribute dissolved mineral products to ground water; mineralized thermal springs furnish an excellent example. Connate waters are usually highly mineralized as they originate from isolated pockets of residual waters entrapped in sedimentary rocks since geologic times. Even rain water entering the ground contains minor salt concentrations picked up in the atmosphere.

Salts are added to ground water passing through soils by soluble products of soil weathering and of erosion by rainfall and flowing water. Excess irrigation water percolating to the water table may contribute substantial quantities of salt. Water passing through the root zone of cultivated areas usually contains saline concentrations several times that of the applied irrigation water. Increases result primarily from the evapotranspiration process which tends to concentrate salts in drainage waters. In addition, soluble soil materials, fertilizers, and selective absorption of salts by plants will modify salt concentrations of percolating waters. Factors governing the increase include soil permeability, drainage facilities, amount of water applied, crops, and climate. Thus, high salinities are found in soils and ground waters of arid climates where leaching by rain water is not effective in diluting the salt solutions. Similarly, poorly drained areas, particularly basins having interior drainage, contain high salt concentrations. Also, some regions contain remnants of sedimentary deposition under saline waters; the designation "badlands" implies the lack of productivity resulting from excess salt contents of the soil and water.

Ground water passing through igneous rocks dissolves only very small quantities of mineral matter because of the relative insolubility of the rock composition. Percolating rain water contains carbon dioxide derived from the atmosphere, which increases the solvent action of the water. The silicate minerals of igneous rocks result in silica being the predominate constituent, although small, of the ground water in contact.

Sedimentary rocks are more soluble than igneous rocks. Because of their high solubility, combined with their great abundance in the earth's crust, they furnish a major portion of the soluble constituents to ground water. Sodium and calcium are commonly added cations; bicarbonate, carbonate, and sulfate are corresponding anions. Chloride occurs to only a limited extent under normal conditions; important sources of chlorides, however, are from sewage, connate waters, and intruded sea water. Nitrate is only rarely an important natural constituent; high concentrations may indicate sources of past or present pollution. In limestone terranes calcium and carbonate ions are added to ground water by solution.

Ground Water Samples

In sampling ground water for analysis of its quality, the water should be collected in one-half gallon glass bottles. After rinsing the bottle with the water being sampled, the sample is then collected and securely corked. The water should be stored in a cool place and transferred promptly to a laboratory for analysis. Samples should be taken from a well only after it has been pumped for some time, otherwise nonrepresentative samples of stagnant or contaminated water may be obtained. With each sample a record should be made of well location, depth of sample, size of casing, date, water temperature, odor, color, turbidity, and operating conditions of the well immediately prior to sampling.

Measures of Water Quality

In specifying the quality characteristics of a water, a complete statement requires chemical, physical, sanitary, bacterial, and biological analyses. For ground water, however, the chemical, physical, and bacterial analyses are most important, the others being pertinent only for unusual situations of a local character.

A complete chemical analysis of a sample of ground water includes the determination of the concentrations of all of the inorganic constituents present. Dissolved salts in ground water occur as dissociated ions; in addition, other minor constituents are present and reported in elemental form only. The common anions and cations found in ground waters, together with minor constituents, are listed in Table 7.1. The analysis also includes measurement of pH and specific electrical conductance. Depending upon the purpose of the water quality investigation, a partial analysis of only particular constituents will sometimes suffice.

Properties of a ground water evaluated in a physical analysis include temperature, color, turbidity, odor, and taste. Bacteriological analysis consists of tests to detect the presence of coliform organisms, which indicate the sanitary quality of water for human consumption. As certain coliform organisms are normally found in intestines of man and animals, the presence of these in ground water is tantamount to its contact with sewage sources.

TABLE 7.1 **Chemical Constituents of Ground Water**

Major Constituents				Minor Constituents
Common Cations	Equivalent Weight	Common Anions	Equivalent Weight	
Calcium (Ca)	20.04	Carbonate (CO_3)	30.00	Iron (Fe)
Magnesium (Mg)	12.16	Bicarbonate (HCO_3)	61.01	Aluminum (Al)
Sodium (Na)	23.00	Sulfate (SO_4)	48.03	Silica (SiO_2)
Potassium (K)	39.10	Chloride (Cl)	35.46	Boron (B)
		Nitrate (NO_3)	62.01	Fluoride (F)
				Selenium (Se)

Standard methods of water analysis are specified by the American Public Health Association and others; [3] most laboratories conducting water analyses follow these procedures.

Chemical Analysis

Once a sample of ground water has been collected and analyzed in a laboratory, methods for reporting water analyses must be considered. From an understanding of expressions and units for describing water quality, standards can be established so that analyses can be interpreted in terms of the ultimate purpose of the water supply. In a chemical analysis of ground water, concentrations of different ions are expressed by weight or by chemical equivalence. Total dissolved solids can be measured in terms of electrical conductivity. These and other measures of chemical quality are described in the following sections.

Concentrations by Weight. Concentrations of the common ions found in ground water are often reported by weight in parts per million (ppm). One ppm defines one part by weight of the ion to a million parts by weight of water. It is numerically equivalent to milligrams per liter. The total ionic concentration (or total dissolved solids) is also reported in this manner. In irrigation practice, the unit tons of dissolved solids per acre-foot of water (taf) is employed. Several useful conversion factors for water quality are listed in Table 7.2.

Chemical Equivalence. Positively charged cations and negative anions combine and dissociate in definite weight ratios. By expressing

TABLE 7.2 Conversion Factors for Water Quality

1 ppm	= 1 mg/l	
1 taf	= 735 ppm	
1 grain/U.S. gallon	= 17.1 ppm	
1 meq/l	= 1 me/l = 1 epm	
meq/l of ion	= ppm of ion/equivalent weight of ion	
1 meq/l of cations	= 100 EC $\times 10^6$	Approximations for most natural waters in the range of 100 to 5000 μmho/cm at 25° C
1 ppm	= 1.56 EC $\times 10^6$	

ion concentrations in equivalent weights these ratios are readily determined because one equivalent weight of a cation will exactly combine with one equivalent weight of an anion. The equivalent weight of an ion is the ratio of its atomic weight to its valence. Table 7.1 includes equivalent weights of the common ions. Because hydrogen with an equivalent weight of one serves as the reference element, these are in reality equivalent weights of hydrogen. For example, the equivalent weight in grams (also known as the gram equivalent weight) of an ion or compound is that weight in grams that combines with or replaces one gram of hydrogen.

For convenience, concentrations are reported in one-thousandth of a gram equivalent weight per liter of solution; consequently, the unit milligram equivalent per liter (meq/l), or simply milliequivalent per liter (me/l) is employed. Furthermore, because one meq/l of hydrogen equals one ppm of hydrogen, it can be said that one meq/l equals one equivalent per million (epm). By definition then, an equivalent per million is an equivalent weight in grams of an ion or salt per one million grams of solution. This identity holds only if the specific gravity of the solution is 1.00; however, errors introduced by this requirement are negligible for ground water. The concentration of an ion in ppm divided by the equivalent weight of the ion yields the number of meq/l of the ion.

In application, therefore, it may be expected that of the total dissolved solids in a ground water sample, the sum of the cations and the sum of the anions when expressed in milliequivalents per liter will each equal half of the total concentration. If the chemical analysis of the various ionic constituents indicates a difference from this balance, it may be concluded either that there are other undetermined constituents present or that errors exist in the analysis. Analyses of nine ground waters used for irrigation in California are shown in Table 7.3; minor constituents other than boron have been omitted.

TABLE 7.3 Chemical Analyses of Selected Ground Waters in California

(After Doneen [19])

Number	EC × 10^6 at 25° C	B, ppm	Major Constituents, me/l: Ca	Mg	Na	CO_3 + HCO_3	Cl	SO_4	Per Cent Na	Water Class *
1	260 †	0.13	1.41	0.44	0.89	1.88	0.34	0.33	32	Good
2	270	0.10	0.21	0.05	2.42	1.20	0.68	0.67	90	Unsuitable
3	790	6.90	0.24	0.02	7.28	2.39	2.47	2.48	96	Unsuitable
4	900	0.51	2.49	5.81	2.83	8.87	1.13	1.02	25	Permissible
5	1090	...	1.20	2.00	8.10	8.10	1.00	2.60	72	Doubtful
6	1370	0.25	8.30	0.75	3.96	2.46	2.73	4.47	30	Permissible
7	1740	0.71	2.14	0.08	12.67	1.02	12.04	1.80	85	Unsuitable
8	2550	0.50	11.40	5.70	12.90	2.80	2.80	23.00	45	Doubtful
9	4330	1.63	12.37	16.71	27.39	2.75	8.55	41.74	49	Unsuitable

* Based on classification in Table 7.7.
† Underlined values determine water class.

Total Dissolved Solids by Electrical Conductivity. A rapid determination of total dissolved solids can be made by measuring the electrical conductance of a ground water sample. Conductance is preferred rather than its reciprocal, resistance, because it increases with salt content. Conductance is measured in mhos (from reciprocal ohms); for comparative purposes results are reported as electrical conductivity (EC), or specific electrical conductance, measured in mhos/cm. Often the conductivity designation EC is replaced by K, but the meaning is identical. Because most natural waters have conductivities much less than one mho/cm, it is convenient to refer to decimal fractions of the unit. For example, a water sample measuring 0.001250 mho/cm could be designated:

$$
\begin{aligned}
\text{EC} &= 0.001250 \text{ mho/cm} \\
&= 1.250 \text{ EC} \times 10^3, \text{ or millimhos/cm (mmho/cm)} \\
&= 125.0 \text{ EC} \times 10^5 \\
&= 1250 \text{ EC} \times 10^6, \text{ or micromhos/cm } (\mu\text{mho/cm})
\end{aligned}
$$

Conductance is a function of water temperature, hence a standard temperature, usually 25° C, must be specified in reporting conductivities. An approximate relation exists between electrical conductivity and concentration for most natural waters [42] in the range of 100 to 5000 micromhos/cm at 25° C, leading to the conversions 1 meq/l of cations = 100 EC × 10^6 and 1 ppm = 1.56 EC × 10^6.

Total Hardness. Total hardness (TH) is a measure of the calcium and magnesium content and is customarily expressed as the equivalent of calcium carbonate. Thus

$$TH = Ca \times \frac{CaCO_3}{Ca} + Mg \times \frac{CaCO_3}{Mg} \tag{7.1}$$

where TH is measured in parts per million of $CaCO_3$, Ca and Mg in parts per million, and the ratios in equivalent weights. Equation 7.1 reduces to

$$TH = 2.497 \text{ Ca} + 4.115 \text{ Mg} \tag{7.2}$$

Graphical Representation. After a chemical analysis has been obtained, there remains the problem of interpreting it for a particular purpose. Such analytic data can aid in solving many practical problems, including the suitability of a water for a given usage, studies of mixtures of waters from different sources, determinations of changes in quality, and movements of saline waters. To assist in these solutions, several graphical representation systems of chemical water quality have been suggested. Collins [15] outlined a bar diagram system for representing analyses, which has been adopted by the U. S. Geological Survey (for an example, see Fig. 12.14). Various other classification diagrams have been advocated by Hill,[29] Langelier and Ludwig,[32] and Piper.[38] None has been generally accepted, mainly because of the variety of needs for water analyses, the difficulty of understanding detailed classifications, and the inadequacy of the simpler representations. The criterion as to the adequacy of a particular system is whether it clearly delineates differences of ground water quality so that the situation can be readily understood.

Physical Analysis

In a physical analysis of ground water, temperature is reported in °C and obviously must be measured immediately after collecting the sample. Color in ground water may be due to mineral or organic matter in solution and is reported in parts per million by comparison with standard solutions. Turbidity is a measure of the suspended and colloidal matter in water, such as clay, silt, organic matter, and microscopic organisms. Measurements are based on the length of a light path through the water which just causes the image of a flame of a standard candle to disappear. The natural filtration produced by unconsolidated aquifers largely eliminates turbidity, but other types of aquifers can produce turbid ground water. Tastes and odors may be derived from bacteria, dissolved gases, mineral matter, or phenols. These characteristics are subjective sensations which can be defined only in terms of the experience of a human being. Quantitative determinations of odor have been developed based on the maximum degree of dilution that can be distinguished from odor-free water. No accepted method has been devised for measuring tastes.[3]

Bacterial Analysis

As mentioned before, bacterial analysis is important for detecting sewage contamination in ground water. Most pathogenic bacteria found in water are indigenous to the intestinal tract of animals and man, but isolating them from natural water is difficult in the laboratory. Because bacteria of the coliform group are relatively easy to isolate and identify, standard tests to determine their presence or absence in a water sample are taken as a direct indication of the safety of the water for drinking purposes. Coliform test results are reported as the most probable number (MPN) of coliform group organisms in a given volume of water. By analysis of a number of separate portions of a water sample, the MPN is computed from probability tables for this purpose.

Water Quality Criteria

Whether a ground water of a given quality is suitable for a particular purpose depends on the criteria or standards of acceptable quality for that use. Quality limits of water supplies for drinking water, industrial purposes, and irrigation apply to ground water because of its extensive development for these purposes.

Drinking Water Standards. Most drinking water supplies in the United States conform to standards established by the U. S. Public Health Service, based on their adoption by the American Water Works Association[2,5] and by most state departments of public health.[12] A summary of the principal provisions relating to quantitative limits is given in Table 7.4.

Industrial Water Criteria. It should be apparent that the quality requirements of waters used in different industrial processes vary widely.[17] Thus, make-up water for high pressure boilers must meet extremely exacting criteria whereas water of as low a quality as sea water can be satisfactorily employed for cooling of condensers. Even within each industry, criteria cannot be established; instead, only recommended limiting values or ranges can be stated.[8,12,39]

TABLE 7.4 Drinking Water Standards [2, 3, 5]

Bacterial Quality:

The minimum number of samples to be collected and analyzed each month and the numbers of these samples and portions thereof that may show presence of coliform organisms are specified. In effect, these requirements limit the average monthly coliform content to an MPN of one per 100 ml.

Physical Characteristics:

Characteristic	Upper Limit
Turbidity	10 ppm (silica scale)
Color	20 (std cobalt scale)
Taste	Not objectionable
Odor	Not objectionable

These limits are mandatory for filtered water supplies; for others, their application is subject to reasonable judgment and discretion based on local conditions.

Chemical Characteristics:

Constituent	Upper Limit, ppm
Lead (Pb)	0.1
Fluoride (F)	1.5
Arsenic (As)	0.05
Selenium (Se)	0.05
Hexavalent chromium	0.05
Copper (Cu)	3.0
Iron (Fe) and Manganese (Mn), together	0.3
Magnesium (Mg)	125
Zinc (Zn)	15
Chloride (Cl)	250
Sulfate (SO_4)	250
Phenol	0.001
Total solids, desirable	500
Total solids, permitted	1000

The limits for the first five constituents are mandatory; the others are recommended.

From an extensive study of industrial water quality by a committee of the New England Water Works Association,[4] suggested quality limits for selected industries are presented in Table 7.5.

Of almost equal importance for industrial purposes as quality of a water supply is the relative constancy of the various constituents. It is often possible to treat a poor quality water or adapt to it so that it

TABLE 7.5 Suggested Water Quality Tolerances for Industrial Uses *

(Allowable limits in ppm)

Industry or Use	Turbidity	Color	Odor and Taste	Iron as Fe †	Manganese as Mn	Total Solids	Hardness as $CaCO_3$	Alkalinity as $CaCO_3$	Hydrogen Sulfide	Health	pH	Other Requirements
Air Conditioning	...	...	Low	0.5	0.5	...	...	...	1.0	...	...	No corrosiveness or slime formation
Baking	10	10	Low	0.2	0.2	...	...	...	0.2	Potable	...	
Boiler Feed												
Pressure 0–150 psi	20	80	...	...	...	3000–500	80	...	5	...	8.0 ‡	No corrosiveness or scale formation §
Pressure 150–250 psi	10	40	...	...	...	2500–500	40	...	3	...	8.4 ‡	No corrosiveness or scale formation §
Pressure 250–400 psi	5	5	...	...	...	1500–100	10	...	0	...	9.0 ‡	No corrosiveness or scale formation §
Pressure >400 psi	1	2	...	...	...	50	2	...	0	...	9.6 ‡	No corrosiveness or scale formation §
Brewing and Distilling												
Light beer, gin	10	...	Low	0.1	0.1	500	...	75	0.2	Potable	6.5–7.0	NaCl 275
Dark beer, whiskey	10	...	Low	0.1	0.1	1000	...	150	0.2	Potable	7.0 ‡	NaCl 275
Canning												
Legumes	10	...	Low	0.2	0.2	...	25–75	...	1.0	Potable	...	
General	10	...	Low	0.2	0.2	...	...	...	1.0	Potable	...	
Carbonated Beverages	2	10	Low	0.2	0.2	850	250	50–100	0.2	Potable	...	Organic matter infinitesimal; oxygen consumed 1.5 ‖
Confectionery	...	...	Low	0.2	0.2	100	...	...	0.2	Potable	7.0	
Cooling	50	...	...	0.5	0.5	...	50	...	5	...	...	No corrosiveness or slime formation
Food, general	10	...	Low	0.2	0.2	...	...	...	...	Potable	...	
Ice	5	5	Low	0.2	0.2	1300	...	...	...	Potable	...	SiO_2 10
Laundering	...	...	...	0.2	0.2	...	50	...	...	...	...	

Plastics, clear	2	2	. . .	0.02	0.02	200	. . .	. . .	. . .	. . .	. . .	
Paper and Pulp												
Ground wood	50	20	. . .	1.0	0.5	. . .	180	. . .	. . .	. . .	. . .	No grit or corrosiveness
Kraft pulp	25	15	. . .	0.2	0.1	300	100	. . .	. . .	. . .	. . .	
Soda and sulphite pulp	15	10	. . .	0.1	0.05	200	100	. . .	. . .	. . .	. . .	
High-grade light papers	5	5	. . .	0.1	0.05	200	50	. . .	. . .	. . .	. . .	No slime formation
Rayon (Viscose)												
Pulp production	5	5	. . .	0.05	0.03	100	8	50	. . .	. . .	. . .	OH 8, Al_2O_3 8, SiO_2 25, Cu 5
Manufacture	0.3	. . .	. . .	0.0	0.0	. . .	55	. . .	. . .	. . .	7.8–8.3	
Steel Manufacture ‖	. . .	. . .	. . .	. . .	. . .	. . .	50	. . .	. . .	. . .	6.8–7.0	Temperature 75° F, Cl 175, suspended matter 25, minimum organic content and corrosiveness
Sugar Manufacture ‖	. . .	. . .	. . .	0.1	. . .	. . .	. . .	. . .	. . .	. . .	. . .	Ca 20, Mg 10, SO_4 20, Cl 20, HCO_3 100
Synthetic Rubber ‖	. . .	. . .	. . .	. . .	. . .	. . .	50	. . .	. . .	. . .	. . .	Oxygen consumed 3.0, minimum organic content and corrosiveness
Tanning	20	10–100	. . .	0.2	0.2	. . .	50–135	135	. . .	. . .	. . .	OH 8
Textiles												
General	5	20	. . .	0.25	0.25	. . .	. . .	. . .	. . .	. . .	. . .	
Dyeing	5	5–20	. . .	0.25	0.25	200	. . .	. . .	. . .	. . .	. . .	Constant composition; residual alumina <0.5

* Data from Reference 4 unless otherwise specified.
† Limit applies to both iron alone and the sum of iron and manganese.
‡ Minimum value.
§ Other limits stated for oxygen consumed, dissolved oxygen, Na_2SO_4/Na_2CO_3 ratio, Al_2O_3, SiO_2, HCO_3, CO_3, and OH.
‖ Data from Reference 12.

TABLE 7.6 Relative Tolerances of Crops to Salt Concentrations [42]

(Electrical conductivity values represent salinity levels at which a 50 per cent decrease in yield may be expected as compared to yields on nonsaline soil under comparable growing conditions.)

Crop Division	Low Salt Tolerance	Medium Salt Tolerance	High Salt Tolerance
Fruit Crops	Avocado Lemon Strawberry Peach Apricot Almond Plum Prune Grapefruit Orange Apple Pear	Cantaloupe Date Olive Fig Pomegranate	Date palm
Vegetable Crops	$EC \times 10^3 = 3$ Green beans Celery Radish $EC \times 10^3 = 4$	$EC \times 10^3 = 4$ Cucumber Squash Peas Onion Carrot Potatoes Sweet Corn Lettuce Cauliflower Bell pepper Cabbage Broccoli Tomato $EC \times 10^3 = 10$	$EC \times 10^3 = 10$ Spinach Asparagus Kale Garden beets $EC \times 10^3 = 12$
Forage Crops	$EC \times 10^3 = 2$ Burnet Ladino clover Red clover Alsike clover Meadow foxtail White Dutch clover	$EC \times 10^3 = 4$ Sickle milkvetch Sour clover Cicer milkvetch Tall meadow oat-grass Smooth brome Big trefoil	$EC \times 10^3 = 12$ Bird's-foot trefoil Barley (hay) Western wheat grass Canada wild rye Rescue grass Rhodes grass Bermuda grass

TABLE 7.6 (*continued*)

Crop Division	Low Salt Tolerance	Medium Salt Tolerance	High Salt Tolerance
Forage Crops	EC × 10^3 = 4	Reed canary Meadow fescue Blue grama Orchard grass Oats (hay) Wheat (hay) Rye (hay) Tall fescue Alfalfa Hubam clover Sudan grass Dallis grass Strawberry clover Mountain brome Perennial rye grass Yellow sweetclover White sweetclover EC × 10^3 = 12	Nuttall alkali grass Salt grass Alkali sacaton EC × 10^3 = 18
Field Crops	EC × 10^3 = 4 Field beans	EC × 10^3 = 6 Castorbeans Sunflower Flax Corn (field) Sorghum (grain) Rice Oats (grain) Wheat (grain) Rye (grain) EC × 10^3 = 10	EC × 10^3 = 10 Cotton Rape Sugar beet Barley (grain) EC × 10^3 = 16

is suitable for a given process, but if the quality fluctuates widely, continued attention and expense may be involved. Fluctuations of water temperature can be equally troublesome. From this standpoint, ground water supplies are preferred to surface water supplies, which commonly display seasonal variations in chemical and physical quality. As a result, an adequate ground water supply of suitable quality has become one of the primary considerations in selecting new industrial plant locations.

Irrigation Water Criteria. The suitability of a ground water for irrigation is contingent upon the effects of the mineral constituents of the water on both the plant and the soil.[6,29,31,42,49] Salts may harm plant growth physically by limiting the uptake of water through modification of osmotic processes, or chemically by metabolic reactions such as caused by toxic constituents. Effects of salts on soils, causing changes in soil structure, permeability, and aeration, indirectly affect plant growth. Specific limits of permissible salt concentrations for irrigation water cannot be stated because of the wide variations in salinity tolerance among different plants; however, field-plot studies of crops grown on soils that are artificially adjusted to various salinity levels provide valuable information relating to salt tolerance. In Table 7.6 relative tolerances of crops to soil-water salt concentrations are listed for major crop divisions. The criterion applied was the relative yield of the crop on a saline soil as compared with its yield on a nonsaline soil under similar growing conditions. Within each group, the crops are listed in order of increasing salt tolerance; electrical conductivity values at the top and bottom of each column represent the range of salinity level at which a 50 per cent decrease in yield may be expected. It should be noted that these concentrations refer to soil water, which may contain concentrations from five to ten times that of applied irrigation water. Soil type, climatic conditions, and irrigation practices may influence the reactions of a given crop to the salt constituents; therefore, the position of each crop in Table 7.6 reflects its relative salt tolerance under customary irrigation conditions.

An important factor allied to the relation of crop growth to water quality is drainage. If a soil is open and well-drained, crops may be grown on it with the application of generous amounts of saline water; but, on the other hand, a poorly drained area combined with application of good-quality water may fail to produce as satisfactory a crop. Poor drainage permits salt concentrations in the root zone to build up to toxic proportions. Today, the necessity of adequate drainage is clearly recognized in order to maintain a favorable salt balance—where the total dissolved solids brought to the land annually by irrigation water is less than the total solids carried away annually by drainage water.[6,46] It is believed that this factor accounted for the failure of many of the elaborate irrigation systems of historical times.

In place of rigid limits of salinity for irrigation water, quality is commonly expressed by classes of relative suitability. As an example, Table 7.7 outlines a classification prepared by Wilcox.[50] Under this scheme the suitability is judged on measurements of electrical con-

TABLE 7.7 Quality Classification of Water for Irrigation

(After Wilcox [50])

Water Class	Per Cent Sodium	EC $\times 10^6$ at 25° C	Boron, ppm: Sensitive Crops	Boron, ppm: Semitolerant Crops	Boron, ppm: Tolerant Crops
Excellent	<20	<250	<0.33	<0.67	<1.00
Good	20–40	250–750	0.33–0.67	0.67–1.33	1.00–2.00
Permissible	40–60	750–2000	0.67–1.00	1.33–2.00	2.00–3.00
Doubtful	60–80	2000–3000	1.00–1.25	2.00–2.50	3.00–3.75
Unsuitable	>80	>3000	>1.25	>2.50	>3.75

ductivity (expressing total dissolved solids), sodium content reported as per cent sodium, and boron concentration. In applying Table 7.7, the lowest rating of any of the three factors determines the water class. Examples of classifications appear in Table 7.3.

A better classification with respect to electrical conductivity and per cent sodium is obtained with the diagram of Fig. 7.1. The interrelationship of high sodium percentage with low total salts has been observed to fit actual conditions.

Sodium concentration is important in classifying an irrigation water because sodium reacts with soil to reduce its permeability (see following section). Soils containing a large proportion of sodium with carbonate as the predominant anion are termed alkali soils; those with chloride or sulfate as the predominant anion, saline soils. Ordinarily, either type of sodium-saturated soil will support little or no plant growth. Sodium content is usually expressed in terms of per cent sodium (also known as sodium percentage and soluble-sodium percentage), defined by

$$\% \text{ Na} = \frac{(\text{Na} + \text{K})100}{\text{Ca} + \text{Mg} + \text{Na} + \text{K}} \tag{7.3}$$

where all ionic concentrations are expressed in milliequivalents per liter. The Salinity Laboratory of the Department of Agriculture [42] recommends the sodium adsorption ratio (SAR) because of its direct relation to the adsorption of sodium by soil. It is defined by

$$\text{SAR} = \frac{\text{Na}}{\sqrt{(\text{Ca} + \text{Mg})/2}} \tag{7.4}$$

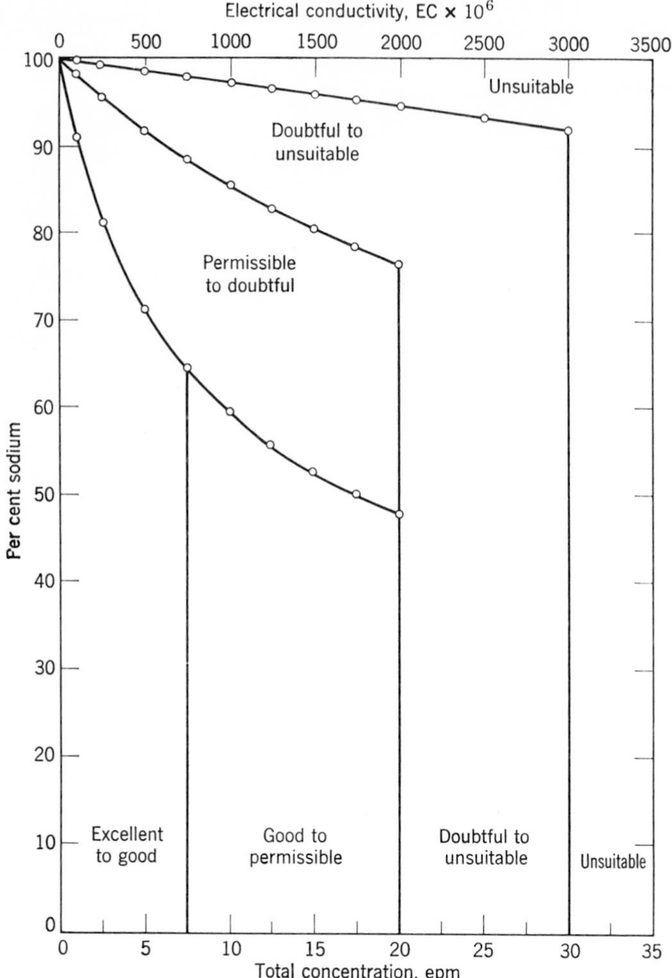

Fig. 7.1. Diagram for irrigation water classification based on electrical conductivity and per cent sodium (after Wilcox [49]).

where the concentrations of the constituents are expressed in milliequivalents per liter. Recommended water classifications for SAR follow:

SAR	Water Class
<10	Excellent
10–18	Good
18–26	Fair
>26	Poor

Boron is necessary in very small quantities for normal growth of all plants, but in larger concentrations it becomes toxic. Quantities needed vary with the crop type; sensitive crops require minimum amounts whereas tolerant crops will make maximum growth on several times these concentrations. Relative boron tolerances of a number of crops were determined by Eaton;[21] boron concentrations of irrigation water classes are listed by crop tolerance in Table 7.7 and the applicable crops appear in Table 7.8.

In investigations relating to quality of water for irrigation and the salinity of the soil solution, particularly regarding sampling programs, it is important to take cognizance of the salt distribution within the soil. As an illustration, the salt distribution under irrigated cotton plants is shown in Fig. 7.2. It is apparent that the leaching effect of the irrigation water in the furrow, together with the movement toward the plants on the ridges, creates wide variations of salt concentration within short distances.

TABLE 7.8 Relative Tolerance of Plants to Boron[42]

(Listed in order of increasing tolerance)

Sensitive	Semitolerant	Tolerant
Lemon	Lima bean	Carrot
Grapefruit	Sweet potato	Lettuce
Avocado	Bell pepper	Cabbage
Orange	Pumpkin	Turnip
Thornless blackberry	Zinnia	Onion
Apricot	Oat	Broadbean
Peach	Milo	Gladiolus
Cherry	Corn	Alfalfa
Persimmon	Wheat	Garden beet
Kadota fig	Barley	Mangel
Grape	Olive	Sugar beet
Apple	Ragged Robin rose	Date palm
Pear	Field pea	Palm
Plum	Radish	Asparagus
American elm	Sweetpea	Athel
Navy bean	Tomato	
Jerusalem artichoke	Cotton	
English walnut	Potato	
Black walnut	Sunflower	
Pecan		

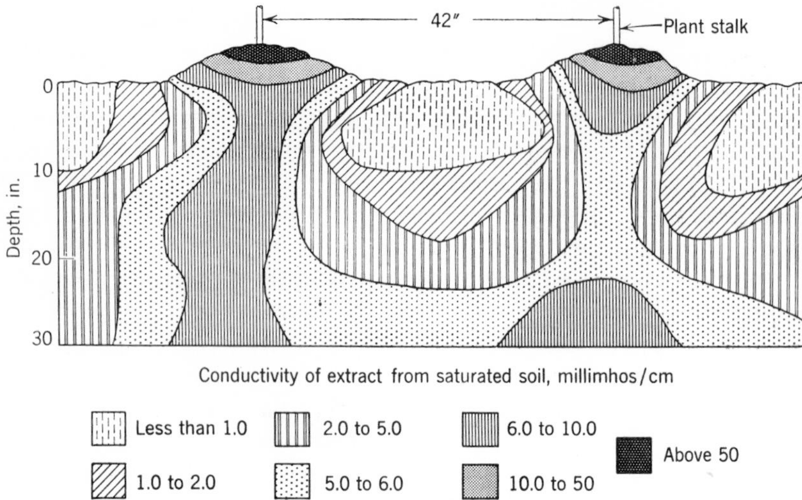

Fig. 7.2. Salt distribution under furrow-irrigated cotton for soil initially salinized to 0.2 per cent salt (3.1 millimhos/cm at 25° C) and irrigated with water of medium salinity (after Wadleigh and Fireman[48]).

Base Exchange

Fine silt, clay, and organic matter fractions of aquifers adsorb and retain cations on their surfaces. Cations are held by minute electrical charges at the surface of the particles; however, they may be replaced by other cations contained in the ground water. This reaction is termed base (or cation) exchange. Sodium, calcium, and magnesium are the principal cations involved; the direction of the exchange is toward an equilibrium of the bases present in the water and on the finer materials of the aquifer.[23, 33]

When high sodium water is applied to soil, the number of sodium ions combined with the soil increases while an equivalent quantity of calcium, or other ions, is displaced. These reactions change the soil characteristics, causing deflocculation and reduction of permeability.[18, 22, 26, 35] In the opposite case where calcium is the dominant cation, the exchange occurs in the reverse direction, creating a flocculated and more permeable soil. The advantage of adding gypsum ($CaSO_4$) to a soil is that by this base exchange process the soil texture and drainability can be improved.

In coastal regions where sea water has entered an aquifer, base exchange may produce a ground water of a quality other than a direct mixture of the two component waters (see Chapter 12).

Deterioration of Ground Water Quality

The quality of ground water depends upon the quality of its source waters; hence changes in source water quality become important. Changes may involve either new source waters or decreased quality of normal supplies. Obvious sources, such as sewage and industrial wastes, entering an aquifer can pollute a ground water supply; if the impairment becomes hazardous to public health, these sources are said to contaminate the supply. Table 7.9 outlines various causes of deterioration. Many of these are discussed individually in other sections and chapters. More than anything else, this listing indicates the wide variety of kinds of deterioration and implies the importance of proper attention and awareness in safeguarding a ground water supply for the future.

Gross organic pollution of ground water rarely occurs because of the inherent difficulties in introducing large quantities of wastes underground (see Chapter 11). Except in consolidated aquifers, such as fractured rocks and limestone, suspended solids are removed by infiltration, bacteria and colloidal matter by biological action. Inorganic solutions, however, pass readily through soil and, once introduced, are difficult to remove. Because natural dilution is slow, artificial flushing is expensive, and treatment is impractical, the effects of such pollution may continue for indefinite periods. Therefore, careful investigation should be made before disposing of any waste material underground to insure that the ground water storage capacity is not irreparably harmed.

Temperature

One of the most conservative properties of ground water is temperature; annual variations under ordinary conditions are almost negligible. The insulating qualities of the earth's crust damp out the extreme temperature variations found at ground surface. Studies have shown that the annual range of the earth's temperature at a depth of 30 ft may be expected to be less than 1° F.[16] Analysis of thousands of records of ground water temperature in the United States revealed that the temperature of ground water occurring at a depth of 30 to 60 ft will generally exceed the mean annual air temperature by 2 to 3° F. This information permitted a ground water temperature map of the United States, shown in Fig. 7.3, to be constructed from climatological data. Below these shallow depths, the temperature increases approximately 1° C for each 100 ft of depth in accordance with the geothermal

TABLE 7.9 Causes of Deterioration of Ground Water Quality [13]

CONTAMINATION AND POLLUTION

Domestic and Municipal Sewage

Industrial Wastes
- Organic wastes
  - food processing
  - lumber processing
- Mineral wastes
  - metal processing industries
  - mining and ore extraction industries
  - oil industries
  - chemical industries
  - miscellaneous
- Cooling water

Solid and Semisolid Refuse

DEGRADATION

Effects of Development, Use, and Reuse of Water
- Irrigation return water
  - surface drainage
  - percolation
- Interchange between aquifers due to improperly constructed, defective, or abandoned wells
- Interchange between aquifers due to differentials in pressure levels resulting from excessive withdrawal
- Overdraft conditions
  - sea water intrusion
  - salt balance
  - upward or lateral diffusion of connate brines and/or juvenile water due to overpumping
- Contamination from the surface due to improperly constructed wells

Natural Causes
- Inflow and/or percolation of juvenile water from highly mineralized springs and streams

Other Causes
- Accelerated erosion
- Mineralization resulting from plant transpiration and/or evaporation

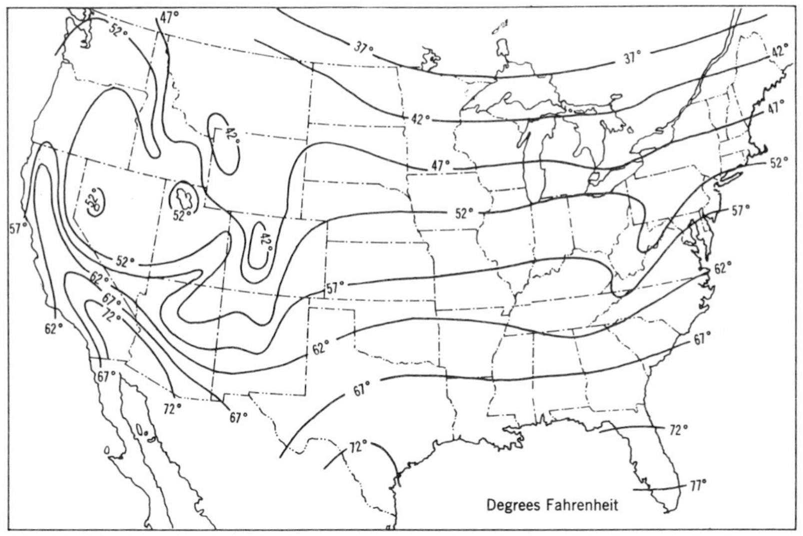

Fig. 7.3. Approximate temperature of ground water in the United States at depths of 30 to 60 feet (after Collins [16]).

gradient of the earth's crust. As extremes, ground water may vary in temperature from below freezing in permafrost to above the boiling point in superheated water emerging from geysers.

References

1. Ackerman, T. V., and E. J. Lynde, Effect of storage reservoir detritus on ground water, *Jour. Amer. Water Works Assoc.*, vol. 36, pp. 315–322, 1944.
2. Amer. Water Works Assoc., *Water quality and treatment*, 2nd ed., Amer. Water Works Assoc., New York, 451 pp., 1950.
3. Amer. Public Health Assoc., Amer. Water Works Assoc., and Federation of Sewage and Industrial Wastes Assocs., *Standard methods for the examination of water, sewage and industrial wastes,* 10th ed., Amer. Public Health Assoc., New York, 522 pp., 1955.
4. Anon., Progress report of the Committee on Quality Tolerances of Water for Industrial Uses, *Jour. New England Water Works Assoc.*, vol. 54, pp. 261–272, 1940.
5. Anon., Drinking water standards—1946, *Jour. Amer. Water Works Assoc.*, vol. 38, pp. 361–370, 1946.
6. Anon., The salt problem in irrigation agriculture, *U. S. Dept. Agric. Misc. Publ.* 607, Washington, D. C., 27 pp., 1946.
7. Anon., Water for irrigation use, *Chem. and Eng. News,* vol. 29, pp. 990–993, 1951.

8. ASTM Committee D-19 on Industrial Water, Manual on industrial water, *Amer. Soc. Test. Materials Spec. Tech. Publ.* 148-A, 420 pp., 1954.
9. Banks, H. O., and J. H. Lawrence, Water quality problems in California, *Trans. Amer. Geophysical Union,* vol. 34, pp. 58–66, 1953.
10. Bodman, G. B., Discussion of Sealing the lagoon at Treasure Island with salt, *Trans. Amer. Soc. Civil Engrs.,* vol. 106, pp. 594–598, 1941.
11. Brenneke, A. M., Control of salt-water intrusion in Texas, *Jour. Amer. Water Works Assoc.,* vol. 37, pp. 579–584, 1945.
12. Calif. State Water Pollution Control Board, Water quality criteria, *Publ.* 3, Sacramento, 512 pp., 1952.
13. Calif. State Water Resources Board, Water utilization and requirements of California, *Bull.* 2, vol. 2, Sacramento, 358 pp., 1955.
14. Clarke, F. W., The data of geochemistry, *U. S. Geological Survey Bull.* 770, Washington, D. C., 841 pp., 1924.
15. Collins, W. D., Graphic representation of water analyses, *Ind. and Eng. Chem.,* vol. 15, p. 394, 1923.
16. Collins, W. D., Temperature of water available for industrial use in the United States, *U. S. Geological Survey Water-Supply Paper* 520-F, Washington, D. C., pp. 97–104, 1925.
17. Collins, W. D., W. L. Lamar, and E. W. Lohr, The industrial utility of public water supplies in the United States, 1932, *U. S. Geological Survey Water-Supply Paper* 658, Washington, D. C., 135 pp., 1934.
18. Doneen, L. D., The quality of irrigation water and soil permeability, *Proc. Soil Sci. Soc. Amer.,* vol. 13, pp. 523–526, 1948.
19. Doneen, L. D., Analyses of irrigation water, *Calif. Agric.,* vol. 4, no. 11, pp. 6, 14, 1950.
20. Doneen, L. D., Salination of soil by salts in the irrigation water, *Trans. Amer. Geophysical Union,* vol. 35, pp. 943–950, 1954.
21. Eaton, F. M., Boron in soils and irrigation waters and its effect on plants, with particular reference to the San Joaquin Valley of California, *U. S. Dept. Agric. Tech. Bull.* 448, Washington, D. C., 131 pp., 1935.
22. Fireman, M., and O. C. Magistad, Permeability of five western soils as affected by the percentage of sodium of the irrigation water, *Trans. Amer. Geophysical Union,* vol. 26, pp. 91–94, 1945.
23. Foster, M. D., Base exchange and sulfate reduction in salty ground waters along Atlantic and Gulf coasts, *Bull. Amer. Assoc. Pet. Geol.,* vol. 26, pp. 838–851, 1942.
24. Foster, M. D., Chemistry of ground water, in *Hydrology* (O. E. Meinzer, ed.), pp. 646–655, McGraw-Hill, New York, 1942.
25. George, W. O., and W. W. Hastings, Nitrate in the ground water of Texas, *Trans. Amer. Geophysical Union,* vol. 32, pp. 450–456, 1951.
26. Harris, A. E., Effect of replaceable sodium on soil permeability, *Soil Sci.,* vol. 32, pp. 435–446, 1931.
27. Hem, J. D., Geochemistry of ground water, *Econ. Geol.,* vol. 45, pp. 72–81, 1950.
28. Hill, R. A., Geochemical patterns in Coachella Valley, *Trans. Amer. Geophysical Union,* vol. 21, pp. 46–53, 1940.
29. Hill, R. A., Salts in irrigation water, *Trans. Amer. Soc. Civil Engrs.,* vol. 107, pp. 1478–1518, 1942.

30. Huberty, M. R., Chemical composition of ground waters, *Civil Eng.*, vol. 11, pp. 494–495, 1941.
31. Kelley, W. P., Permissible composition and concentration of irrigation water, *Trans. Amer. Soc. Civil Engrs.*, vol. 106, pp. 849–861, 1941.
32. Langelier, W. F., and H. F. Ludwig, Graphical methods for indicating the mineral character of natural waters, *Jour. Amer. Water Works Assoc.*, vol. 34, pp. 335–352, 1942.
33. Love, S. K., Cation exchange in ground water contaminated with sea water near Miami, Florida, *Trans. Amer. Geophysical Union*, vol. 25, pp. 951–955, 1944.
34. Magistad, O. C., and J. E. Christiansen, Saline soils, their nature and management, *U. S. Dept. Agric. Circ.* 707, Washington, D. C., 32 pp., 1944.
35. Menichikovsky, F., Effect of nature of exchangeable bases on soil porosity and soil-water properties in mineral soil, *Soil Sci.*, vol. 26, pp. 169–181, 1946.
36. Morse, R. R., The nature and significance of certain variations in composition of Los Angeles Basin ground waters, *Econ. Geol.*, vol. 38, pp. 475–511, 1943.
37. Palmer, C., The geochemical interpretation of water analyses, *U. S. Geological Survey Bull.* 479, Washington, D. C., 31 pp., 1911.
38. Piper, A. M., A graphic procedure in the geochemical interpretation of water analyses, *Trans. Amer. Geophysical Union*, vol. 25, pp. 914–928, 1944.
39. Powell, S. T., Some aspects of the requirements for the quality of water for industrial purposes, *Jour. Amer. Water Works Assoc.*, vol. 40, pp. 8–23, 1948.
40. Renick, B. C., Base exchange in ground-water by silicates as illustrated in Montana, *U. S. Geological Survey Water-Supply Paper* 520-B, Washington, D. C., pp. 53–72, 1924.
41. Revelle, R. R., Criteria for recognition of sea water in ground waters, *Trans. Amer. Geophysical Union*, vol. 22, pp. 593–597, 1941.
42. Richards, L. A. (ed.), Diagnosis and improvement of saline and alkali soils, *Agric. Handbook* 60, U. S. Dept. Agric., Washington, D. C., 160 pp., 1954.
43. Robaux, A., Physical and chemical properties of ground water in the arid countries, *Proc. Ankara Symposium on Arid Zone Hydrology*, UNESCO, Paris, pp. 17–28, 1953.
44. Rossum, J. R., Chemical quality of underground water supplies, *Water and Sewage Works*, vol. 95, pp. 69–71, 1948.
45. Scofield, C. S., The salinity of irrigation water, *Ann. Rep. The Smithsonian Institution*, Washington, D. C., pp. 275–287, 1935.
46. Scofield, C. S., Salt balance in irrigated areas, *Jour. Agric. Research*, vol. 61, pp. 17–39, 1940.
47. Thomas, H. E., Sanitary quality of ground-water supplies, *The Sanitarian*, vol. 11, pp. 147–151, 1949.
48. Wadleigh, C. H., and M. Fireman, Salt distribution under furrow and basin irrigated cotton and its effect on water removal, *Proc. Soil Sci. Soc. Amer.*, vol. 13, pp. 527–530, 1948.
49. Wilcox, L. V., The quality of water for irrigation use, *U. S. Dept. Agric. Tech. Bull.* 962, Washington, D. C., 40 pp., 1948.
50. Wilcox, L. V., Classification and use of irrigation waters, *U. S. Dept. Agric. Circ.* 969, Washington, D. C., 19 pp., 1955.

Basin-Wide Ground Water Development

CHAPTER 8 ....

To provide maximum development of ground water resources for beneficial use requires thinking in terms of an entire ground water basin. By visualizing a basin as a large natural underground reservoir, it is clear that utilization of ground water by one landowner affects the water supply of all other landowners. In order to maintain the resource indefinitely, a hydrologic equilibrium must exist between all waters entering and leaving the basin. At the same time economic, legal, and quality aspects must be considered. Safe yield defines the basin draft on a ground water supply which can be continued indefinitely without harming the supply or basin landowners. Pumpage in excess of safe yield is overdraft. Several methods are available for computing safe yield under specified conditions. In terms of maximum development of all water resources of an area, there are economic benefits in coordinating the use of surface and ground water reservoirs. This concept of conjunctive utilization deserves investigation in planning all new water resource developments as well as in improving existing systems.

Safe Yield and Overdraft

The safe yield of a ground water basin is the amount of water which can be withdrawn from it annually without producing an undesired result. Any draft in excess of safe yield is overdraft.

At first glance the concept of safe yield appears quite simple—only so much water enters a basin, hence only that amount can be pumped. Consideration of the definition, however, reveals that there can be more than one "undesired result" from pumping a ground water basin, that the safe yield may be limited to an amount less than the net amount of water supplied to the basin, and that the safe yield can vary as the conditions governing it vary.

If ground water is regarded as a renewable natural resource, then only a certain quantity of water may be withdrawn annually from a ground water basin. The maximum quantity of water which can be extracted from an underground reservoir, yet still maintain that supply unimpaired, depends upon the safe yield. Overdraft areas constitute the largest ground water problem in the United States.[28] Until overdrafts are reduced to safe yields in these basins, permanent damage or depletion of the ground water supplies must be anticipated.

Factors Governing Safe Yield

The determination of the safe yield of a ground water basin requires analysis of undesired results which may accrue if safe yield is exceeded. Four factors are generally considered: [3] water supply available to the basin, economics of pumpage from the basin, quality of the ground water, and water rights in and near the basin. If any one of these is modified to create an undesired result, then an overdraft exists. The water supply criterion is the most important and also the most subject to quantitative determination.

Water Supply. It should be apparent that safe yield cannot exceed the long-time mean annual water supply to the basin. Withdrawals exceeding this supply must come from storage within the aquifer. Such permanent depletion is often referred to as *mining* of ground water because of its analogy to mining of ores and petroleum. In most basins the quantity of water in storage is many times the annual recharge or draft; therefore, in any one year the draft can exceed the recharge without causing permanent depletion. But on a long-term basis, when series of wet and dry years would tend to average out, the draft becomes an overdraft if the mean supply is exceeded.

The water supply to a basin can be limited either by the physical size of the underground basin or by the rate at which water moves through the basin from the recharge area to the withdrawal area. Determinations of safe yield may thus refer to the quantity concept or the rate concept; Thomas [28] preferred the designations reservoir problems and pipeline problems, respectively. In basins where both may apply, the smaller value governs. The quantity concept is usually more important for unconfined aquifers where supply and disposal areas are near, whereas the rate concept is more applicable to confined aquifers where supply and disposal areas may be many miles apart.

Economics. Economic considerations may govern safe yield in basins where the cost of pumping ground water becomes excessive. If the investment in developing a ground water supply is lost by abandonment in favor of other more economical sources of water, a damage has resulted. Excessive pumping costs are usually associated with lowered ground water levels, which may also necessitate deepening of wells, lowering of pump bowls, and installing larger pumps. In the Western states, where pumpage is largely for irrigation, agricultural economics, which involves such items as crop prices and government farm subsidies, may set an economic limit for pumping ground water. Establishment of such a limit for safe yield hinges upon specification of maximum pumping lifts, or minimum ground water levels.

Water Quality. Safe yield can also be exceeded if draft on a basin produces a ground water of inferior quality. Any of several possibilities could exist (see Chapter 7): pumping in a coastal aquifer could induce sea water intrusion into the basin; lowered ground water levels could lead to pumping of underlying connate brines; or poor quality water from adjacent areas might be drawn into the pumping aquifer. A quality limitation on safe yield depends on the minimum acceptable standard of water quality, which, in turn, depends upon the use made of the pumped water. From this it follows that changes in the purpose for which a water is pumped can affect the safe yield of a basin.

Water Rights. Legal considerations may limit safe yield if there is interference with prior water rights within a basin or in adjacent basins. Any legal restrictions on pumpage would have to be established before the safe yield could be determined. The problem of water rights in overdraft areas is discussed in Chapter 13.

If no economic, quality, or legal problems are created by pumpage from a ground water basin, the available water supply will govern the safe yield. In many instances one or more of the other undesired results will be induced by pumpage exceeding supply. Quantitative determination of safe yield where water supply is the limiting factor can be made under specified conditions if there is adequate knowledge of the hydrology of the basin available. Most methods are based on simplified solutions of the equation of hydrologic equilibrium.

Equation of Hydrologic Equilibrium

The hydrologic cycle and its elements were reviewed in Chapter 1. In terms of the hydrologic cycle for a particular ground water basin, a balance must exist between the quantity of water supplied to the basin and the amount stored within or leaving the basin. The equation of hydrologic equilibrium provides a quantitative statement of this balance. In its most general form it may be expressed as in Eq. 8.1.

$$\begin{bmatrix} \text{Surface inflow + Subsurface inflow + Precipitation} \\ \text{+ Imported water + Decrease in surface storage} \\ \text{+ Decrease in ground water storage} \end{bmatrix} = \begin{bmatrix} \text{Surface outflow + Subsurface outflow + Con-} \\ \text{sumptive use + Exported water + Increase in} \\ \text{surface storage + Increase in} \\ \text{ground water storage} \end{bmatrix} \tag{8.1}$$

In this form the equation includes all waters—surface and subsurface—entering and leaving a basin. There are many situations in which it is possible to eliminate certain items from the equation because they are negligible or because they do not effect the solution. For example, a confined aquifer may have a hydrologic equilibrium independent of overlying surface waters; therefore, items of surface flow, precipitation, consumptive use, imported and exported water, and changes in surface storage can be omitted from the equation.

Each item of the equation represents a discharge, a volume of water per unit of time. Any consistent units of volume and time can be adopted; acre-feet per year is common in the United States. The water year, extending from October 1 to September 30, is preferable to the calendar year. For safe yield calculation, long-time mean values for each item are necessary for some methods. The equation can be applied to areas of any size, although for meaningful results a hydrologic entity, such as an aquifer, a ground water basin, or a river valley, is best.

The equation of hydrologic equilibrium in theory must balance. In practice, if all items can be evaluated, it will rarely balance exactly. This may be attributed to inaccuracies of measurements, lack of adequate basic data, or incorrect approximations. The amount of unbalance should not exceed the limits of accuracy of the basic data. In order to achieve a balance, adjustments should be made in items subject to large error. If the unbalance exceeds the limits of accuracy of the basic data, further investigation is necessary. Application of the equation requires good judgment, adequate hydrologic data, and careful analysis of the geology and hydrology of the particular area.

With the equation, the safe yield and/or overdraft from a ground water basin can be determined under existing conditions as well as under any specified future conditions. Also, any one unknown item can be determined if all others are known. This last application can be misleading, however, for inaccuracies in one or more of the known quantities may exceed the magnitude of the unknown quantity.

Data Collection for Basin Investigations

To solve the equation of hydrologic equilibrium requires a comprehensive collection of basic data within the basin under study. The following outline summarizes types of basic data required and methods of their analysis for use in the equation. Much of it is based on recommendations of Simpson.[25]

Surface Inflow and Outflow; Imported and Exported Water. These quantities are measurable by standard hydrographic and hydraulic procedures. Where complete data on surface flows to and from the basin are not available from the Geological Survey or other agencies, supplemental stream gaging stations should be installed.

Precipitation. Records of precipitation can be obtained from Weather Bureau *Climatological Data.* Gages should be well distributed over the basin to provide a good estimate of the weighted average annual precipitation from the isohyetal or Thiessen polygon methods.* If gages are not so located, supplemental stations should be established.

Consumptive Use. All water, surface and subsurface, released into the atmosphere by processes of evaporation and transpiration is consumptive use, or evapotranspiration. To compute this discharge from a given basin it is first necessary to make a land use, or cultural, survey which will yield the amount of each type of water-consuming area. Aerial photographs are helpful for this task. Unit values of consumptive use must then be determined. For crops and native vegetation, methods based on available heat, such as the Blaney-Criddle method † are generally satisfactory. For water surfaces local evaporation records should be employed. Urban and industrial areas require careful estimates from samples of representative areas. Multiplying the unit value

* See, for example: Linsley, R. K., M. A. Kohler, and J. L. H. Paulhus, *Applied Hydrology,* McGraw-Hill, New York, 689 pp., 1949.

† See, for example: Blaney, H. F., and others, "Consumptive Use of Water—A Symposium," *Trans. Amer. Soc. Civil Engrs.,* vol. 117, pp. 948–1023, 1952.

of consumptive use by the corresponding acreage gives the water consumption for each area. The sum of these products yields the total consumptive use over the basin.

Changes in Surface Storage. These can be computed directly from changes in water levels of surface reservoirs.

Changes in Ground Water Storage. In practice these are limited to changes in storage of the zone of saturation. Changes of water content can and do occur in the zone of aeration; however, they are difficult to determine on a field basis and can be minimized by selecting periods of storage change in which the amount of water in unsaturated storage at the beginning and end of the period is nearly equal. In irrigated areas period limits should correspond to beginnings or endings of irrigation seasons.

Determination of changes in ground water storage can only be accomplished from an adequate knowledge of the occurrence of ground water in the basin. A general geologic study should be made which includes an analysis of all well logs. Aquifers must be delimited and their degree of confinement established. Antecedent information on ground water levels, pumping records, pumping tests, and artificial recharge must be collected. Specific yields of unconfined aquifers and storage coefficients of confined aquifers within the basin must be evaluated.

Select a grid of measuring wells spaced about three-fourths mile apart over the basin. Supplement with jetted test holes where required. Water levels in these wells should be measured under conditions as nearly static as possible, preferably after the season of heavy draft and again after the season of recharge. A few control wells should be equipped with automatic water level recorders or have their water levels measured monthly to facilitate detailed study of ground water fluctuations. A basin map showing lines of equal change in ground water levels is then prepared. The product of change in water level times specific yield (or storage coefficient) times area gives the change of ground water storage for each uniform stratum of the basin. The sum of these products yields the total change in storage.

Subsurface Inflow and Outflow. These items of the equation are the most difficult to evaluate because they cannot be directly measured. Often one of them, or the difference, is fixed by being the only unknown in the equation. From geologic investigation it may be found that either subsurface inflow or outflow is lacking, or both. Many times after study, subsurface inflow may be estimated to equal that of subsurface outflow so that the items cancel. Difficulties arise in situations where underground flow from one basin to another is known to occur. The direction of flow can be established from water tables or piezometric slopes. From estimates or measurements of slopes, permeabilities, and cross-sectional areas of flow, the subsurface flow can be computed from Darcy's law. Where surface streams and subsurface drainage systems control ground water levels, better estimates of subsurface flow are usually possible because more data are available.

Methods of Computing Safe Yield

Safe yield was defined in terms of an annual quantity of water which could be withdrawn from a basin. In a confined aquifer where no connection with surface water exists in the basin, safe yield can be defined in terms of gross annual pumpage. In unconfined aquifers safe yield can be defined as actual annual consumptive use of pumped ground water plus exported ground water; this is equivalent to gross annual pumpage minus return flow. The following methods have been developed to compute safe yield where supply is the governing criterion. In any given basin one or more methods may be applicable, depending upon geologic conditions, degree of ground water development, and available data. It should be noted that these methods, although not specifying an item-by-item evaluation, are predicated upon the general equation of hydrologic equilibrium. Thus, when supply to a basin is required, all sources of water entering the basin must be included.

Hill Method—Based on Draft and Change in Ground Water Elevation. This method was developed by R. A. Hill for ground water investigations in Arizona and Southern California.[9] Annual change in elevation of ground water levels—water table or piezometric—in a basin are plotted against annual drafts. If the water supply to the basin is reasonably constant, the points can be fitted by a straight line. The draft corresponding to zero change in elevation equals the safe yield. The supply during the period of record should approximate the long-time mean supply. The method has the advantage that the draft during the entire period of record may be an overdraft, yet the prolongation of the fitted straight line defines the safe yield at the intercept of the zero change in elevation line.

Figure 8.1 illustrates the procedure for the Pasadena basin, Los Angeles County, Calif. Data were available for the period 1922–1938 and were plotted as five-year moving averages to smooth out annual variations in supply. The indicated safe yield of 12,000 acre-ft per

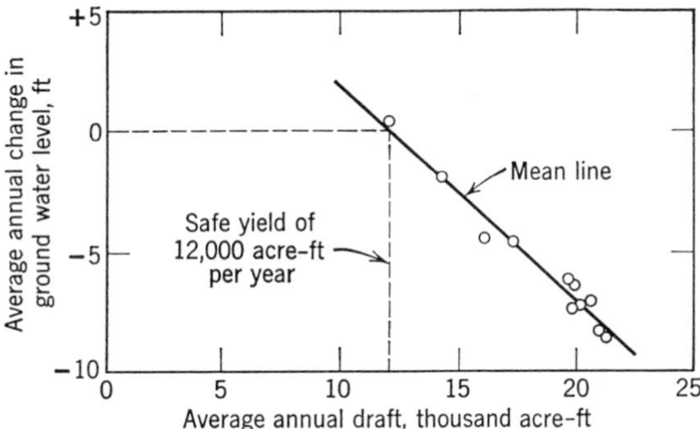

Fig. 8.1. Determination of safe yield by the Hill Method for the Pasadena Basin, Los Angeles County, Calif. (after Conkling[9]).

year is substantially less than the average annual pumpage of 18,500 acre-ft per year; therefore, a sizable overdraft occurred in the basin.

Harding Method—Based on Annual Retained Inflow and Change in Water Table Elevation. S. T. Harding developed this method for analysis of ground water resources in San Joaquin Valley, Calif.[14] Annual values of retained basin inflow are plotted against annual changes in water table elevation. As in the Hill method, the points are fitted by a straight line, and the retained inflow corresponding to zero change in water table elevation is the safe yield. The draft on the basin should be reasonably constant from year to year, which implies that there are no significant variations in irrigated acreage or consumptive use. This requirement is met in arid irrigated areas where precipitation supplies only a minor amount of water and the deficiency is made up by pumping from ground water. The annual retained inflow is the difference between total inflow and total outflow. The average supply during the period should approximate the long-time mean to obtain a good estimate of safe yield. An important limitation of the method is that there must be direct connection between surface and subsurface waters, restricting it to unconfined aquifers.

An example of the method by Ingerson[15] for the Tule River-Deer Creek area of the San Joaquin Valley, Calif., is given in Fig. 8.2. Data covered the 18-year period from 1921 to 1939. Underflow was neglected so the abscissa shows annual surface inflow minus outflow per acre irrigated. It can be seen that the safe yield equaled 2.22 acre-ft per acre. The average annual retained inflow, however, amounted to 1.53 acre-ft per acre. This overdraft produced a 2.06 ft annual average lowering of the water table for the 18-year period.

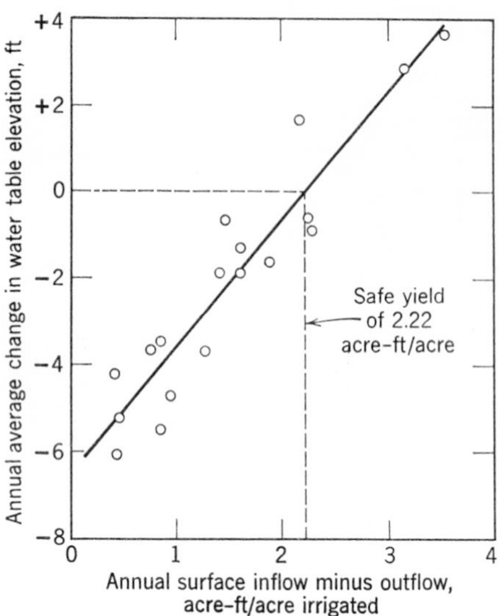

Fig. 8.2. Determination of safe yield by the Harding Method for the Tule River-Deer Creek area, San Joaquin Valley, Calif. (after Ingerson[15]).

Method Based on Zero Net Ground Water Level Fluctuation. If the ground water elevation at the beginning and end of a period of time, amounting to at least several years, is the same, the average annual net draft on the basin is a measure of the safe yield. For unconfined aquifers the net draft is the consumptive use of pumped ground water plus any exported ground water; for confined aquifers it is the gross pumpage. The average annual supply should approximate the long-time mean, and the draft before and after the period should approach overdraft conditions.

An estimate of the safe yield for the South Santa Clara Valley, Calif., was prepared[13] from data in Fig. 8.3. Ground water levels in the 1932–1933 and 1947–1948 seasons were nearly equal. Therefore, the average annual net draft of 41,600 acre-ft during the period between these seasons, when corrected for differences between mean and period values of percolation and precipitation and for the small change in ground water storage, gave the safe yield—39,300 acre-ft.

Simpson Method—Based on a Pumping Trough in a Coastal Aquifer. Overdrafts in coastal aquifers extending to the ocean lead to sea water intrusion when water table or piezometric levels fall below sea level (see Chapter 12). Safe yield can be computed with a method developed by T. R. Simpson [24] during investigation of the Salinas River Valley, Calif. Assume a confined aquifer intersects the coast, as shown in Fig. 8.4. When the basin draft equals safe yield the piezometric surface slopes downward toward the ocean (Fig. 8.4*a*) and a small amount of fresh water is wasted into the ocean in order to stabilize the position of the wedge of sea water (this relation is described in Chapter 12). Under overdraft conditions, however, the down-valley flow is less than the draft, causing the piezometric surface to fall. A pumping trough, as shown in Fig. 8.4*b*, is formed. Its position and dimensions are determined by the pattern and magnitude of the basin pumpage. From the hydraulic gradients it is clear that draft on the inland side of the trough is supplied by down-valley flow from the recharge area, whereas draft on the seaward side of the trough comes from ground water moving inland from the sea. The latter action extends the sea water wedge further into the aquifer; wells near the coast begin to pump highly saline water from the aquifer and must be

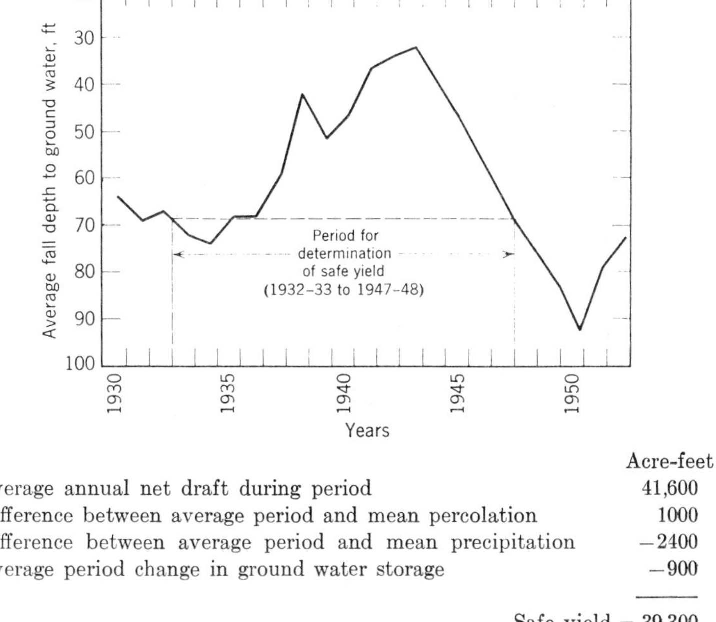

	Acre-feet
Average annual net draft during period	41,600
Difference between average period and mean percolation	1000
Difference between average period and mean precipitation	−2400
Average period change in ground water storage	−900
Safe yield =	39,300

Fig. 8.3. Determination of safe yield based on zero net ground water fluctuation for South Santa Clara Valley, Calif. (after Haley and others [13]).

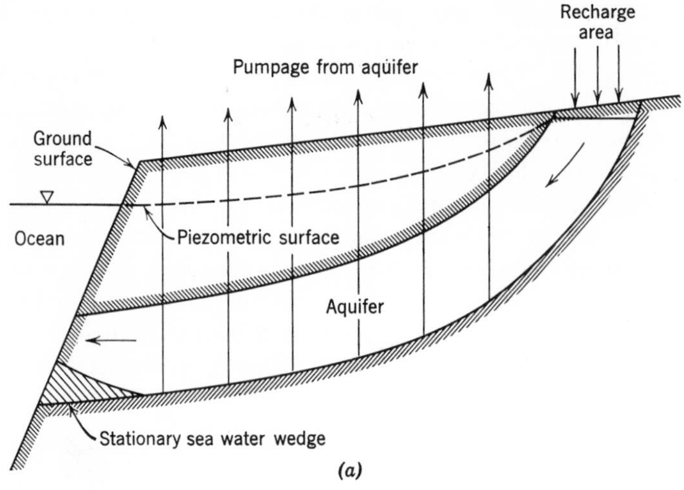

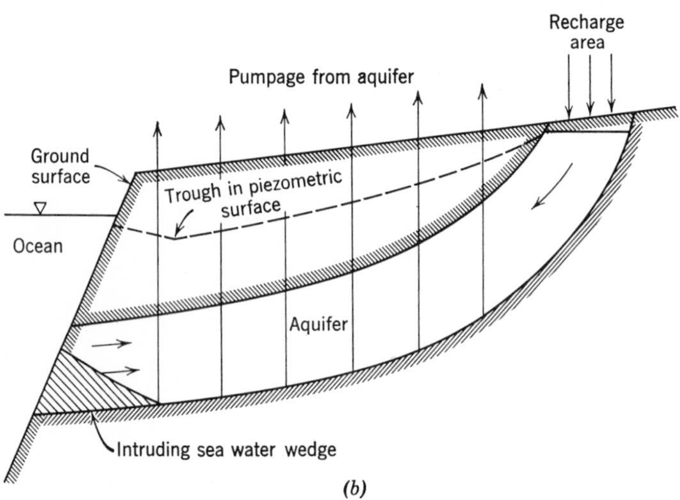

Fig. 8.4. Illustrations of (*a*) safe yield and (*b*) overdraft conditions for a confined aquifer intersecting the coast.

abandoned. It follows then that the basin draft just prior to the appearance of the trough or immediately after its disappearance is the safe yield.

In the Salinas River Valley, where the major aquifer has a configuration similar to that shown in Fig. 8.4, it was observed that a pumping trough formed each spring as the irrigation season advanced and receded each fall after the peak of the irrigation season. While the trough was present, the draft inland from the trough was determined from representative control wells and expressed as a continuous down-valley flow. At the same time, the average slope of the piezometric surface from the recharge area to the centerline of the trough was measured. These values were inserted in the Darcy equation to obtain, by approximation, the product of coefficient of permeability and cross-sectional area (KA). Finally, the inland piezometric slope was estimated for the trough's disappearance, that is, when its elevation was up to sea level and its position was at the coast. By substituting this slope and the previously determined value of KA into the Darcy equation, a draft is obtained which is the safe yield. An example, taken from Simpson,[24] follows:

Observations

Date of trough measurement: June 3, 1945
Continuous down-valley flow: 250 cfs
Difference in elevation of piezometric surface from recharge area to centerline of trough: 104.5 ft
Distance from recharge area to centerline of trough: 130,000 ft

Therefore, from Darcy's law,

$$KA = \frac{Q}{h/L} = \frac{250}{104.5/130{,}000} = 311{,}000 \text{ cfs}$$

Computation of Safe Yield

Difference in elevation of piezometric surface from recharge area to sea level: 100 ft
Distance from recharge area to coast line: 135,000 ft
KA (from above) = 311,000 cfs

Hence,

$$\text{Safe yield} = Q = KA\,\frac{h}{L} = 311{,}000\left(\frac{100}{135{,}000}\right) = 230 \text{ cfs}$$

The supply from the recharge area at the time of basin observations should approximate the long-time mean. The method is unique in that it is based on Darcy's law but does not require separate determination of the coefficient of permeability and cross-sectional area. It could be applied to an unconfined coastal aquifer provided that essentially all of the inflow is lateral and originates from a source of nearly uniform elevation. There is even the possibility that the method might prove useful for inland aquifers where legal considerations specify that draft on a basin shall not induce inflow from an adjoining basin.

Method Based on Darcy's Law. If the inflow into a basin is lateral and the direction is known, the safe yield can be obtained from the average long-time inflow by Darcy's law. The average hydraulic gradient, aquifer permeability, and cross-sectional area perpendicular to flow must be known. These can be determined from ground water levels, pumping tests, and geologic data, respectively. The method is most advantageous for confined aquifers having unidirectional flow. The Geological Survey has applied this method in many areas to determine well yields and spacings.[21]

Method Based on Specific Yield and Average Annual Rise in Water Table. In unconfined aquifers the annual recharge can be expressed as the product of the specific yield, annual rise in water table, and area of aquifer. Specific yield can be determined from methods described in Chapter 2, water table changes can be measured in observation we'ls, and the areal extent of an aquifer can be found from geologic data. The average annual rise should approximate the long-time mean. The method has been employed by Kazmann [9] to estimate the safe yield of the Miami River Valley near Hamilton, Ohio.

Variability of Safe Yield

It is seldom that any single value of safe yield from a ground water basin can be correct for an extended time. Any determination of safe yield is based upon specified conditions, either existing or assumed, and any changes in these conditions will change the safe yield. This fact applies to the degree and pattern of ground water development within the basin as well as to other factors, previously described, which govern safe yield. Even land subsidence resulting from lowered ground water levels (see Chapter 6) may impose a limit. The concept of safe yield has been severely criticized; [16,17] the chief difficulty arises because it is often misinterpreted by persons unfamiliar with ground water hydrology as meaning a fixed underground water supply.

Most methods for estimating safe yield are based on analysis of several years of hydrologic data and ground water usage in a basin. It is unfortunate, perhaps, that most investigations to ascertain safe yield are not initiated until basin developments have produced overdrafts. Yet this is almost necessary in order to obtain an accurate value for safe yield. Conkling [9] pointed out that it would be extremely difficult to determine safe yield in a virgin basin—one full of water with a balance existing between natural inflow and outflow and no pumping. Similarly, estimating the future safe yield of a basin under greater development than at present requires careful evaluation of items in the equation of hydrologic equilibrium.

In basins where the quantity of water in underground storage governs safe yield, the lowering of ground water levels will increase the water supply by increasing subsurface inflow and decreasing subsurface outflow, by increasing recharge from influent streams and decreasing discharge to effluent streams, and by reducing uneconomic evapotranspiration losses. Conversely, a rise in water levels will have the opposite effects. Therefore, where recharge is sufficient, the greater the utilization of underground water, the larger the safe yield. The maximum would be controlled by economic pumping lifts, water quality, or legal considerations.

An unconfined basin fed by an adequate recharge source can increase its safe yield, not only by increasing pumpage but also by rearrangement of pumping patterns. If the concentration of wells is shifted to near the recharge source, greater inflow will be induced. The rearrangement has the additional advantage that a greater supply may be obtained without necessarily increasing pumping lifts. For example, in the cross-section shown in Fig. 8.5*a*, it is assumed that the stream is the principal recharge source. By moving the well field nearer to the

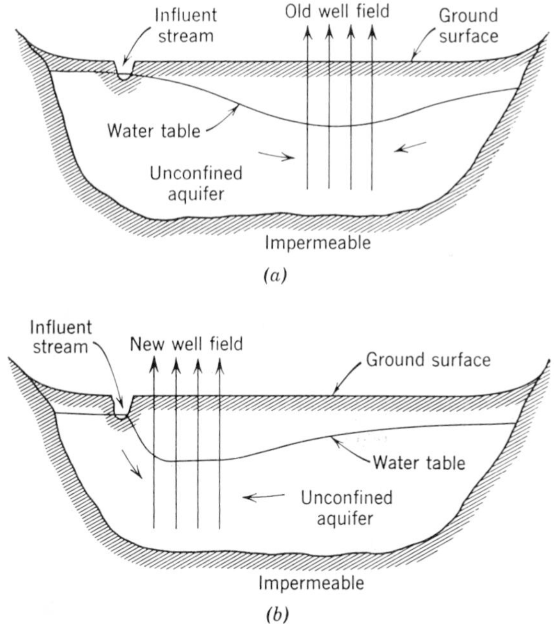

Fig. 8.5. Example of increased ground water yield for same pumping depths obtained by shifting wells nearer to recharge source.

stream as in Fig. 8.5*b*, the water table slope is increased and a greater yield for equal pumping depths results.

For a confined aquifer with its recharge area located at some distance from the pumping area, the rate of flow through the aquifer will govern the safe yield. In large confined aquifers, pumpage of water from storage can be carried on for many years without establishing an equilibrium with basin recharge. Although the slope of the piezometric surface will increase, the permeability of the aquifer is seldom sufficient to maintain a compensating flow into the basin. Thomas [28] has described several basins in the United States where this situation exists.

As pointed out by Baker,[2] gradual and subtle modifications in a basin will often change its safe yield. Changes in vegetation and even in crops, particularly where root depth is affected, may affect surface infiltration and subsequent percolation to the water table. Urbanization of an area, accompanied by greater surface runoff and installation of storm sewers, would be expected to reduce recharge. Changes in the purpose of pumping ground water, such as from irrigation to municipal or industrial use, may from an economic viewpoint allow greater pumping lifts; consequently, the safe yield can be increased. Other economic factors include changes in the value of irrigated crops and increased efficiency of new wells and pumps.

Conjunctive Use of Surface and Ground Water Reservoirs

In the Western United States, future demands for water cannot be met entirely from new surface reservoirs, for sufficient economically feasible storage sites do not exist. Maximum water development can only be attained by conjunctive utilization of surface and ground water reservoirs. Essentially this requires that surface reservoirs impound streamflow which is then transferred at an optimum rate to ground water storage. Surface storage supplies most annual water requirements while ground water reservoirs, generally being many times larger,* can be retained primarily for cyclic storage covering series of years having subnormal precipitation. Thus, ground water levels would be lowered during a cycle of dry years and raised during the ensuing wet period. The optimum rate of transfer from surface to ground water storage must be large enough so that the surface reservoir will be drawn

* For example, in the Central Valley of California the gross ground water storage capacity has been estimated to be 130,000,000 acre-ft, or more than four times the 30,000,000 acre-ft of surface storage planned in the entire Central Valley Project.[6]

down enough to retain the next high runoff. To have a maximum feasible transfer, water must be artificially recharged into the ground. Common methods include: spreading of water in ponds or basins for infiltration and percolation to the ground water, recharge pits, recharge wells, and return flow from irrigation. Seepage from canals and reservoirs also artificially recharges ground water. Present methods are as yet imperfect; however, research is expected to improve recharge rates and thereby reduce economic and physical limitations. Artificial recharge is treated in Chapter 11.

The basic difference between the usual surface water development with its associated ground water development and conjunctive operation of surface and ground water reservoirs is that the separate firm yields of the former may be replaced by a more economic joint yield in the latter.

Plans for ultimate development of water supplies in California are predicated upon conjunctive use of surface and ground water reservoirs.[3,10,29] Such coordination will provide more water at less cost than would otherwise be possible. Conjunctive use requires little in the way of special facilities other than for artificial recharge. It is more a matter of proper operation for maximum effectiveness of surface and ground water reservoirs. Instigation of conjunctive use requires careful analysis of water supplies, water requirements, and geologic conditions.

Because every water development project is unique, it is impossible to present economic considerations generally of conjunctive operation and have them apply specifically to any given situation. Nevertheless, it is possible to summarize the principal ones which may be encountered. The following outline of positive and negative economic factors compares conjunctive use relative to development of surface supplies only; not all, of course, may apply to any given situation. This summary is based on work of F. B. Clendenen.[5,6]

Positive Economic Factors of Conjunctive Use.

(*a*) Greater water conservation—operation of both surface and underground reservoirs provides for larger water storage.

(*b*) Smaller surface storage—ground water storage can provide for water requirements during a series of dry years.

(*c*) Smaller surface distribution system—greater utilization of ground water from widely distributed wells.

(*d*) Smaller drainage system—pumping from wells aids in controlling the water table.

(*e*) Reduced canal lining—seepage from canals is an asset because it provides artificial recharge to ground water.

(*f*) Greater flood control—release of stored surface waters for artificial recharge requires less flood control reservation and furnishes both water conservation and flood protection.

(*g*) Ready integration with existing development—generally conjunctive operation occurs after extensive basin development, but integration can be made to increase water supplies without loss of investment in existing pumping plants.

(*h*) Stage development facilitated—final completion of projects may require 20 to 40 years, hence development by stages is desirable as it reduces the idle potential of the project; stage construction of surface reservoirs is costly, but can be minimized with smaller reservoirs.

(*i*) Smaller evapotranspiration losses—greater underground water storage with lowered ground water levels reduces losses.

(*j*) Greater control over outflow—surface waste and subsurface outflow are reduced by conjunctive use, thereby providing greater water conservation.

(*k*) Improvement of power load and pumping plant use factors—in areas which can be served by either surface or ground water, surface water can be released for irrigation during peak power demand periods to effect a saving in power costs.

(*l*) Less danger from dam failure—should failure ever occur, the smaller the dam and reservoir storage, the smaller the damage.

(*m*) Reduction in weed seed distribution—with a smaller surface distribution system there is less opportunity for spread of noxious weed seeds.

(*n*) Better timing of water distribution—an irrigator prefers to have water available when he wants it, as from a pump, than to take water on schedule from surface conduits.

Negative Economic Factors of Conjunctive Use.

(*a*) Less hydroelectric power—smaller surface reservoirs generate less energy and conjunctive use operation provides less firm power.

(*b*) Greater power consumption—more pumping and from greater depths.

(*c*) Decreased pumping efficiency—large fluctuations in ground water levels reduce pumping efficiency.

(*d*) Greater water mineralization—natural and artificially recharged ground waters contain more dissolved solids than surface water does.

(*e*) More complex project operation—greater supervision of project operation is required and artificial recharge works need careful management.

(*f*) More difficult cost allocation—varying water supplies from two different sources require analysis to fix equitable water rates.

(*g*) Artificial recharge is required—this is costly to operate, difficult to accomplish on land containing relatively impermeable subsoil, and occupies land otherwise available for agricultural purposes.

(*h*) Danger of land subsidence—reduced ground water levels, particularly in confined aquifers, may promote land subsidence which can damage canals and other surface works.

The procedure for developing a sound conjunctive use operation requires estimation of the various elements of the water supply and distribution. A trial operation is run assuming conditions existing during the most critical drought period of record. Initial estimates are modified until the most effective practicable water utilization is obtained. Examples of the procedure can be found in studies by Clendenen [5] and Thomas.[29]

References

1. Baker, D. M., Safe-yield of ground water reservoirs, *Assemblée Générale de Bruxelles, Assoc. Intl. d'Hydrologie Scientifique*, vol. 2, pp. 160–164, 1951.
2. Baker, D. M., Yield from ground-water reservoirs, *West. Const.*, vol. 28, no. 2, pp. 74–76, 117, 1953.
3. Banks, H. O., Utilization of underground storage reservoirs, *Trans. Amer. Soc. Civil Engrs.*, vol. 118, pp. 220–234, 1953.
4. Boke, R. L., and D. S. Stoner, The application of hydrologic techniques to ground-water problems in California's Central Valley Project, *Proc. Ankara Symposium on Arid Zone Hydrology,* UNESCO, Paris, pp. 134–139, 1953.
5. Clendenen, F. B., *A comprehensive plan for the conjunctive utilization of a surface reservoir with underground storage for basin-wide water supply development: Solano Project, California,* D. Eng. thesis, Univ. Calif., Berkeley, 160 pp., 1954.
6. Clendenen, F. B., Economic utilization of ground water and surface storage reservoirs, Paper presented before meeting of Amer. Soc. Civil Engrs., San Diego, Calif., Feb. 1955.
7. Clyde, G. D., Utilization of natural underground water storage reservoirs, *Jour. Soil and Water Conserv.*, vol. 6, pp. 15–19, 1951.
8. Conkling, H., The depletion of underground water-supplies, *Trans. Amer. Geophysical Union,* vol. 15, pp. 531–539, 1934.
9. Conkling, H., Utilization of ground-water storage in stream system development, *Trans. Amer. Soc. Civil Engrs.,* vol. 111, pp. 275–354, 1946.
10. Dolcini, A. J., and others, The California water plan, *Bull.* 3, Calif. Dept. Water Resources, Sacramento, 246 pp., 1957.
11. Foose, R. M., Ground-water conservation and development, *Monthly Bulletin,* Penn. Dept. Internal Affairs, Harrisburg, vol. 19, no. 2, pp. 17–28, 1951.

12. Gleason, G. B., South Coastal Basin investigation—overdraft on ground water basins, *Bull.* 53, Calif. Div. Water Resources, Sacramento, 256 pp., 1947
13. Haley, J. M., and others, Santa Clara Valley investigation, *Bull.* 7, Calif. State Water Resources Board, Sacramento, 154 pp., 1955.
14. Harding, S. T., Ground water resources of Southern San Joaquin Valley, *Bull.* 11, Calif. Div. Eng. and Irrig., Sacramento, 146 pp., 1927.
15. Ingerson, I. M., The hydrology of Southern San Joaquin Valley, California, and its relation to imported water-supplies, *Trans. Amer. Geophysical Union,* vol. 22, pp. 20–45, 1941.
16. Kazmann, R. G., The role of aquifers in water supply, *Trans. Amer. Geophysical Union,* vol. 32, pp. 227–230, 1951.
17. Kazmann, R. G., "Safe yield" in ground water development, reality or illusion? *Proc. Amer. Soc. Civil Engrs.,* vol. 82, no. IR3, 12 pp., 1956.
18. Lull, H. M., and E. N. Munns, Effect of land use practices on ground water, *Jour. Soil and Water Conserv.,* vol. 5, pp. 169–179, 1950.
19. McDonald, H. R., The irrigation aspects of ground-water development, *Proc. Amer. Soc. Civil Engrs.,* vol. 81, sep. 707, 17 pp., 1955.
20. Meinzer, O. E., Quantitative methods of estimating ground-water supplies, *Bull. Geol. Soc. Amer.,* vol. 31, pp. 329–338, 1920.
21. Meinzer, O. E., Outline of methods for estimating ground-water supplies, *U. S. Geological Survey Water-Supply Paper* 638-C, Washington, D. C., pp. 99–144, 1932.
22. Meinzer, O. E., Problems of the perennial yield of artesian aquifers, *Econ. Geol.,* vol. 40, pp. 159–163, 1945.
23. Porter, N. W., Concerning conservation of underground water with suggestions for control, *Trans. Amer. Soc. Heat. Vent. Engrs.,* vol. 47, pp. 309–322, 1941.
24. Simpson, T. R., Salinas Basin investigation, *Bull.* 52, Calif. Div. Water Resources, Sacramento, 230 pp., 1946.
25. Simpson, T. R., Utilization of ground water in California, *Trans. Amer. Soc. Civil Engrs.,* vol. 117, pp. 923–934, 1952.
26. Snyder, J. H., Ground water in California—the experiences of Antelope Valley, *Giannini Foundation Ground-Water Studies* 2, Univ. Calif., Berkeley, 171 pp., 1955.
27. Stringfield, V. T., Geologic and hydrologic factors affecting perennial yield of aquifers, *Jour. Amer. Water Works Assoc.,* vol. 43, pp. 803–816, 1951.
28. Thomas, H. E., *The conservation of ground water,* McGraw-Hill, New York, 327 pp., 1951.
29. Thomas, R. O., General aspects of planned ground-water utilization, *Proc Amer. Soc. Civil Engrs.,* vol. 81, sep. 706, 11 pp., 1955.
30. Turner, S. F., and L. C. Halpenny, Ground-water inventory in the Upper Gila Valley, New Mexico and Arizona; scope of investigation and methods used, *Trans. Amer. Geophysical Union,* vol. 22, pp. 738–744, 1941.
31. Wentworth, C. K., The problem of safe yield in insular Ghyben-Herzberg systems, *Trans. Amer. Geophysical Union,* vol. 32, pp. 739–742, 1951.
32. Williams, C. C., and S. W. Lohman, Methods used in estimating the ground-water supply in Wichita, Kansas, well-field area, *Trans. Amer. Geophysical Union,* vol. 28, pp. 120–131, 1947.

Surface Investigations of Ground Water

CHAPTER 9

By working on the earth's surface, it is sometimes possible to estimate where ground water occurs and, under special conditions, to obtain information on water quality. Investigating ground water from the surface is at best not easy, nor are results always successful; however, such methods are normally less costly than subsurface investigations. Geophysical methods, developed in the last thirty years for petroleum and mineral exploration, have proved useful for locating and analyzing ground water. Although several methods can be enumerated under the geophysical heading, only the electrical resistivity and seismic refraction methods have more than limited application to ground water. Geologic investigation and reconnaissance represent a second approach to the problem. A third approach is based on the interpretation of aerial photographs of the earth's surface. All methods provide only indirect indications of ground water, as underground hydrologic data must be inferred from surface information. Correct interpretation requires supplemental data from subsurface investigations (described in Chapter 10) to substantiate surface findings.

Geophysical Exploration

Geophysical exploration refers to the scientific measurement of physical properties of the earth's crust for investigation of mineral deposits or geologic structure.[7,16,18] With the discovery of oil by geophysical methods in 1926, economic pressures for the location of petroleum and mineral deposits stimulated the development and improvement of many geophysical methods and equipment. Application to ground water investigations was slow because the commercial value of oil overshadows that of water. In recent years, however, refinement of geophysical techniques as well as an increasing recognition of the advantages of the methods for ground water study has changed the situation. Today, many organizations responsible for meeting water supply demands are employing geophysical methods. The methods are frequently inexact or difficult to interpret, and they are most useful when supplemented by subsurface investigations.

Geophysical methods detect differences, or anomalies, of physical properties within the earth's crust. Density, magnetism, elasticity, and electrical resistivity are properties most commonly measured. Experience and research have enabled differences in these properties to be interpreted in terms of geologic structure, rock type and porosity, water content, and water quality.

Electrical Resistivity Method

The electrical resistivity of a rock formation limits the amount of current passing through the formation when an electrical potential is applied. It may be defined as the resistence in ohms between opposite faces of a unit cube of the material. If a material of resistance R has a cross-sectional area A and a length L, then its resistivity can be expressed as

$$\rho = \frac{RA}{L} \tag{9.1}$$

In the metric system, units of resistivity are ohm-m^2/m, or simply ohm-m.

Resistivities of rock formations vary over a wide range, depending upon the material, density, porosity, pore size and shape, water content and quality, and temperature. There are no fixed limits for resistivities of various rocks; igneous and metamorphic rocks yield values in the range 10^2 to 10^8 ohm-m, sedimentary and unconsolidated rocks, 10^0 to 10^4 ohm-m. In relatively porous formations, the resistivity is controlled more by water content and quality within the formation than by the rock resistivity;[41] therefore, for aquifers composed of unconsolidated materials, the resistivity of the ground water governs. Aquifer resistivity can be expressed in terms of resistivity of the ground water and of porosity for uniform packings of spherical mineral grains. If ρ is the aquifer resistivity, ρ_w is that of the ground water (assumed to fill all of the voids), and α is porosity, then it can be shown [16] that

$$\frac{\rho}{\rho_w} = \frac{3 - \alpha}{2\alpha} \tag{9.2}$$

This relation applies only for isotropic conditions; for anisotropic conditions, orientation of the current with respect to stratifications will produce resistivity differences.

Actual resistivities are determined from an apparent resistivity which is computed from measurements of current and potential differences between pairs of electrodes placed in the ground surface. The procedure involves measuring a potential difference between two electrodes (P in Fig. 9.1) resulting from an applied current through two other electrodes (C in Fig. 9.1) outside but in line with the potential electrodes. If the resistivity is everywhere uniform in the subsurface zone beneath

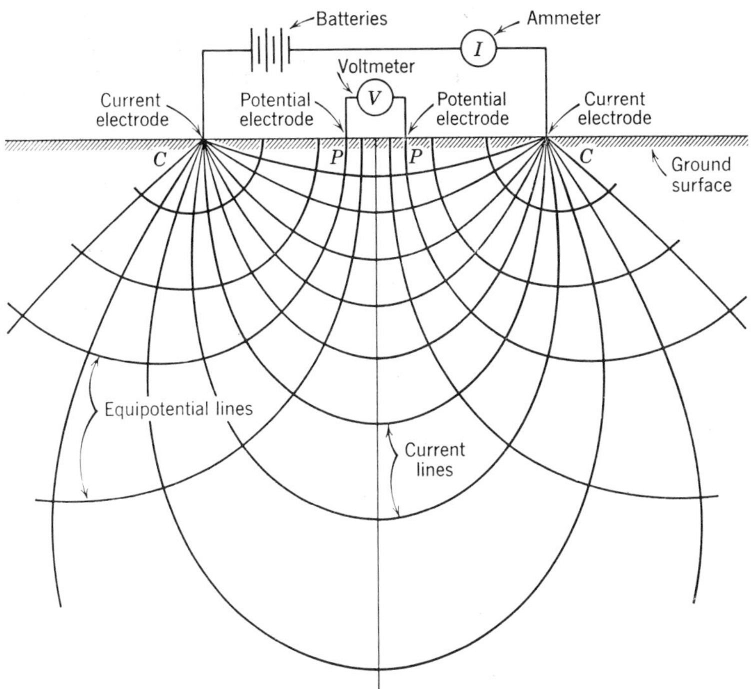

Fig. 9.1. Electrical circuit for resistivity determination and electrical field for a homogeneous subsurface stratum.

the electrodes, an orthogonal network of circular arcs will be formed by the current and equipotential lines, as shown in Fig. 9.1. The measured potential difference is a weighted value over a subsurface region controlled by the shape of the network. Thus, the measured current and potential differences yield an apparent resistivity over an unspecified depth. If the spacing between electrodes is increased, a deeper penetration of the electrical field occurs and a different apparent resistivity is obtained. In general, actual subsurface resistivities vary with depth; therefore, apparent resistivities will change as electrode spacings are increased, but not in a like manner. Because changes of resistivity at great depths have only a slight effect on the apparent resistivity compared to those at shallow depths, the method is seldom effective for determining actual resistivities below a few hundred feet.

Current electrodes consist of metal stakes driven into the ground; potential electrodes are porous cups filled with a saturated solution of copper sulfate to inhibit electrical fields from forming around them. To minimize polarization effects either an a-c low frequency current or a reversible direct current is preferable. In practice, various standard electrode spacing arrangements have been adopted; most common are the Wenner and Schlumberger arrangements.

The Wenner [13, 48] arrangement, shown in Fig. 9.2a, has the potential electrodes located at the third points between the current electrodes. The apparent resistivity is given by the ratio of voltage to current times a spacing factor. For the Wenner arrangement, the apparent resistivity

$$\rho_a = 2\pi a \frac{V}{I} \tag{9.3}$$

where a is the distance between adjacent electrodes, V is the voltage difference between the potential electrodes, and I is the applied current.

The Schlumberger arrangement, shown in Fig. 9.2b, has the potential electrodes close together. The apparent resistivity is given by

$$\rho_a = \pi \frac{(L/2)^2 - (b/2)^2}{b} \frac{V}{I} \tag{9.4}$$

where L and b are the current and potential electrode spacings, respectively (Fig. 9.2b). Theoretically, $L \gg b$, but for practical application good results can be obtained if $L \geqslant 5b$.[20]

When apparent resistivity is plotted against electrode spacing (a for Wenner, and $L/2$ for Schlumberger) for various spacings at one location, a smooth curve can be drawn through the points. The inter-

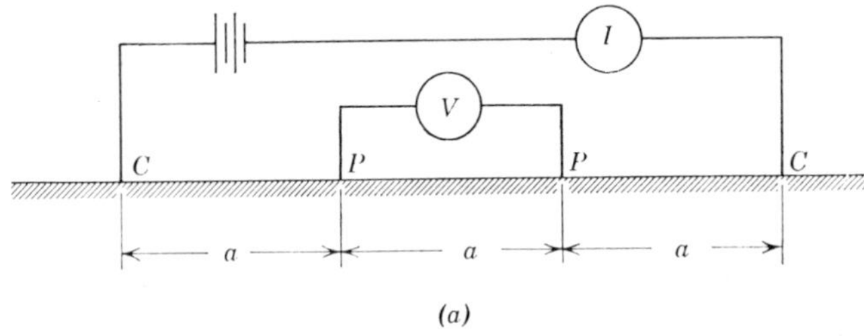

(a)

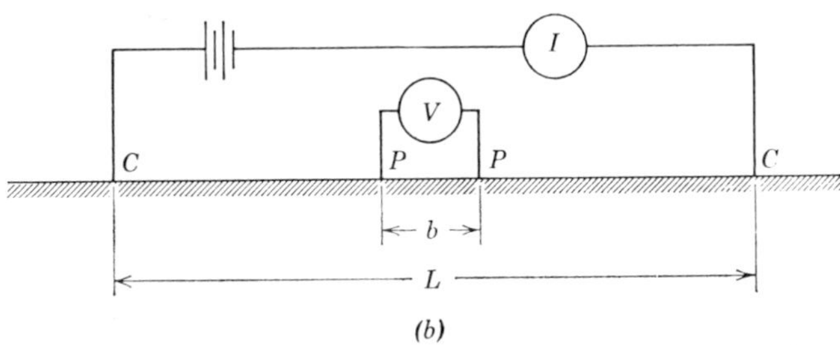

(b)

Fig. 9.2. Common electrode arrangements for resistivity determination: (*a*) Wenner and (*b*) Schlumberger.

pretation of such a resistivity-spacing curve in terms of subsurface conditions is a complex and frequently difficult problem. The solution can be obtained in two parts: (*a*) interpretation in terms of various layers of actual (as distinguished from apparent) resistivities and their depths; and (*b*) interpretation of the actual resistivities in terms of subsurface geologic and ground water conditions. Part (*a*) can be accomplished with theoretically computed resistivity-spacing curves of 2-, 3-, and 4-layer cases for various ratios of resistivities. Curves and explanation of curve-matching techniques have been published by Mooney and Wetzel [29] for the Wenner configuration; by La Compagnie Générale de Géophysique [20] for the Schlumberger configuration.* Part (*b*) depends upon supplemental data. Comparing actual resistivity variations with depth to data from a nearby logged test hole enables a correlation to be established with subsurface geologic and ground water conditions. This information can then be applied for interpretation of resistivity measurements in surrounding areas.[46]

* Also, curves for the Schlumberger arrangement can be computed from tables of potentials about a point electrode in Mooney and Wetzel.[29]

Figure 9.3*a* shows a graph of apparent resistivity and electrode spacing, while Fig. 9.3*b* gives the interpretation of the measurement. Depths and actual resistivities were determined by matching with Schlumberger curves.[20] Geologic data were obtained from nearby test holes, but estimated chloride contents of the ground water were based upon a relation between actual resistivity of the saturated aquifer and resistivity of the ground water obtained from measurements at surrounding test holes. It should be noted that the resistivities here are unusually low because of severe sea water intrusion (see Chapter 12);

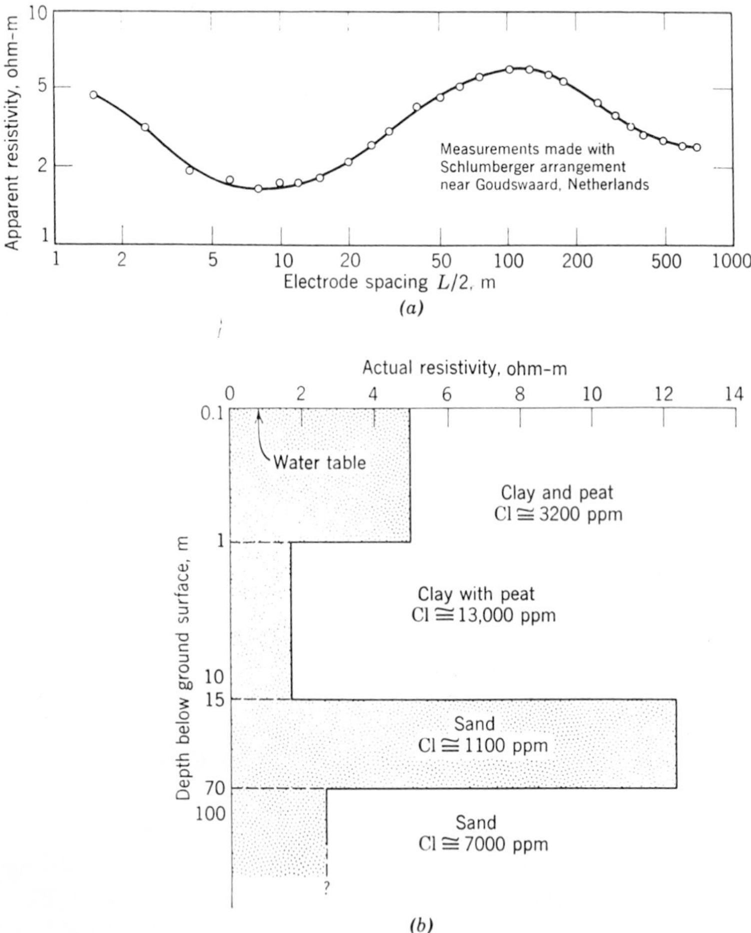

Fig. 9.3. Example of electrical resistivity measurement showing (*a*) results and (*b*) interpretation.

values 10 to 100 times higher can be expected under ordinary conditions.

Resistivity surveys can cover either vertical investigations at selected locations by varying electrode spacings, or they can furnish isoresistivity maps of an area.[3, 21, 31, 39, 44, 47] In areal studies a constant spacing may be adopted to measure resistivities only at a particular depth of interest, such as an aquifer. Areal resistivity changes can be interpreted in terms of aquifer limits and changes in ground water quality, whereas variable depth surveys may indicate aquifers, water tables, salinities, impermeable formations, and bedrock depths.

Any factors which disturb the electrical field in the vicinity of the electrodes may invalidate the resistivity measurements. Buried pipe lines, cables, and wire fences are common hazards. Extremely dry conditions may necessitate moistening the ground around electrodes to establish proper earth contact.

Of all surface geophysical methods, the electrical resistivity method has been applied most widely for ground water investigations. Its portable equipment and ease of operation facilitate rapid measurements. The method is often helpful in planning efficient and economical test drilling programs. It is especially well adapted for locating subsurface salt water boundaries because the decrease in resistance when salt water is encountered becomes apparent on a resistivity-depth curve.[37] In the Hawaiian Islands, predicted depths from resistivity measurements and observed depths from drilling agreed (for the fresh water-salt water interface) to within one foot in a majority of measurements of depths of the order of 100 ft.[42, 43] In the Netherlands, deep deposits of sand under polders enabled resistivity curves to be interpreted in terms of concentration variations of underlying saline waters.[46] In Illinois,[2, 3] applying the method to locate municipal water supplies in unconsolidated materials gave an unusually good record of 92 per cent correct interpretations, verified by test drilling of recommended sites. The method has been considered for locating seepage loss areas along canals.[5]

Seismic Refraction Method

The seismic refraction method involves the creation of a small shock at the earth's surface either by the impact of a heavy instrument or by exploding a small dynamite charge and measuring the time required for the resulting sound, or shock, wave to travel known distances. Seismic waves follow the same laws of propagation as light rays and may be reflected or refracted at any interface where a velocity change occurs. Seismic reflection methods provide information on geologic structure thousands of feet below the surface, whereas seismic refraction methods—of interest in ground water studies—cover only a few hundred feet in depth. The travel time of a wave depends upon the media through which it is passing; velocities are greatest in solid igneous rocks and least in unconsolidated materials. Wave velocities in unconsolidated, unsaturated strata are the order of 1500 to 3000 ft/sec, 3000 to 6000 ft/sec in unconsolidated aquifers, and 6000 to 10,000 ft/sec in poor aquifers with appreciable clay or silt content.

Changes in seismic wave velocities are governed by changes in elastic properties of the formations. The greater the contrast of these properties, the clearer the formations and their boundaries can be identified. In sedimentary rocks, the texture and geologic history are more important than the mineral composition. Porosity tends to decrease wave velocity, but water content increases it.

A spherical wave expands outward from a shock point, as shown in Fig. 9.4*a*. It travels at a speed governed by the material through which it is passing. If, for example, a homogenous unconsolidated material is assumed with a water table, the wave upon reaching the water table will travel along the interface. As it travels along the interface, a series of waves are propagated back into the unsaturated layer. Positions of the wave front drawn at intervals of a few milliseconds in Fig. 9.4*a* illustrate this refraction. At any location on the surface, the first wave will arrive either directly from the shot point or from a refracted path. By measuring the time interval of the first arrival at varying distances from the shot point, a time-distance graph can be plotted. Reciprocals of the slopes in the time-distance graph of Fig. 9.4*b* give 1500 ft/sec for the velocity v_1 above the water table and 6000 ft/sec for the velocity v_2 below. For the horizontal two-layer case here described, the depth H to the water table can be computed from the velocities v_1 and v_2 and the distance s to the intersection on the graph, as shown in Fig. 9.4*b*. The equation is

$$H = \frac{s}{2}\sqrt{\frac{v_2 - v_1}{v_2 + v_1}} \tag{9.5}$$

which, when the values of the example are substituted, gives 23 ft.

Multilayered problems may be solved in a similar manner. Different surface elevations, sloping formations, faults, and changes in the interfacial configuration require special analysis. Computational procedures are described in textbooks of geophysics.[7,16,18]

The field procedure for seismic refraction investigations has been simplified with the help of compact and efficient instruments. With dynamite, a charge of less than one pound is ordinarily sufficient. It is placed in a hand-augered hole of 3 to 5 ft depth and the hole is backfilled. Some types of equipment are so sensitive that the blow

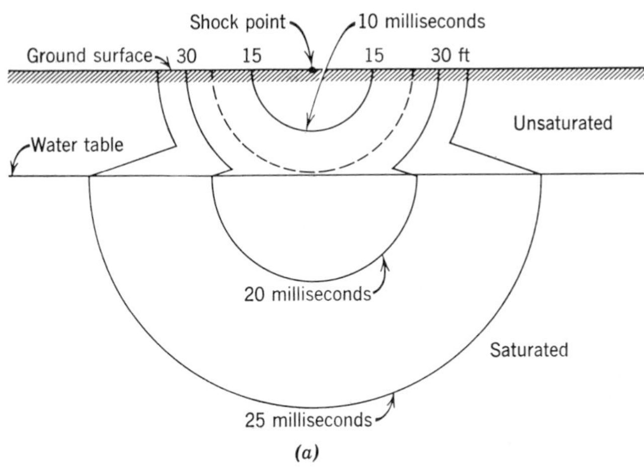

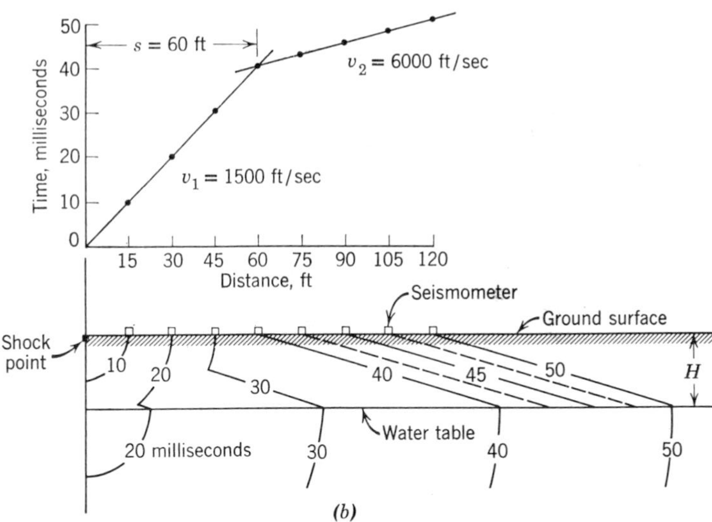

Fig. 9.4. Seismic refraction method applied to determine the depth to a water table; (*a*) wave front advance and (*b*) time-distance graph.

of a sledge hammer on the ground surface will produce a recordable shock wave. Seismometers, also known as geophones, detectors, or pickups, are spaced in a line from the shock point 10 to 50 ft apart. They receive the shock wave and convert the vibration into electrical impulses. An electrical circuit connects the seismometers to an amplifier and a recording oscillograph, which automatically records the instant of firing and the various first arrivals of the shock wave. Depth determinations to 200 to 300 ft are typical with this equipment, although satisfactory work to depths of 2000 ft has been accomplished.

Interpretation of seismic refraction data assumes homogeneous layers bounded by interfacial planes. Where no distinct boundary exists, but rather a gradual transition zone, a curve replaces the break in slope on the time-distance graph. Fortunately, water tables approximate planes, so that many of the problems imposed by irregular configurations of geologic structure are avoided. Efficient application of the method requires skill in proper interpretation in terms of rock materials, depths, and irregularities. Other knowledge of subsurface materials and configurations aids in proper analysis of field records. The actual presence of ground water is difficult to determine without supplemental information because velocities overlap in saturated and unsaturated zones. Seismic wave velocities must increase with depth in order to obtain satisfactory results; as a result, a dense layer overlying an unconsolidated aquifer will mask the presence of the aquifer.

The seismic refraction method in applicable areas can eliminate rapidly and economically areas unfavorable for test drilling. It is not readily adapted to small areas. Minimum distances of several hundred feet are needed for seismic profiles in different directions. Local noise or vibrations, from sources such as highways, airports, and construction sites, interfere with seismic work.

The seismic method, because it requires special equipment and trained technicians for operation and interpretation, has been applied to only a relatively limited extent for ground water investigations.[4] Incidental to foundation explorations by seismic refraction for proposed dams in the Ohio River Basin,[38] locations of water tables were made based on velocity differences between saturated and unsaturated overburden. The successful work by Linehan [24, 25] and others in locating ground water supplies in Massachusetts and Connecticut provides notable examples of the applicability of the method. Here, investigations were directed toward finding gravel strata for water supplies which could then be confirmed by test drilling.

Gravity and Magnetic Methods

The gravity method measures differences in density on the earth's surface which may indicate geologic structure. As the method is expensive and because differences in water content in subsurface strata seldom involve measurable differences in specific gravity at the surface, the method has little application to ground water prospecting. It is possible that special geologic conditions, such as thick alluvial deposits bordering a mountain area or intrusive bodies forming an aquifer boundary, might be detected from gravity variations.

The magnetic method enables magnetic fields of the earth to be mapped. As magnetic contrasts are seldom associated with ground water occurrence, the method has little relevance. Indirect information pertinent to ground water studies, such as dikes which form aquifer boundaries or limits of a basaltic flow, has been obtained with the method.

Geologic Methods

Intelligent utilization of published geologic data, supplemented by geologic field reconnaissance, will often furnish a tentative appraisal of ground water conditions.[10, 23] This approach should be regarded as a first step in any evaluation of subsurface water supply, as no expensive equipment is required and information on geologic composition and structure will permit evaluation of need for field exploration by other methods.

A knowledge of the depositional and erosional events in an area may indicate the extent and regularity of water-bearing formations. The type of rock formation will suggest the magnitude of water yield to be expected; one formation may be adequate for a domestic supply but entirely unsatisfactory for an industrial or municipal supply. Stratigraphy and geologic history of an area may reveal aquifers beneath unsuitable upper strata, the continuity and interconnection of aquifers, or important aquifer boundaries. The nature and thickness of overlying beds, as well as the dip of water-bearing formations, will enable estimates of drilling depths to be made. Similarly, confined aquifers may be noted and the possibility of flowing wells or low pumping lifts foretold. Meinzer [27] has emphasized the influence of rock structure on ground water.

The fundamental relationships between geologic structure and ground water are presented elsewhere: geologic formations in terms of their capabilities as aquifers in Chapter 2; the quality of ground water as affected by different geologic sources in Chapter 7.

Air Photo Interpretation

Because the occurrence of ground water depends to a considerable extent upon terrain characteristics, proper interpretation of aerial photographs of a region can provide valuable information in this regard.[17] Vegetation, land form and use, drainage patterns, erosion, color, and special ground features such as eskers, terraces, alluvial planes, and gravel pits are apparent on air photos and indicate subsurface conditions.

Individual air photos taken over an area under investigation are assembled into a mosaic map covering the area. From study of this and stereoscopic study of individual photo pairs, drainage and soil maps can be prepared. These tools can then be employed to develop a ground water prediction map. Howe, Wilke, and Bloodgood,[17] for example, prepared such a map for Tippecanoe County, Indiana. The county was divided into areas of good, fair, and poor ground water yields by the classification given in Table 9.1. Examination of well data confirmed the analysis.

Ground water maps prepared from air photos can delineate the most and least promising areas for ground water supplies. Such maps aid in selecting test drilling sites, reduce costs of ground water investigations, and assist in locating industrial plants requiring large water supplies.

TABLE 9.1 Areal Ground Water Classification, Tippecanoe County, Indiana

(After Howe, Wilke, and Bloodgood [17])

Class	Classification Basis	Ground Water Yield
A	Granular deposits in stream terraces, alluvial plains, outwash plains, glacial sluiceways and filled valleys, all at low elevations	Good (>200 gpm)
B	Morainal deposits, eskers, kames; all of small extent and generally at higher elevations	Fair (50 to 200 gpm)
C	Upland till and organic topsoils	Poor (<50 gpm)

Dowsing

The art of using a divining rod to locate water is known as dowsing, or water witching. Although lacking scientific justification for the method, water witches diligently follow the dictates of their divining rods wherever people can be persuaded of their potential value. The method, as commonly practiced, consists of holding a forked stick in both hands and walking over the local area until the butt end is attracted downward—ostensively by subsurface water. Diviners find the method profitable not only for locating ground water, but also for such diverse purposes as finding ore deposits, treasure, criminals, property boundaries, and lost animals.[9] Heiland [15] went to the heart of the matter when he wrote:

It may be perfectly possible that certain persons of supernormal faculties can sense the presence of water, but this is something to be discussed by a psychologist and not a geophysicist. Besides, if the numerous wiggle-stick and doodle-bug men who pretend to be able to locate water possessed such faculty, there would be no need for them to employ any of their mysterious devices.

It is amazing that the idea of supernatural powers has such a continued fascination for people.* The literature on the subject is extensive and spans four centuries.[8] The statement by Dr. O. E. Meinzer,[8] former Chief of the Ground Water Branch, U. S. Geological Survey, should suffice to dispel the naïveté of persons seeking to locate water on the basis of this method:

It is doubtful whether so much investigation and discussion have been bestowed on any other subject with such absolute lack of positive results. It is difficult to see how for practical purposes the entire matter could be more thoroughly discredited, and it should be obvious to everyone that further tests by the United States Geological Survey of this so-called "witching" for water, oil, or other minerals would be a misuse of public funds.

It is by no means true that all persons using a forked twig or some other device for locating water or other mineral are intentional deceivers. Some of them are doubtless men of good character and benevolent intentions. However, as anything that can be deeply veiled in mystery affords a good opportunity for swindlers, there can be no reasonable doubt that many of the

* A recent perpetrator of the dowsing legend was the late novelist, Kenneth Roberts. His novels advocating dowsing (including *Henry Gross and His Dowsing Rod*, 1951, *The Seventh Sense*, 1953, and *Water Unlimited*, 1957, Doubleday & Co., Garden City, N. Y.) are interesting to read. For a humorous and sometimes scathing rebuttal to Mr. Roberts, see the paper by Riddick.[33]

large group of professional finders . . . are deliberately defrauding the people, and that the total amount of money they obtain is large.

To all inquirers the United States Geological Survey therefore gives the advice not to expend any money for the services of any "water witch" or for the use or purchase of any machine or instrument devised for locating underground water or other minerals.

References

1. Bays, C. A., Prospecting for ground-water—geophysical methods, *Jour. Amer. Water Works Assoc.*, vol. 42, pp. 947–956, 1950.
2. Bays, C. A., and S. H. Folk, Developments in the application of geophysics to ground-water problems, *Illinois Geological Survey Circ.* 108, Urbana, 25 pp., 1944.
3. Buhle, M. B., Earth resistivity in ground water studies in Illinois, *Min. Eng.*, vol. 5, pp. 395–399, 1953.
4. Burwell, E. B., Jr., Determination of ground-water levels by the seismic method, *Trans. Amer. Geophysical Union,* vol. 21, pp. 439–440, 1940.
5. Conwell, C. N., Application of the electrical resistivity method to delineation of areas of seepage along a canal—Wyoming Canal—Riverton Project, *Geol. Rep.* G-114, U. S. Bureau Reclamation, Denver, Colo., 10 pp., 1951.
6. Dizioglu, M. Y., Underground-water investigations by means of geophysical methods (particularly electrical) in Central Anatolia, *Proc. Ankara Symposium on Arid Zone Hydrology,* UNESCO, Paris, pp. 199–215, 1953.
7. Dobrin, M. B., *Introduction to geophysical prospecting,* McGraw-Hill, New York, 435 pp., 1952.
8. Ellis, A. J., The divining rod—a history of water witching, *U. S. Geological Survey Water-Supply Paper* 416, Washington, D. C., 59 pp., 1917.
9. Emmart, B. D., All-purpose dowsing, *Atlantic Monthly,* vol. 190, no. 1, pp. 90–92, 1952.
10. Fent, O. S., Use of geologic methods in ground-water prospecting, *Jour. Amer. Water Works Assoc.,* vol. 41, pp. 590–598, 1949.
11. Foster, J. W., and M. B. Buhle, An integrated geophysical and geological investigation of aquifers in glacial drift near Champaign-Urbana, Illinois, *Econ. Geol.,* vol. 46, pp. 368–397, 1951.
12. Frommurze, H. F., Scientific methods of water finding, *Proc. Geol. Soc. South Africa,* vol. 46, pp. 23–38, 1943.
13. Gish, O. H., and W. J. Rooney, Measurement of resistivity of large masses of undisturbed earth, *Terrestrial Magnetism and Atmospheric Electricity,* vol. 30, pp. 161–188, 1925.
14. Hallenbeck, F., Geo-electrical problems of the hydrology of West German area, *Geophysical Prospecting,* vol. 1, pp. 241–249, 1953.
15. Heiland, C. A., Prospecting for water with geophysical methods, *Trans. Amer Geophysical Union,* vol. 18, pp. 574–588, 1937.
16. Heiland, C. A., *Geophysical exploration,* Prentice-Hall, New York, 1013 pp., 1940.
17. Howe, R. H. L., H. R. Wilke, and D. E. Bloodgood, Application of air

photo interpretation in the location of ground water, *Jour. Amer. Water Works Assoc.*, vol. 48, pp. 1380–1390, 1956.

18. Jakosky, J. J., *Exploration geophysics,* 2nd ed., Times Mirror Press, Los Angeles, 1195 pp., 1950.
19. Kelly, S. F., Geophysics in the exploration, exploitation, and conservation of water, *Mines Mag.*, vol. 39, pp. 13–22, 38, Nov. 1949.
20. La Compagnie Générale de Géophysique, Abaques de sondage électrique, *Geophysical Prospecting,* vol. 3, suppl. 3, 7 pp. + set of curves, 1955.
21. Landes, K. K., and J. T. Wilson, Ground-water exploration by earth-resistivity methods, *Papers Mich. Acad. Arts, Sci., Let.*, vol. 29, pp. 345–354, 1943.
22. Lee, F. W., Geophysical prospecting for underground waters in desert areas, *Information Circ.* 6899, U. S. Bureau Mines, Washington, D. C., 27 pp. 1936.
23. Leggette, R. M., Prospecting for ground water—geologic methods, *Jour. Amer. Water Works Assoc.*, vol. 42, pp. 945–946, 1950.
24. Linehan, D., Seismology applied to shallow zone research, *Amer. Soc. Test. Materials Spec. Tech. Publ.* 122, pp. 156–170, 1951.
25. Linehan, D., and S. Keith, Seismic reconnaissance for ground-water development, *Jour. New England Water Works Assoc.*, vol. 63, pp. 76–95, 1949.
26. Mazloum, S., Boring and prospecting for ground-water in arid zones, *Proc. Ankara Symposium on Arid Zone Hydrology,* UNESCO, Paris, pp. 184–187, 1953.
27. Meinzer, O. E., The occurrence of ground water in the United States, *U. S. Geological Survey Water-Supply Paper* 489, Washington, D. C., 321 pp., 1923.
28. Meinzer, O. E., The value of geophysical methods in ground-water studies, *Trans. Amer. Geophysical Union,* vol. 18, pp. 385–387, 1937.
29. Mooney, H. M., and W. W. Wetzel, *The potentials about a point electrode and apparent resistivity curves for a two-, three-, and four-layered earth,* Univ. Minnesota Press, Minneapolis, 146 pp. + set of curves, 1956.
30. Paver, G. L., On the application of the electrical resistivity method of geophysical surveying to the location of underground water, with examples from the Middle East, *Proc. Geol. Soc. London,* pp. 46–51, Apr. 18, 1945.
31. Paver, G. L., Iso-resistivity mapping for the investigation of underground water supplies, *Assemblée Générale d'Oslo, Assoc. Intl. d'Hydrologie Scientifique,* vol. 3, pp. 290–295, 1948.
32. Paver, G. L., The geophysical interpretation of underground water supplies; a geological analysis of observed resistivity data, *Jour. Inst. Water Engrs.,* vol. 4, pp. 237–266, 1950.
33. Riddick, T. M., Dowsing—an unorthodox method of locating underground water supplies or an interesting facet of the human mind, *Proc. Amer. Philosophical Soc.,* vol. 96, pp. 526–534, 1952.
34. Robertshaw, J., and P. D. Brown, Geophysical methods of exploration and their application to civil engineering problems, *Proc. Inst. Civil Engrs.,* pt. 1, vol. 4, pp. 644–690, 1955.
35. Rose, N. A., Ground water and relation of geology to its occurrence in the Houston district, Texas, *Bull. Amer. Assoc. Pet. Geol.,* vol. 27, pp. 1081–1101, 1943.
36. Ryder, L. W., The case for water witching, *Jour. New England Water Works Assoc.,* vol. 63, pp. 232–237, 1949.
37. Sayre, A. N., and E. L. Stephenson, The use of resistivity-methods in the

location of salt-water bodies in the El Paso, Texas, area, *Trans. Amer. Geophysical Union,* vol. 18, pp. 393–398, 1937.

38. Shepard, E. R., and A. E. Wood, Application of the seismic refraction method of subsurface exploration to flood-control projects, *Trans. Amer. Inst. Min. and Met. Engrs.,* vol. 138, pp. 312–325, 1940.
39. Spicer, H. C., Electrical resistivity studies of subsurface conditions near Antigo, Wisconsin, *U. S. Geological Survey Circ.* 181, Washington, D. C., 19 pp., 1952.
40. Stickel, J. F., Jr., L. E. Blakeley, and B. B. Gordon, Geophysics and water, *Jour. Amer. Water Works Assoc.,* vol. 44, pp. 23–35, 1952.
41. Sundberg, K., Effect of impregnating waters on electrical conductivity of soils and rocks, *Trans. Amer. Inst. Min. and Met. Engrs.,* vol. 97, pp. 367–391, 1932.
42. Swartz, J. H., Resistivity studies of some salt-water boundaries in the Hawaiian Islands, *Trans. Amer. Geophysical Union,* vol. 18, pp. 387–393, 1937.
43. Swartz, J. H., Geophysical investigations in the Hawaiian Islands, *Trans. Amer. Geophysical Union,* vol. 20, pp. 292–298, 1939.
44. Tattam, C. M., Application of electrical resistivity prospecting to ground water problems, *Colo. School of Mines Quart.,* vol. 32, no. 1, pp. 117–138, 1937.
45. Todd, D. K., Investigating ground water by applied geophysics, *Proc. Amer. Soc. Civil Engrs.,* vol. 81, sep. 625, 14 pp., 1955.
46. Volker, A., and J. Dijkstra, Détermination des salinités des eaux dans le sous-sol du Zuiderzee par prospection géophysique, *Geophysical Prospecting,* vol. 3, pp. 111–125, 1955.
47. Way, H. J. R., An analysis of the results of prospecting for water in Uganda by the resistivity method, *Trans. Inst. Min. and Met.,* vol. 51, pp. 285–310, 1942.
48. Wenner, F., A method of measuring earth-resistivity, *Bull. Bureau Standards,* vol. 12, Washington, D. C., pp. 469–478, 1916.
49. Woollard, G. P., and G. F. Hanson, Geophysical methods applied to geologic problems in Wisconsin, *Wis. Geological Survey Bull.* 78, Madison, 255 pp., 1954.
50. Workman, L. E., and M. M. Leighton, Search for ground-waters by the electrical resistivity-method, *Trans. Amer. Geophysical Union,* vol. 18, pp. 403–409, 1937.
51. Ziemke, P. C., Water witching, *Water and Sewage Works,* vol. 96, p. 136, 1949.

Subsurface Investigations of Ground Water

CHAPTER 10

Detailed and comprehensive study of ground water and conditions under which it occurs can only be made by subsurface investigations. Whether the information needed concerns an aquifer (its location, thickness, composition, permeability, and yield) or ground water (its location, movement, quality), quantitative data can be obtained from subsurface examinations. It should be emphasized that all such work classed as subsurface investigations is conducted entirely by personnel on the surface who operate equipment extending underground. Test drilling furnishes information on substrata in a vertical line from the surface. Logging techniques within a well can provide data on properties of the formation, water quality, size of well cavity, and rate of ground water movement. Evaluation of these factors aids in proper location, construction, and development of wells.

Test Drilling

Test drilling of small diameter holes to ascertain geologic and ground water conditions is useful in checking other means of investigation and to obtain assurance of underground conditions prior to well drilling.[27,30] Many times, if a test hole proves fruitful it is redrilled or reamed to a larger diameter to form a pumping well. Test holes also serve as observation wells for measuring water levels or for conducting pumping tests. Logs, or samples of rock strata encountered in drilling, enable aquifers to be delineated. A well log constructed from drilling samples is shown in Fig. 10.1. Water samples collected at the same time indicate water quality, while measurements of water levels will reveal confined or unconfined aquifers and circulation up or down the hole from one stratum to another.

Almost any well drilling method can be used for test drilling; however, in unconsolidated formations, cable tool and hydraulic rotary

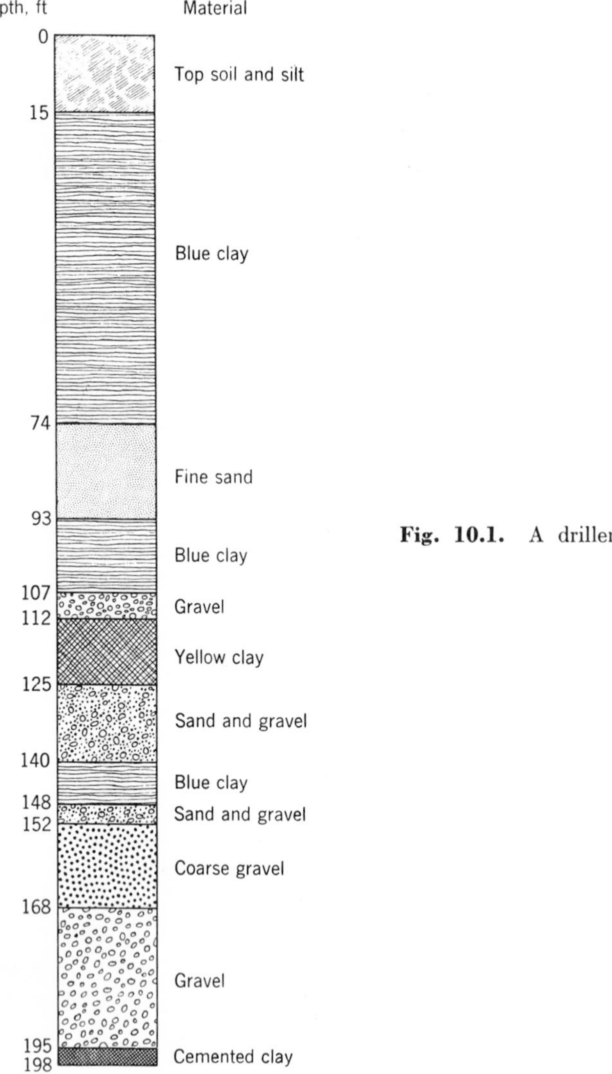

Fig. 10.1. A driller's well log.

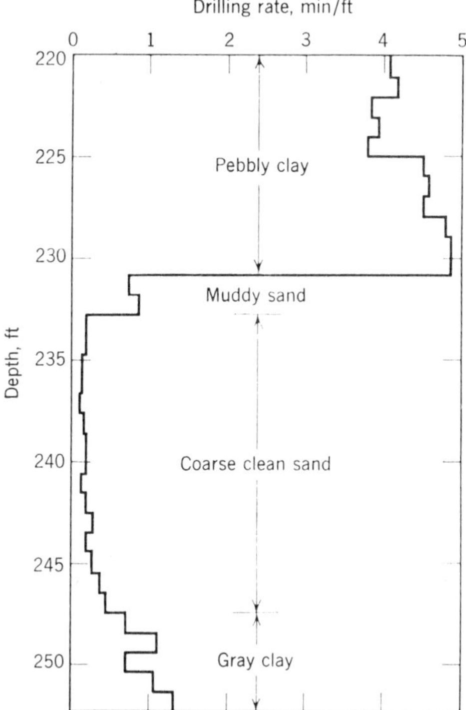

Fig. 10.2. Drilling-time log and strata penetrated (after Kirby [19]).

methods are most common (drilling methods are described in Chapter 5). The former is slower but provides more accurate samples from the bailer, whereas the latter is faster but it is sometimes difficult to determine the exact character of the formations. This fact is particularly true where fine-grained materials are encountered as these mix with the drilling fluid. For great depths and fairly uniform sands, the hydraulic rotary method is quicker and cheaper. Accurate samples can be obtained by pulling the drill stem and using a sampler at the bottom of the hole, or if intact cores are desired in exploratory drilling, a hollow-stem cutter head may be affixed to cut cylindrical cores. For test holes in soft ground and shallow depths, drilling with an auger is quick and economical. Jetting has proved to be an economic method of drilling shallow small-diameter holes for investigational purposes. The rapidity of the jetting operation combined with its lightweight portable equipment gives it important advantages, but the lack of good samples is a disadvantage. The choice of a method for test drilling depends on what information is necessary, the type of material encountered, drilling depth, and location.

A drilling-time log is a useful supplement to test drilling.[19] It consists of an accurate record of the time, in minutes and seconds, required to drill each foot of the hole. The technique is most practical with hydraulic rotary drilling although it is applicable to other methods as well. Because the texture of a stratum being penetrated largely governs the drilling rate, a drilling-time log may be readily interpreted in terms of formation types and depths. A portion of one obtained by the hydraulic rotary method is shown in Fig. 10.2 together with the log of the test hole based on cuttings.

Resistivity Logging

Within an uncased well, current and potential electrodes can be lowered to measure electrical resistivities of the surrounding media and to obtain a trace of their variation with depth. The result is a resistivity (or electric) log. Such a log is affected by fluid within a well, by well diameter, by the character of surrounding strata, and by ground water.

Of several possible methods for measuring underground resistivities, the multielectrode method is most commonly employed, as it minimizes effects of the drilling fluid and well diameter and also makes possible a direct comparison of several recorded resistivity curves.[28] Four electrodes, two for emitting current and two for potential measurement, constitute the system. Recorded curves are termed *normal* or *lateral*, depending on the electrode arrangement as shown in Fig. 10.3. In the normal arrangement the effective spacing is considered to be the distance AM (Fig. 10.3*a*) and the recorded curve is designated AM. The spacing for lateral (AO) curves is taken as the distance AO, measured between M and a point midway between the electrodes A and B (Fig. 10.3*b*). Sometimes a long normal curve (AM') is recorded based on the same electrode arrangement as the normal but with the distance AM increased several times. Similarly, a long lateral curve (AO') has a longer AO distance than the regular lateral. Boundaries of formations having different resistivities are located most readily with a short electrode spacing, whereas information on fluids in permeable formations can be obtained best with long spacings.

An electric log of a well usually consists of vertical traverses that record the normal and lateral, possibly either or both the long normal and long lateral, and the spontaneous potential curves (see following section). An illustration of an electric log is given as Fig. 10.4. Accurate interpretation of resistivity logs is difficult, requires careful analysis,[2] and is best done by specialists.

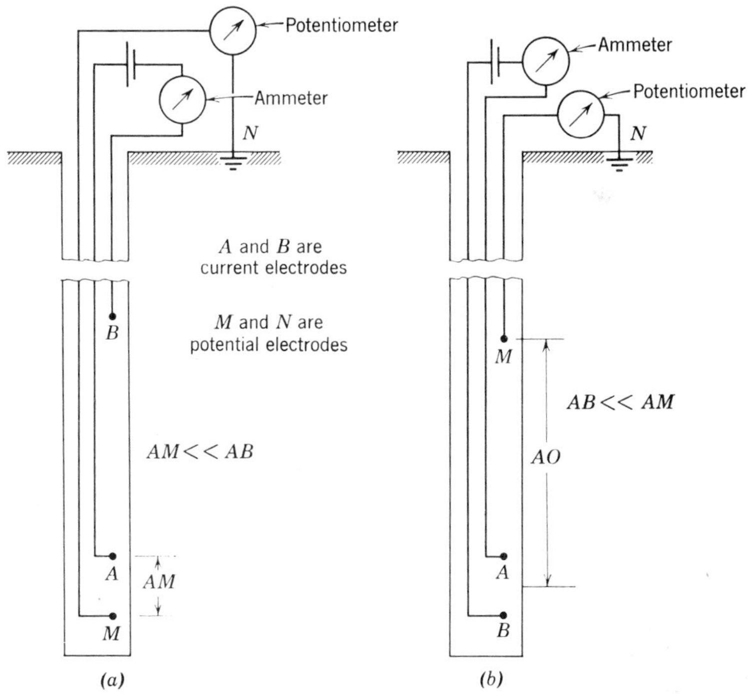

Fig. 10.3. Electrode arrangements for recording (*a*) normal and (*b*) lateral resistivity well logs.

Resistivity curves indicate the lithology of rock strata penetrated by the well and enable fresh and salt waters to be distinguished in the surrounding material.[4, 5, 9] In old wells exact locations of casings can be determined. Resistivity logs may be used to determine specific resistivities of strata, or they may indicate qualitatively changes of importance. As mentioned in the previous chapter, resistivity of an unconsolidated aquifer is controlled primarily by the porosity, packing, water resistivity, degree of saturation, and temperature. Although specific resistivity values cannot be stated for different aquifers, on a relative basis shales, clays, and salt water sands give low values, fresh water sands moderate to high values, and cemented sandstones and nonporous limestones high values.[15] Of course, casings and metallic objects will indicate very low resistivities. Correlation of rock samples, taken from wells during drilling, with resistivity curves furnishes a sound basis for interpretation of curves measured in nearby wells without available samples.

Resistivity of a ground water depends upon ionic concentration and

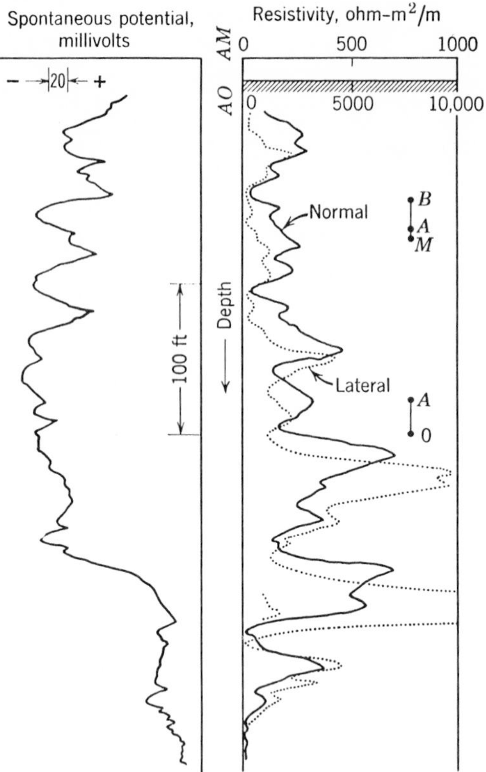

Fig. 10.4. Spontaneous potential and resistivity logs of a well (courtesy Schlumberger Well Surveying Corp.).

ionic mobility of the salt solution. This mobility is related to the molecular weight and electrical charge, so that large differences exist for various compounds. For example, the ion mobility of a sodium chloride solution is several times that of a comparable calcium carbonate solution. Poland and Morrison [25] showed that salinity-resistivity curves differ between sea water and ground water for this reason. Relationships between resistivity and total dissolved solids for several salt solutions and natural ground waters are shown in Fig. 10.5.

As the temperature of a ground water increases it has a greater ionic mobility, associated with a decrease in viscosity. Hence, an inverse relation exists between resistivity and temperature. The relation, expressed as a correction factor, is shown in Fig. 10.6. Resistivity at the measurement temperature when multiplied by the correction

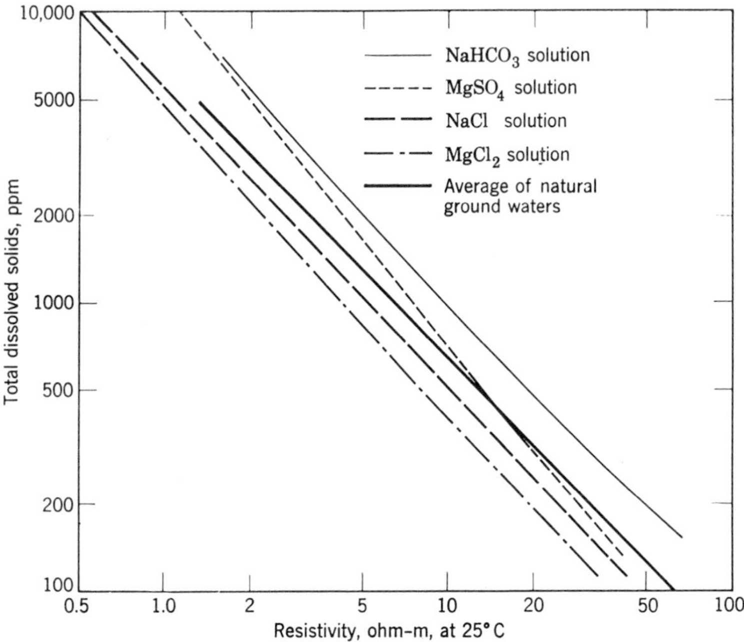

Fig. 10.5. Resistivity-concentration curves for various salt solutions and natural ground waters (after *Agric. Handbook* 60, U. S. Dept. Agric.).

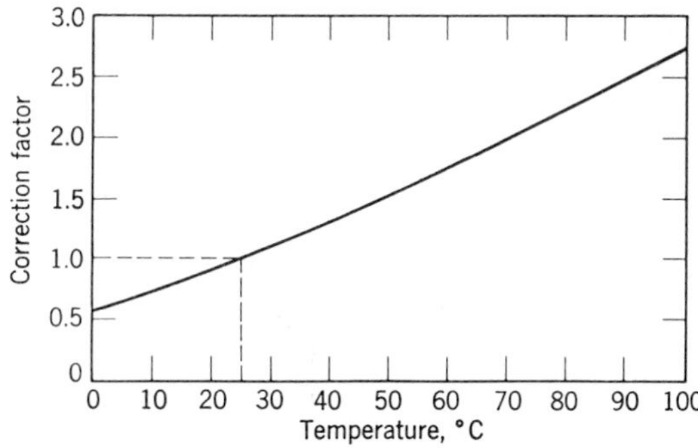

Fig. 10.6. Correction factor to convert resistivities at other temperatures to resistivities at 25° C (after Jones and Buford [16]).

factor for that temperature yields the resistivity at the standard temperature of 25° C.

From an investigation of Louisiana aquifers, Jones and Buford [16] extended the applicability of resistivity logs by establishing empirical relations for estimating aquifer porosity and the chemical analysis of a ground water. The porosity α was determined from [3]

$$\alpha^m = \frac{\rho_w}{\rho} \tag{10.1}$$

where ρ is the formation resistivity in place, ρ_w is the water resistivity, and m is a void-distribution coefficient, or cementation factor. Laboratory tests on a variety of sand samples from aquifers gave a median value for m of 1.56 and a range from 0.97 to 2.71. Estimating the chemical composition of ground water in an extensive aquifer is contingent upon the existence of a systematic variation of ion concentrations with total dissolved solids. Graphs showing ion concentrations versus total dissolved solids were prepared for each of the major Louisiana aquifers under study. As an example, data from one aquifer are shown in Fig. 10.7. Knowing the source aquifer and the measured aquifer resistivity, estimates of concentrations of important ions were prepared. Data from one representative determination, presented in Fig. 10.8 and the following example, indicate that the chemical composition estimate was satisfactory but that the porosity determination was not. Refinement of such procedures may increase the usefulness of resistivity logs.

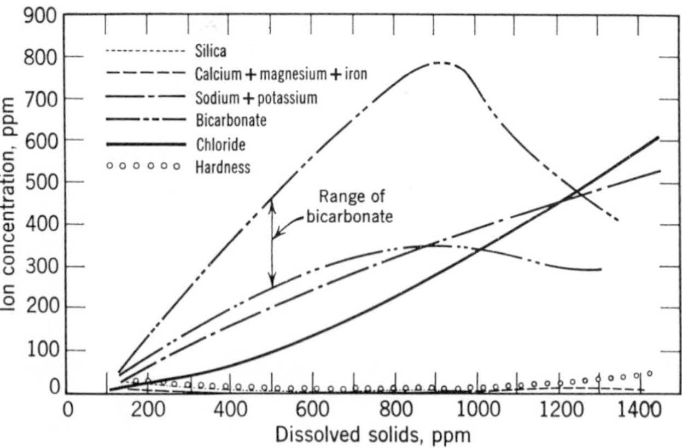

Fig. 10.7. Variation of ion concentration with total dissolved solids in a Louisiana aquifer (after Jones and Buford [16]).

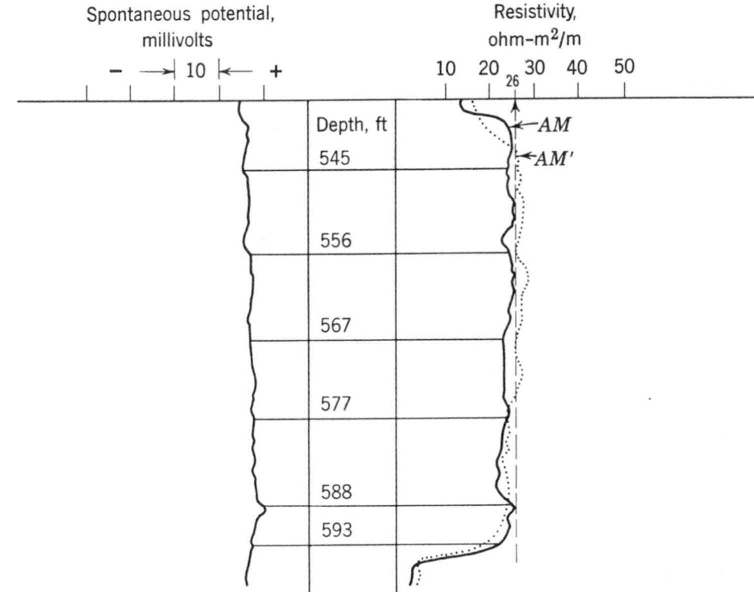

Fig. 10.8. Portion of electric log through an aquifer (after Jones and Buford [16]).

Example of Interpretation of Resistivity Log for Porosity and Chemical Composition (After Jones and Buford [16])

Well: USGS Na-57, Natchitoches, La.; aquifer temperature = 24.4° C.

Chemical Determination: Given ρ = 26 ohm-m²/m (from Fig. 10.8); m = 1.66 (average from formation samples); and α = 41.4 per cent (average from formation samples). From $\rho_w = \rho\alpha^m$ (Eq. 10.1), ρ_w = 6.01 ohm-m²/m. Applying a correction factor of 0.98 from Fig. 10.6, ρ_w at 25° C = 5.88 ohm-m²/m. From a graph (not shown) similar to Fig. 10.5 but for the ground water of the individual aquifer, total dissolved solids = 920 ppm. With this value and Fig. 10.7, the following chemical analysis is obtained:

	Hypothetical concentration, ppm (from Fig. 10.7)	Actual concentration, ppm (from lab. analysis)
SiO_2	20	. . .
Ca + Mg + Fe	20	5
Na + K	360	321
HCO_3	350–790	262
Cl	290	347
Total hardness as $CaCo_3$	14	12
Total dissolved solids	920	818

Porosity Determination: Given $\rho = 26$ ohm-m^2/m; $\rho_w = 5.58$ ohm-m^2/m (lab. measurement); and $m = 1.52$ (average for aquifer sands). From $\alpha^m = \rho_w/\rho$ (Eq. 10.1), $\alpha = 23.1$ per cent. Measured value = 41.4 per cent.

One of the most common uses of an electric log is to determine the proper place to set well screens. A log provides a basis for selecting proper lengths of screens and for setting them opposite the best formations. Because of this application, many well drillers have their own "loggers" for this purpose.

Resistivity logs are useful for estimating salt concentrations in well waters.[20] Salt may be present from connate sources leaking into wells or from sea water intrusion (see Chapter 12). Wells intersecting both fresh and salt water aquifers may act as sources of contamination because of the interconnection. The circulation under nonpumping conditions depends upon the relative hydrostatic heads, water densities, positions, aquifer thicknesses, and the physical structure and conditions of the well. Various hydrologic conditions for pumping and nonpumping wells are shown diagrammatically in Fig. 10.9 together with corresponding resistivity curves. Resistivity logs are also employed for locating aquifers, determining bed sequences, correlating aquifers, and estimating changes in ground water quality.

Potential Logging

The potential method measures natural electrical potentials found within the earth. Potentials are referred to also as self-potentials, spontaneous potentials, or simply "SP." Measurements, usually in millivolts, are obtained from a recording potentiometer connected to two like electrodes. Usually one electrode is lowered into the well and the other connected to the ground surface, as illustrated by electrodes M and N in Fig. 10.3.

Interpretation of potential logs to obtain maximum information is difficult[11,28] and should be done by specialists. The exact nature of phenomena giving rise to observed potentials is not entirely known.[10,22,23] Electrofiltration resulting from the flow of drilling mud into surrounding formations or of water through porous media[26] and electrochemical potentials arising from fluid concentration differences, as between drilling mud and ground water, are believed to be the major causes. Energy from chemical reactions occurring at formation boundaries, oxidation, and pH gradients also have been suggested as possible causes. Potential values range from zero to several hundred millivolts; positive values occur with flow from the formation into the well, negative values for the reverse flow. Potential

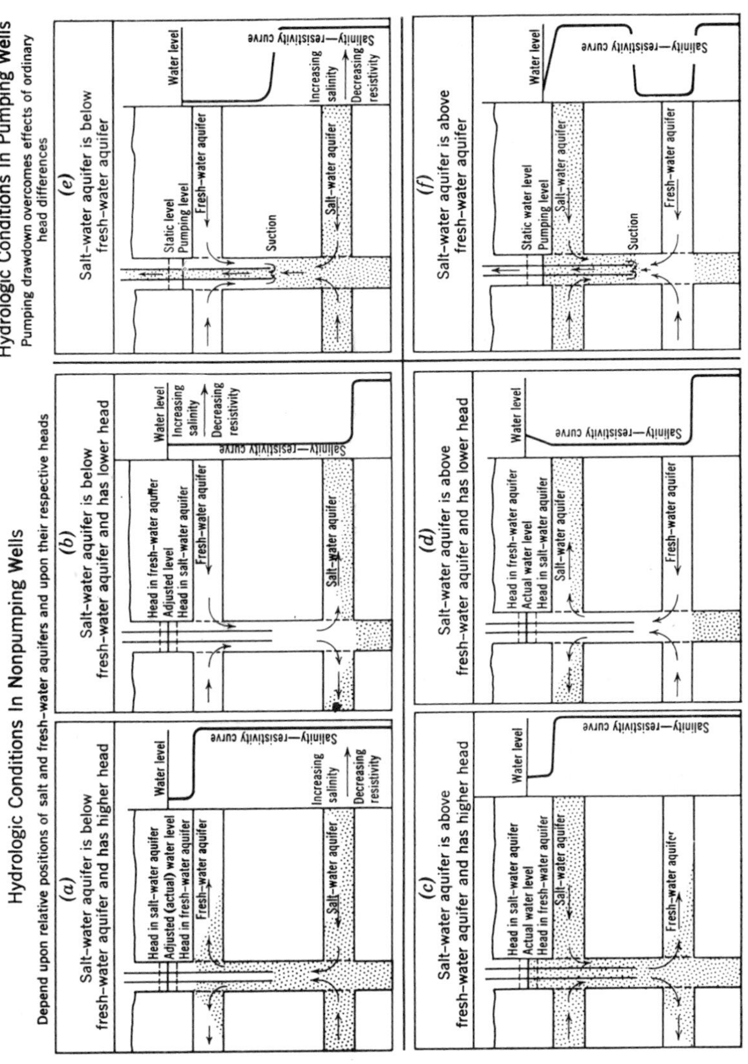

Fig. 10.9. Hydrologic conditions and resistivity curves for wells penetrating two aquifers of different salinities (after Poland and Morrison [25]).

logs are read in terms of positive and negative deflections from an arbitrary base line which might be either a permeable or impermeable formation of considerable thickness. Therefore, potential logs indicate permeable zones but not in absolute terms.[11] Frequently, changing the natural water level in a well will modify flows and also potential values, thereby enabling better definition to be achieved of permeable zones. In areas where there are no sharp contrasts in permeable zones, potential curves lack relief and are of little value. In urban and industrial areas, spurious earth currents may occur, such as from electric railroads, which interfere with potential logging.

Spontaneous potentials resulting from electrochemical potentials can be expressed by [28]

$$\mathrm{SP} = M \frac{\rho_f}{\rho_w} \tag{10.2}$$

where ρ_f is the drilling fluid resistivity in ohm-m, ρ_w is the ground water resistivity in ohm-m, and M is a factor dependent upon the chemical composition of the two fluids and upon the character of the formations adjoining an aquifer. From a study of potential logs in wells drilled by the hydraulic rotary method in the San Joaquin Valley, Calif., Bryan [9] found that a value of $M = 70$ proved satisfactory. Knowing M and measuring SP and ρ_f enables estimates of the ground water resistivity to be computed.

In practice, potential and resistivity logs are usually recorded together as shown in Fig. 10.4. The two logs often indicate the same subsurface conditions and thereby supplement one another; however, occasionally the pair of logs will furnish information not available directly from either alone.

Temperature Logging

A vertical traverse measurement of ground water temperature in a well can be readily obtained with a recording resistance thermometer. Such data may be of value in analyzing subsurface conditions. Ordinarily temperatures will increase with depth in accordance with the geothermal gradient, amounting to roughly 1° C for each 100 feet in depth. Departures from this normal gradient may provide information on circulation or geologic conditions in the well. Bays [7] pointed out that abnormally cold temperatures may indicate the presence of gas or, in deep wells, may suggest contamination from near the surface. Likewise, abnormally warm water may occur from water of deep-seated origin. Temperatures may indicate waters from different aquifers intersected by a well. In a few instances [8] temperature logs have aided the location of the approximate top of new concrete behind a casing as the heat generated during setting produces a marked temperature increase of the water within the casing.

Caliper Logging

Well diameters can be measured along a well by means of a hole caliper. One such instrument, developed by the Illinois Geological Survey,[8] consists of four arms extended by springs, and an electric resistor motivated by the arms. With the arms closed the instrument is lowered to the bottom of a well where the arms are released by detonating a small shot. The average hole diameter is then logged as a continuous graph by recording resistance changes while the caliper is run up the well. A hole caliper and the resulting log are shown in Fig. 10.10. Such data are useful for measuring diameters of old wells, for locating caving zones, and for furnishing information on casings.

Other Subsurface Methods

Current meters of several designs have been developed to measure flow velocities in wells.[12,13] Such instruments must not only be compact, but also must be sensitive to small water movements and their directions. Measurements reveal strata contributing water to the well, flow from one stratum to another via the well, and leaks around and through casings.

Certain other logging procedures in wells have been practiced to a limited extent. Fluid samplers which obtain water samples at specified depths measure water quality and serve as checks on electric logs. Photographs of interior well surfaces enable lithology and casings [17] to be inspected. Logs of pH have been run to study chemical characteristics of ground water. Radioactive logs, using gamma and neutron rays, have had wide application in the petroleum industry to analyze formations in oil wells. The method has been extended to water wells for estimating porosities and moisture contents.*

By tracer techniques, estimates of ground water velocity can be obtained. These methods are described in Chapter 3.

* For an excellent discussion of radioactive logging, as well as other logging methods, see: Jones, P. H., and H. E. Skibitzke, "Subsurface geophysical methods in ground-water hydrology," in *Advances in Geophysics* (H. E. Landsberg, ed.), vol. 3, Academic Press, New York, pp. 241–300, 1956.

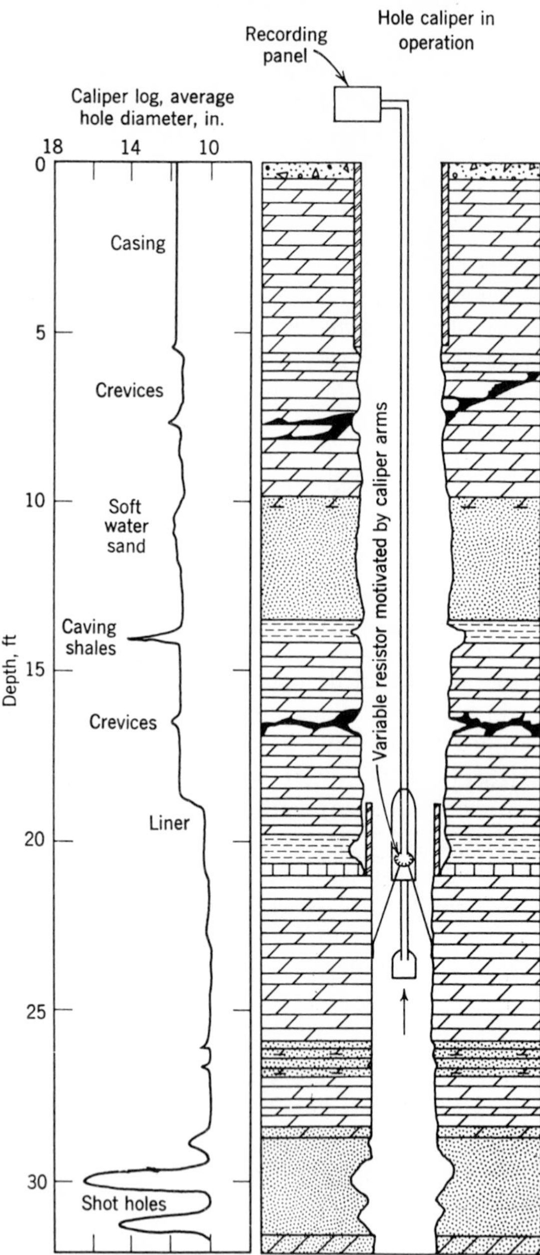

Fig. 10.10. Hole caliper and resulting log (after Bays and Folk [8]).

From pumping tests of wells, aquifer yield and permeability can be measured. Procedures for this purpose are discussed in Chapter 4.

References

1. Amer. Soc. Test. Materials, *Symposium on radioactive isotopes in soil investigations,* Philadelphia, 42 pp., 1952.
2. Anon., Interpretation handbook for resistivity logs, *Doc.* 4, Schlumberger Well Surveying Corp., Houston, Texas, 148 pp., 1951.
3. Archie, G. E., The electrical resistivity log as an aid in determining some reservoir characteristics, *Trans. Amer. Inst. Min. and Met. Engrs.,* vol. 146, pp. 54–62, 1942.
4. Baffa, J. J., The utilization of electrical and radioactivity methods of well logging for ground-water supply development, *Jour. New England Water Works Assoc.,* vol. 62, pp. 207–219, 1948.
5. Barnes, B. A., and P. P. Livingston, Value of the electrical log for estimating ground-water supplies and the quality of the ground water, *Trans. Amer. Geophysical Union,* vol. 28, pp. 903–911, 1947
6. Bays, C. A., New developments in ground-water exploration, *Jour. Amer. Water Works Assoc.,* vol. 35, pp. 911–920, 1943.
7. Bays, C. A., Prospecting for ground water—geophysical methods, *Jour. Amer. Water Works Assoc.,* vol. 42, pp. 947–956, 1950.
8. Bays, C. A., and S. H. Folk, Developments in the application of geophysics to ground-water problems, *Illinois Geological Survey Circ.* 108, Urbana, 25 pp., 1944.
9. Bryan, F. L., Application of electric logging to water well problems, *Water Well Jour.,* vol. 4, no. 1, pp. 3–7, 1950.
10. Dickey, P. A., Natural potentials in sedimentary rocks, *Trans. Amer. Inst. Min. and Met. Engrs.,* vol. 164, pp. 256–266, 1945.
11. Doll, H. G., The S. P. log: theoretical analysis and principles of interpretation, *Trans. Amer. Inst. Min. and Met. Engrs.,* vol. 179, pp. 146–185, 1949.
12. Erickson, C. R., Vertical water velocity in deep wells, *Jour. Amer. Water Works Assoc.,* vol. 38, pp. 1263–1272, 1946.
13. Fiedler, A. G., The Au deep-well current meter and its use in the Roswell artesian basin, New Mexico, *U. S. Geological Survey Water-Supply Paper* 596, Washington, D. C., pp. 24–32, 1928.
14. Heiland, C. A., Prospecting for water with geophysical methods, *Trans. Amer. Geophysical Union,* vol. 18, pp. 574–588, 1937.
15. Heiland, C. A., *Geophysical exploration,* Prentice-Hall, New York, 1013 pp., 1940.
16. Jones, P. H., and T. B. Buford, Electric logging applied to ground water exploration, *Geophysics,* vol. 16, pp. 115–139, 1951.
17. Kelly, S. F., Photographing rock-walls and casings of boreholes, *Trans. Amer. Geophysical Union,* vol. 20, pp. 269–271, 1939.
18. Kent, D. F., Techniques used in mine-water problems of the east Tennessee zinc district, *U. S. Geological Survey Circ.* 71, Washington, D. C., 9 pp., 1950.
19. Kirby, M. E., Improve your work with drilling-time logs, *Johnson National Drillers Jour.,* vol. 26, no. 6, pp. 6–7, 14, 1954.

20. Livingston, P. P., and W. Lynch, Methods of locating salt-water leaks in water wells, *U. S. Geological Survey Water-Supply Paper* 796-A, Washington, D. C., 20 pp., 1937.

21. Maher, J. C., and P. H. Jones, Ground water exploration on the Natchitoches area, *U. S. Geological Survey Water-Supply Paper* 968-D, Washington, D. C., 52 pp., 1949.

22. McCardell, W. M., W. O. Winsauer, and M. Williams, Origin of the electric potential observed in wells, *Trans. Amer. Inst. Min. and Met. Engrs.*, vol. 198, pp. 41–50, 1953.

23. Mounce, W. D., and W. M. Rust, Jr., Natural potentials in well logging, *Trans. Amer. Inst. Min. and Met. Engrs.*, vol. 164, pp. 288–294, 1945.

24. Mylander, H. A., Oil-field techniques used for water-well drilling, *Jour. Amer. Water Works Assoc.*, vol. 45, pp. 764–772, 1953.

25. Poland, J. F., and R. B. Morrison, An electrical resistivity-apparatus for testing well-waters, *Trans. Amer. Geophysical Union*, vol. 21, pp. 35–46, 1940.

26. Ramachandar Rao, M. B., Self-potential anomalies due to subsurface water flow at Garimenapenta, Madras State, India, *Min. Eng.*, vol. 5, pp. 400–403, 1953.

27. Rose, N. A., W. N. White, and P. P. Livingston, Exploratory water-well drilling in the Houston district, Tex., *U. S. Geological Survey Water-Supply Paper* 889-D, Washington, D. C., 25 pp., 1944.

28. Stratton, E. F., and R. D. Ford, Electric logging, in *Subsurface geologic methods* (L. W. LeRoy, ed.), 2nd ed., Colorado School of Mines, Golden, pp. 364–392, 1951.

29. Texas Agric. and Mech. College, Well logging methods conference, *Texas Eng. Exp. Sta. Bull.* 93, College Station, 171 pp., 1946.

30. Thorpe, T. W., Prospecting for ground water—test drilling, *Jour. Amer. Water Works Assoc.*, vol. 42, pp. 957–960, 1950.

31. Walstrom, J. E., The quantitative aspects of electric log interpretation, *Trans. Amer. Inst. Min. and Met. Engrs.*, vol. 195, pp. 47–58, 1952.

Artificial Recharge of Ground Water

CHAPTER 11

In order to increase the natural supply of ground water, man has attempted to artificially recharge ground water basins. Artificial recharge may be defined as augmenting the natural infiltration of precipitation or surface water into underground formations by some method of construction, spreading of water, or by artificially changing natural conditions. A variety of methods have been developed, including water spreading, recharging through pits, excavations, wells, and shafts, and pumping to induce recharge from surface water bodies.[15,16,34,46] The choice of a particular method is governed by local topographic, geologic, and soil conditions, the quantity of water to be recharged, and the ultimate water use. In special circumstances land value, water quality, or even climate may be an important factor. A comprehensive annotated bibliography on the subject has been published by the U. S. Geological Survey.[72]

Artificial Recharge in the United States

Recharging in the United States began near the end of the nineteenth century; since then recharge installations have steadily increased. Quantities of water from various sources artificially recharged during 1955 were summarized by MacKichan[44] and are shown in Table 11.1. California recharged 375 million gallons per day (mgd) of surface

TABLE 11.1 Artificial Recharge * of Ground Water in the United States, 1955

(After MacKichan [44])

Source	Quantity, mgd
Air conditioning return	41
Industrial wastes	49
Surface water	540
Public water supplies	71
Total	701

* Excluding induced recharge.

water, or more than half of all water artificially recharged in the United States. The national total amounts to 1.5 per cent of the total ground water use in the United States (see Chapter 1).

Water Spreading

The term *water spreading* refers to the releasing of water over the ground surface in order to increase the quantity of water infiltrating into the ground and percolating to the water table. Although field studies of spreading have shown that many factors govern the rate at which water will enter the soil, from a quantitative standpoint, area of recharge and length of time water is in contact with soil are most important. Spreading efficiency is measured in terms of the recharge rate, expressed as the velocity of downward water movement over the wetted area. In the United States the unit, feet per day (or its numerical equivalent, acre-feet/acre/day) is commonly employed.

Spreading methods may be classified as flooding, basin, ditch or furrow, natural channel, and irrigation. Each is described briefly in the following sections.

Flooding Method. In relatively flat topography, water may be diverted to spread evenly over a large area.[48] In practice, canals and earthen distributing gullies are usually needed to release the water at intervals over the upper end of the flooding area. It is desirable to form a thin sheet of water over the land, which moves at a minimum velocity to avoid disturbing the soil. Tests indicate that highest infiltration rates occur on areas with undisturbed vegetation and soil covering. Compared with other spreading methods, flood spreading costs least for land preparation. In order to control the water at all times, banks or ditches should surround the entire flooding area. To obtain maximum efficiency at least one man must be on the grounds during flooding operations, as frequently movement of a few shovelfuls of dirt will effectively increase the wetted area.

Basin Method. Water may be recharged by releasing it into basins which are formed by excavation or by construction of dikes or small dams. Horizontal dimensions of such basins vary from a few feet to several hundred feet. The most common system consists of individual basins fed by pumped water from nearby surface water sources. Silt-free water aids in preventing sealing of basins during submergence. Even so, most basins require periodic cleaning by scraping of the bottom surface when dry.

In California, series of basins have been successfully built and operated in abandoned stream channels. In alluvial plains, basins may parallel existing channels with water being led into the upper basin by canal. As the first basin fills, it spills into the second, the process being repeated through the entire chain of basins (see Fig. 11.1). From the lowest basin, excess water is returned to the main channel. By this method spreading is accomplished on what otherwise may be waste land and permits water contact over 75 to 80 per cent of the gross area.

Basins, because of their general feasibility, efficient use of space, and ease of maintenance, are the most favored method of artificial recharge.

Fig. 11.1. Spreading basins paralleling the Arroyo Seco in Pasadena, Calif. (courtesy Los Angeles County Flood Control District).

TABLE 11.2 **Representative Spreading Basin Recharge Rates** [72]

Location	Rate, ft/day
Santa Cruz River, Ariz.	1.1–3.8
Los Angeles County, Calif.	2.2–6.2
Madera, Calif.	1.0–4.1
San Gabriel River, Calif.	1.9–5.4
Santa Ana River, Calif.	1.8–9.6
Santa Clara Valley, Calif.	1.4–7.3
Tulare County, Calif.	0.4
Ventura County, Calif.	1.2–1.8
Des Moines, Iowa	1.5
Newton, Mass.	4.3
East Orange, N. J.	0.4
Princeton, N. J.	0.1
Long Island, N. Y.	3.1
Richland, Wash.	7.7

No exact statement can be made regarding recharge rates; however, Table 11.2 summarizes representative rates obtained for basins in the United States.

Ditch or Furrow Method. In this method water is distributed to a series of ditches, or furrows, which are shallow, flat-bottomed, and

Fig. 11.2. Spreading ditches in Tujunga Wash, Los Angeles, Calif. (courtesy City of Los Angeles Dept. of Water and Power).

Fig. 11.3. Channel spreading with rock-and-wire check dams in Cucamonga Creek near Upland, Calif. (courtesy D. C. Muckel).

closely spaced to obtain maximum water contact area. Figure 11.2 shows typical spreading ditches on an alluvial plain. Gradients of major feeder ditches should be sufficient to carry suspended material through the system. Deposition of fine-grained material clogs soil surface openings. Although a variety of ditch plans have been devised, a particular plan should be tailored to the configuration of the local area. A collecting ditch is needed at the lower end of each area to convey excess water back into the main stream channel. The method is adaptable to irregular terrain but seldom provides water contact area equal to that obtainable with basins.

Natural Channel Method. Water spreading in a natural stream channel may use any of the three methods described above. Where a flood hazard may result from large channel barriers forming basins, flooding or ditch methods are preferable. Whatever method is adopted, the primary purpose is to extend the time and area over which water is recharged from a naturally influent channel. In California, small check dams have successfully distributed streams over wide flat channels.[32,71] Dams are built of reinforced concrete or of rock and wire.[48] The effect of check dams in distributing water over a channel is shown in Fig. 11.3.

Channel spreading can also be conducted without specific spreading works. In streams having storage reservoirs primarily for flood control, releases of clear water may be entirely recharged into downstream reaches. A majority of the spreading works in and near Los Angeles County, Calif.,* are part of an integrated water conservation and flood protection plan.[23,38,39,41,64]

Irrigation Method. In irrigated areas water is sometimes spread by irrigating with excess water during dormant, winter, or nonirrigating seasons. The method requires no additional cost for land preparation as the distribution system is already installed. Even keeping irrigation canals full will contribute to recharge by seepage from the canals. Where a large portion of the water supply is pumped, the method has the advantage of raising the water table and consequently reducing power costs.

Research on Water Spreading

The economy of water spreading hinges upon maintenance of a high infiltration rate. Typical rate curves, however, show a pronounced tendency to decrease with time. To determine the cause of this decrease and how to counteract it has led to extensive research programs. A variety of soil treatments and operational methods have been undertaken to study the problem.

In Fig. 11.4 is shown a typical curve of recharge rate versus time. The initial decrease is attributed to dispersion and swelling of soil particles after wetting, the subsequent increase accompanies elimination of entrapped air by solution in passing water, while the final gradual decrease results from microbial growths clogging the soil pores.[1,12,21,49] Laboratory tests with sterile soil and water give nearly constant maximum recharge rates, thereby substantiating the effect of microbial growths.

On a cooperative basis the U. S. Agricultural Research Service has conducted an extensive series of field tests in California to evaluate factors governing recharge rates.[49,60,61] Generally, recharge rates decrease as the mean particle size of soil on a spreading area decreases. Efforts to maintain soil pores free for water passage have led to additions of organic matter and chemicals to the soil as well as to growing vegetation on the spreading area. Cotton-gin trash,† for example, when mixed with soil and given a moist incubation period was effec-

* Los Angeles County Flood Control District reported that 3100 acres of spreading grounds were in operation in Los Angeles County during 1957. The average recharge capacity over the gross area exceeded 1.2 ft per day. For the 25-year period, 1932–1957, an average of 56,500 acre-ft of water was recharged annually.

† Cotton-gin trash consists of boll hulls, leaves, stems, a few seeds, and a small amount of lint.

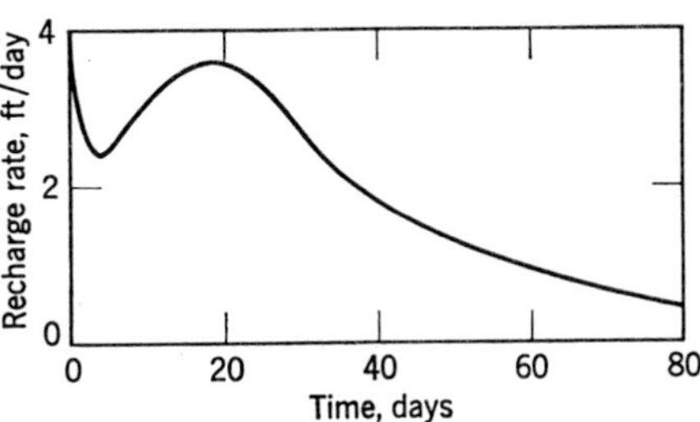

Fig. 11.4. Typical recharge rate variation with time for water spreading on undisturbed soil (after Muckel[49]).

tive in increasing rates. Of several grasses tried, Bermuda grass best survived prolonged wetting and improved intake rates. Chemical soil conditioners, which tend to aggregate the soil, show promise in soils of certain textures. Alternating wet and dry periods on a basin generally furnishes a greater total recharge than does continuous spreading in spite of the fact that water is in contact with the soil for as little as one-half of the total time. Drying kills microbial growths, and this, combined with scarification of the soil surface, reopens the soil pores.

Other factors contribute to recharge rates. Surface compaction by heavy equipment in preparing a spreading area may adversely affect infiltration. Studies in small ponds have confirmed that infiltration rates are directly proportional to head of water.[59] Where less pervious strata lie below the surface stratum, the recharge rate depends on the rate of subsurface lateral flow. Hence, spreading only in narrow, widely spaced strips recharges nearly as much water as spreading over an entire area.[60, 62] Sunlight, affecting bacterial action in soil, water temperature, and algal growths in water, has not been fully evaluated as a recharge factor. A high water temperature with accompanying low viscosity should increase infiltration, but this effect may be more than compensated by the stimulation to bacterial activity. Water containing silt or clay is known to clog soil pores, leading to rapid reductions in recharge rates. Rapid sand filtration to eliminate fine material may be economically justified where municipal water supplies are involved.[34] Wave action in large, shallow ponds may stir bottom sediments and seal pores which would otherwise remain open. Water quality can be an important factor; thus, recharging a water of high sodium content tends to deflocculate colloidal soil particles and thereby hinder water passage. Because high water tables limit the downward flow of recharged water, they should be at least 10 to 20 feet below spreading surfaces.

Sewage Recharge

Sewage constitutes a valuable source of water for recharging ground water. In the present day when conservation, reclamation, and reuse of water are receiving increasing emphasis, sewage recharge is and has been practiced in a variety of ways throughout the world. Septic tanks act as small recharge units. Sewage farms, in which treated sewage irrigates forage and orchard crops, are common in European countries and in the Western United States.[50] Although public opinion generally opposes the idea of reusing sewage waters, it seems likely that through education and conclusive demonstrations of the safety and advantages of the method, based on research investigations, this attitude will change in the future.

Because of higher concentrations of suspended matter and bacteria, spreading rates for sewage effluents are lower than for fresh water. Typical rates for sewage farms are the order of 0.01 to 0.09 ft per day. In recent years several investigations have been undertaken in California to evaluate the technical feasibility of sewage spreading for water reclamation.[5,18] At Lodi, results with final effluents from a sewage treatment works gave a rate of about 0.5 ft per day.[29] Comparable values of 1.0 ft per day at Whittier, 1.2 ft per day at Azusa,[66] and 0.2 to 0.8 ft per day on lysimeter tests involving five California soils have been measured.[56] Most studies recommend alternate wetting and drying periods of 7 to 14 days. With cultivation during the dry cycle, maximum spreading rates can be obtained. Tests for *B. coli* bacteria beneath the spreading areas show that natural filtration through fine-grained materials makes the water potable after only a few feet of percolation.

Little is known concerning the possibilities of sewage recharge through wells. Recharge experiments through a well at Richmond, Calif., showed a steady clogging of the well with settled sewage, whereas this did not occur with fresh water.[19] The clogging rate, indicated by an increase in the recharge well head pressure, was proportional to the suspended solids content of the sewage water. Biological growths and gas binding of the aquifer by fine gas bubbles also contributed to the clogging. Continuous operation was possible by weekly chlorine injection and redevelopment by pumping 4 or 5 per cent of the recharged water.

Recharging waste waters from a vegetable quick-freezing plant near Seabrook, N. J., has been accomplished by spraying the effluent from large rotating nozzles over a wooded area.[45] Recharge rates of up to 0.53 ft per day have been maintained through permeable sandy soil. The applied water becomes potable after filtering through the ground. Marked rises in the water table accompany the recharging, but the increased storage is largely dissipated by subsurface outflow before the beginning of the next season.

Recharge Through Pits and Shafts

Water spreading cannot be effective in areas where subsurface strata restrict the downward passage of water. In California, for example, hardpans and clay layers are common deterrents to recharge by spreading. In areas where the impervious layer is not too far below the ground surface, recharging can be conducted by digging pits or shafts.[55] If these penetrate to more permeable substrata, water can percolate directly into an aquifer. Because pits and shafts cost more to construct and recharge smaller volumes of water than do spreading areas, they have limited application. Abandoned gravel pits have been utilized occasionally for this purpose.

An important contribution to knowledge of pit recharge is being made by a project conducted by the Illinois State Water Survey at Peoria.[69,70] Water for industrial and municipal use is obtained from gravels and sands in the Illinois River valley. Increased pumping demands created a serious overdraft in the area, but recharge from the river was small because of silt deposits on the river bed. As preliminary tests indicated that recharging might improve the situation,

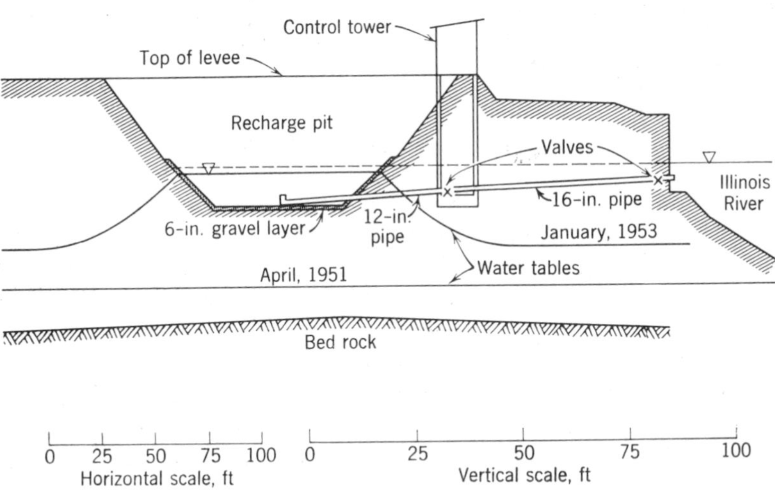

Fig. 11.5. Cross-section of recharge pit at Peoria, Ill. (after Suter[70]).

TABLE 11.3 **Operating Data for Peoria, Illinois, Recharge Pit**

(From Illinois State Water Survey)

Season	1951–52	1952–53	1953–54	1954–55	1955–56
Total operating time, days	146	208	199	165	196
Total inflow, acre-ft	795	659	641	1120	1300
Average inflow, cfs	2.8	1.6	1.6	3.4	3.3
Average chlorination, ppm	3.6	8.8	8.8	4.0	5.3
Accumulated silt, tons	64	89	78	131	159

a full-scale recharge study was begun in 1951. A pit with bottom dimensions 40 ft by 62.5 ft and 30 ft deep was excavated near the Illinois River (see Fig. 11.5). A pipe feeds river water by gravity to a control tower containing chlorination equipment, metering devices, and control valves. The pit is operated only during the cold-water period of the river (usually October to May) in order to keep ground water temperature below 60° F. Table 11.3 summarizes operating results for five seasons. The increased inflow beginning with the 1954–55 season accompanied the replacement of a 6-inch sand layer on the bottom and sides of the pit with uniform pea gravel. The pit is cleaned periodically, as required, with a suction cleaner which removes the silt layer collected on the bottom. The successful results achieved with this pit can be attributed to the porous formations which the pit penetrates, the large ground water demand in the vicinity which maintains a low water table, chlorination of the water, and close supervision of the pit's recharge capacity.

Recharge through Wells

A recharge well * may be defined as a well which admits water from the surface to underground formations. Its flow is the reverse of a pumping well, but its construction may or may not be the same. Well recharging is practicable where deep confined aquifers must be recharged, or where economy of space, such as in urban areas, is an important consideration.[65]

If water is admitted into a well, a cone of recharge will be formed which is similar in shape but is the reverse of a cone of depression surrounding a pumping well. The equation for the curve can be derived

* Recharge wells are known also as injection wells, inverted wells, diffusion wells, disposal wells, and even dumb wells.

with the Dupuit assumptions in a similar manner to that done for a pumping well (see Chapter 4). For a confined aquifer with water being recharged into a completely penetrating well at a rate Q_r, the expression

$$Q_r = \frac{2\pi Kb(h_w - h_0)}{\ln (r_0/r_w)} \tag{11.1}$$

is applicable. Symbols are identified in Figure 11.6*a*. For a recharge well penetrating an unconfined aquifer (see Fig. 11.6*b*),

$$Q_r = \frac{\pi K(h_w^2 - h_0^2)}{\ln (r_0/r_w)} \tag{11.2}$$

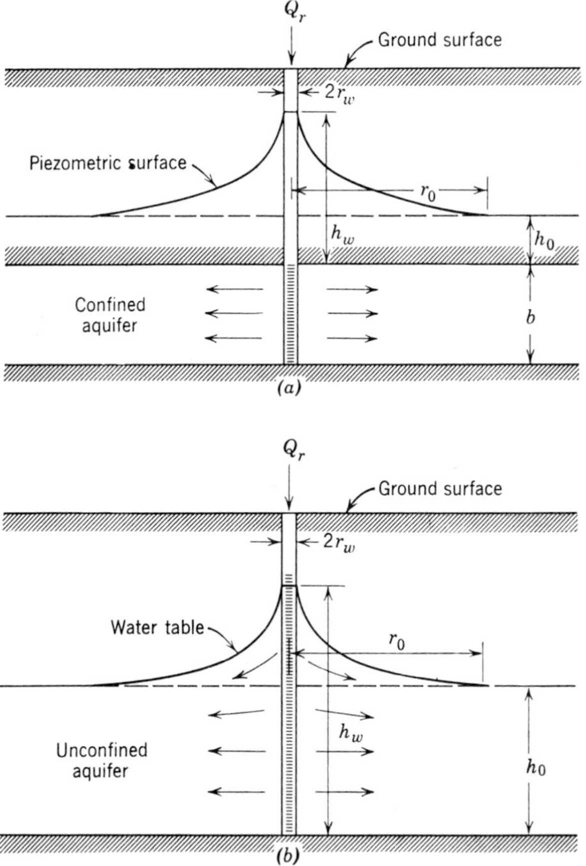

Fig. 11.6. Radial flow from recharge wells penetrating (*a*) confined and (*b*) unconfined aquifers.

By comparing the discharge equations for pumping and recharge wells, it might be anticipated that the recharge capacity would equal the pumping capacity of a well if the recharge cone has dimensions equivalent to the cone of depression. Field measurements, however, rarely support this reasoning; recharge rates seldom equal pumping rates. The difficulty lies in the fact that pumping and recharging differ by more than a simple change of flow direction.

As water is pumped from a well fine material present in the aquifer is carried through the coarser particles surrounding the well and into the well. But contrariwise, any silt carried by water into a recharge well is filtered out and tends to clog the aquifer surrounding the well. Similarly, recharge water may carry large amounts of dissolved air, tending to reduce the permeability of the aquifer by air binding. Recharge water may contain bacteria which can form growths on the well screen and the surrounding formation, thereby reducing the effective flow area. Chemical constituents of the recharge water may differ sufficiently from the normal ground water to cause undesired chemical reactions, for example, base exchange in aquifers containing sizable fractions of silt and clay. These factors all act to reduce recharge rates; as a result, well recharging has been limited to a few areas where local conditions and experience have shown the practicality of the method.[20]

Measured inflow rates of recharge wells at several locations in the United States are tabulated in Table 11.4. In most cases these figures

TABLE 11.4 Average Well Recharge Rates[72]

Location	Rate, cfs
Fresno, Calif.	0.2–0.9
Los Angeles, Calif.	1.2
Manhattan Beach, Calif.	0.4–1.0
Orange Cove, Calif.	0.7–0.9
San Fernando Valley, Calif.	0.3
Tulare County, Calif.	0.12
Orlando, Fla.	0.2–21
Mud Lake, Idaho	0.2–1.0
Jackson County, Mich.	0.1
Newark, N. J.	0.6
Long Island, N. Y.	0.2–2.2
El Paso, Texas	2.3
Williamsburg, Va.	0.3

represent average rates based upon continued operation. Recharge wells, like spreading areas, may show initial large intake rates followed by nearly constant or slowly decreasing values. Greatest intake rates are found in extremely porous formations such as limestones and lavas.

It should be noted that supply wells can alternate as recharge wells. During World War II, distilleries in Louisville, Ky., recharged municipal water into their own pumping wells as an emergency measure to alleviate a serious ground water overdraft.[3,30]

Two outstanding examples of well recharging are described in the following sections.

The Manhattan Beach Recharge Project

A comprehensive well recharge investigation, sponsored by the State of California, was begun in 1951 at Manhattan Beach, Calif.[9,10] The purpose of the project was to determine the feasibility of establishing a fresh-water barrier to prevent further intrusion of sea water in a confined aquifer (see Chapter 12). Nine 12-in. diameter wells for recharging were drilled at 500-ft intervals to form a line near and paralleling the coast, while 54 observation wells were located in the vicinity of the well line. The wells penetrated an extensive confined aquifer about 110 ft thick and lying about 100 ft below ground surface (see Fig. 12.9). The aquifer is composed of fine sand and gravel and has a coefficient of permeability in the range 800–1500.

Recharging began early in 1953 with treated Colorado River water by applying heads of 40 to 50 ft of water to the wells. Injection rates of up to 1 cfs per well were obtained. In order to prevent the formation of slime-forming bacteria in and around the well, chlorination of 5 to 10 ppm was required. Recharging has continued successfully after several years of operation.

A lesson learned from the Manhattan Beach project was the need for properly constructed recharge wells. Shortly after recharging began, a sudden caving occurred over a considerable area adjacent to one well casing. Similar actions, or evidences thereof, were observed at other recharge wells. Settlements were attributed to a high pumping rate for development of the wells, causing creation of large caverns surrounding the perforated well casings in the aquifer. Gravel packing was recommended for new recharge wells. A gravel envelope around a well reduces entrance velocities from the aquifer (because of the larger diameter) and settles to fill any cavities which may tend to form around the well during development. Gravel can be replenished at the surface as needed. It was also found that sealing of the wells by grouting at the clay layer above the aquifer was necessary to prevent movement of water upward around the casing during recharging.

Recharge Wells on Long Island, New York

More than 1100 recharge wells have been drilled on Long Island, N. Y., since 1933.[14,35,42] Usual recharge rates fall in the range 0.2 to 0.5 cfs. These wells were drilled to comply with a New York State Water Power and Control Commission requirement that water pumped from new wells for cooling and air conditioning must be returned to the aquifer from which it is withdrawn. The results of this policy have shown the conditions favoring or limiting successful recharge well operation in unconsolidated formations. A typical supply and recharge well installation is illustrated by Fig. 11.7.

Two basic types of recharge wells have been drilled on Long Island —the dry type and the wet type. The dry type consists of a perforated cased hole ending above the water table, whereas the wet type (Fig.

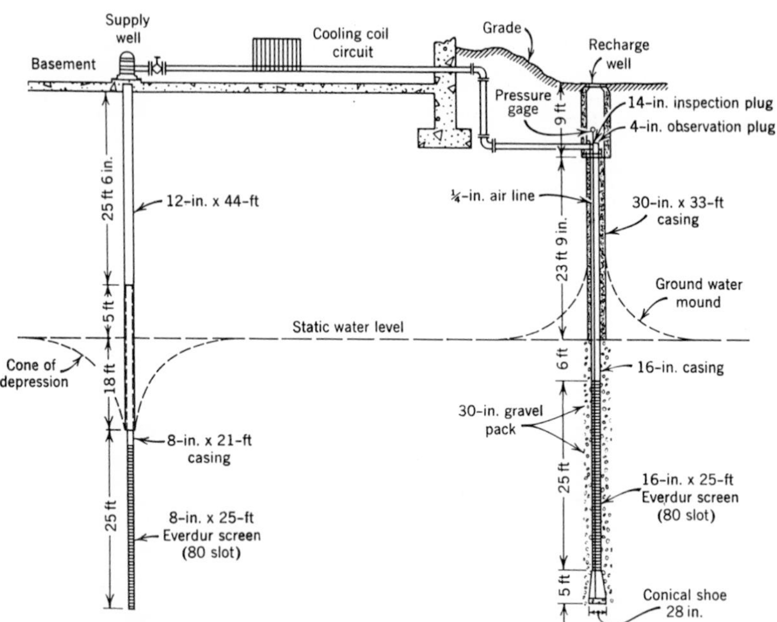

Fig. 11.7. A typical supply and recharge well installation for cooling purposes on Long Island, N. Y. (after Johnson [35]).

11.7) has screened casing extending to below the water table. The dry type of well permits some heat dissipation of the returned warm water before it reaches the water table, and also, because it is shallower, is cheaper to construct. On the other hand, excessive clogging is reported in some of these wells, believed to be caused by release of dissolved gases as water leaves the wells and by water-oxygen contact in the surrounding unsaturated strata. Another important disadvantage of the dry type of well is that conventional redevelopment methods are not effective. The wet type of well is regarded as the more successful of the two, and about three-quarters of all Long Island recharge wells are of this type.

Experience showed that wells having a 36-in. outer casing, gravel filters, and an inner well screen are most satisfactory. Recharged water should be as free of sediment as possible. Thus, it has been estimated that 1 oz of silt in 100 gal of water would deposit over 11 tons of silt in a typical recharge well during a single season. Fortunately, most water for cooling and air conditioning has little opportunity to collect suspended matter. Recharge and supply wells should be separated as far as possible, both horizontally and vertically, to minimize direct recirculation of ground water.

With the concentration of recharge wells on western Long Island, one problem of concern is the effect of continually recharging warm water into the aquifer.[13] Temperatures of recharged water average 2° to 20° F higher than of water pumped from the ground. A gradual rise of ground water temperatures has been noted, the largest occurring, as might be anticipated, in the most heavily recharged areas.

Recharge Wells for Storm Drainage

In a few localities recharge wells replace sewer systems to dispose of storm runoff.[2] Noteworthy examples are the cities of Orlando, Fla.[73] and Fresno, Calif.[31] At Orlando, wells penetrate from 120 to 1000 ft into limestone, have casings to depths of 70 to 400 ft, and range from 5 to 18 in. in diameter. Capacities extend from 0.2 to several cubic feet per second. Although considerable rubbish is carried into the wells, the cavernous limestone formations seldom become clogged. The water table lies about 30 to 50 ft below ground surface. A danger of pollution exists in such formations, which do not provide adequate filtration, if subsurface water supplies are located nearby.

At Fresno, several hundred wells were installed at gutter inlets to solve an acute storm drainage problem. Thirty-inch diameter wells are bored 30 to 40 ft deep through alluvium, and backfilled with gravel around 8-in. casings. The bottoms of the wells are located at least 10 ft above the normal water table to prevent contamination of underground water supplies. To minimize clogging and to provide for ease of maintenance, a special filter system is built into the top of each well. This includes a perforated metal basket at the entrance to each well which can be cleaned rapidly of leaves and debris after major storms. The average recharge well capacity is about 0.2 cfs for a 24-hr period. With a routine maintenance schedule established, the wells have successfully solved the city's drainage problem; additional wells are constructed as required.

Induced Recharge

Direct methods of artificial recharge described above involve the conveyance of surface water to some point where it enters the ground. Distinguished from these is the method of induced recharge, accomplished by withdrawing ground water at a location adjacent to a lake or stream so that lowering of the ground water level will induce water to enter the ground from the surface source. The schematic cross-sections of a river valley in Fig. 11.8 show flow patterns with and without induced infiltration from a stream. On the basis of this definition, wells, infiltration galleries, and collector wells located directly adjacent to and fed largely by surface water serve as means of artificial recharge.* The hydraulics of wells located near streams is described in Chapter 4; the construction and operation of wells, collectors, and galleries, in Chapter 5.

Induced infiltration where supplied by a perennial stream assures a continuing water supply even though overdraft conditions may exist in nearby areas supplied only by natural recharge. The method has proved effective in unconsolidated formations of permeable sand and gravel hydraulically connected between stream and aquifer.[36,37,54] The amount of water induced into the aquifer depends upon the rate of pumping, permeability, type of well, distance from surface stream, and natural ground water movement. It is important that the velocity of

* Although induced recharge is treated here as a method of artificial recharge, it should be noted that many individuals do not consider it so. Their opinion is based on the following points: (1) ground water must be extracted to obtain recharge; (2) the amount of recharge is difficult to determine; and (3) the method is ill-defined (theoretically any well induces recharge from the nearest related surface water body).

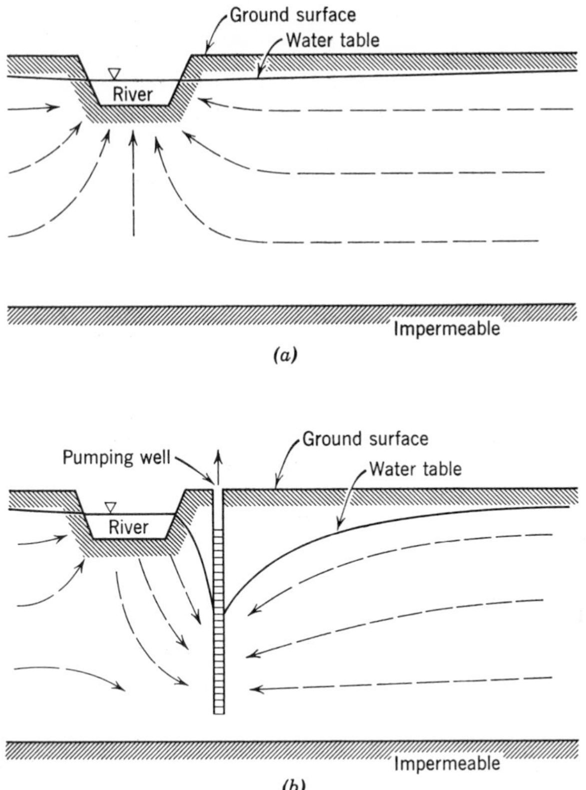

Fig. 11.8. Induced recharge resulting from a well pumping near a river; (*a*) natural flow pattern and (*b*) flow pattern with pumping well.

the surface stream be sufficient to prevent silt deposition from sealing the stream bed. In river reaches where currents have been reduced by regulation or where flood flows no longer provide periodic scouring of the bed, the method results in gradually reduced infiltration.

Studies of water quality have been made for several collector wells inducing recharge.[36,37] These show that induced recharge furnishes water free of organic matter and pathogenic bacteria. Because surface water commonly is less mineralized than ground water, water obtained by induced infiltration, being a mixture of ground and surface waters, is of higher quality than natural ground water. Changes of water quality following installation of a collector well along the Mississippi River are shown in Fig. 11.9. Improvement of iron and chloride contents and total hardness are indicated. In a similar manner, temperatures of water from induced recharge will lie between those of the surface and underground sources. Figure 11.10 illustrates this effect for a group of collectors on the north bank of the Ohio River at Charlestown, Ind. The mixture of the nearly constant ground water temperature with river water has a temperature range less than that of the river and lags the seasonal river temperature oscillations by about 2½ months.

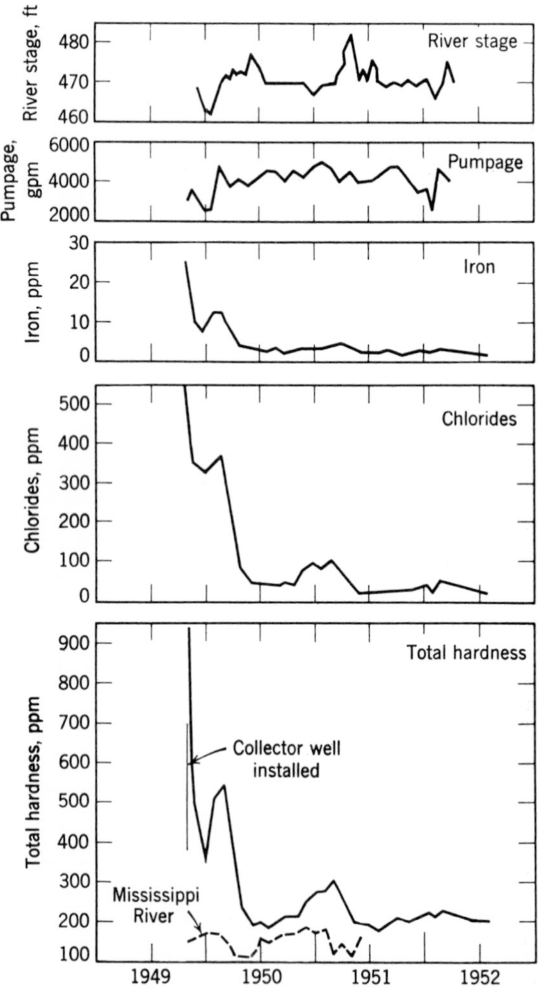

Fig. 11.9. River stage, pumpage, iron content, chloride content, and total hardness of water from a collector well along the Mississippi River (after Klaer[37]).

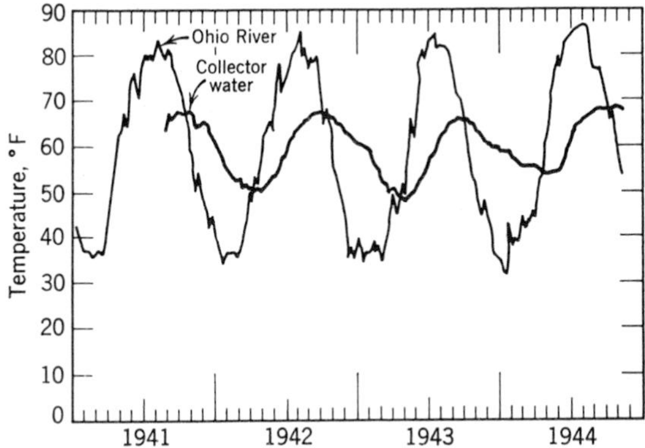

Fig. 11.10. Temperature of the Ohio River and water from a group of collector wells at Charlestown, Ind. (after Kazmann[36]).

European Recharge Practices

Artificial recharge in Europe dates from early in the nineteenth century. Most early installations were based on induced recharge with galleries placed near and under stream beds. In 1897, Richert[51] built the first infiltration basin for recharging at Göteborg, Sweden. The success of this and succeeding installations led to wide application of the method in Sweden, Germany, and the Netherlands. To a more limited extent artificial recharge is practiced in France, Great Britain, and Spain.[16, 34, 72]

Infiltration basins are integral parts of many Swedish municipal water supply systems. Most are located on glacial eskers, which are long narrow alluvial ridges deposited during the last glacial period under the retreating ice sheet by streams draining from beneath the ice. These gravel and sand deposits serve as excellent conduits (and storage reservoirs) for carrying recharged water to pumping installations. Nearby river or lake water is passed through mechanical and rapid sand filters before recharging. Most plants employ rectangular-shaped basins with unprotected side slopes of 1:2 although a few basins have vertical concrete walls. A layer of uniform sand up to three feet in thickness is placed on the basin bottoms. Data on several Swedish infiltration basins, taken from a comprehensive report by Jansa,[34] appear in Table 11.5. The high infiltration rates experienced in Sweden result from the very permeable formations to which the water is applied and from the pretreatment of the recharged water. Distances between basins and pumping wells collecting the recharged

TABLE 11.5 Data on Infiltration Basins in Sweden

(After Jansa [34])

City	Capacity, cfs	Height of Basin above Water Table, ft	Infiltration Rate, ft/day	Distance from Basins to Pumping Wells, ft
Eksjö	0.4	0–6	10–16	1000
Eskilstuna	5.3	72–82	13	1600
Göteborg	3.3	0–6	5	1700–2100
Hälsingborg	6.5	9	13	>1000
Karlskoga	2.0	39	23	2100
Katrineholm	1.6	23	52	1500
Kristinehamn	1.2	9	33	750
Landskorna	2.0	0–6	16	300–1600
Luleå	3.7	43	8	700
Malmö	2.0	16–33	7–10	1600–3300
Sodertalje	4.1	30–56	16	1300–5600
Västerås	16.3	50	13	700–1600
Örebro	4.9	26–43	33	300–1000

water for use are sufficient to purify the water from a bacteriological standpoint, to control tastes and odors, and to equalize surface water temperature fluctuations. Plan and geologic sections for the installation of Karlskoga appear in Fig. 11.11.

Artificial recharge is widely practiced in Germany where basins and ditches, and, more recently, wells have been utilized.[27,33,52,72] Installations are prevalent along the Lippe, Main, Rhine, and Ruhr rivers, as these streams are polluted and natural ground water supplies are insufficient for industrial and municipal demands. Many cities combine induced recharge methods and spreading by locating wells or infiltration galleries so as to be fed by a river and basins simultaneously. Figure 11.12 illustrates schematically two of several arrangements employed for recharge. River water is usually passed through settling basins and treated to remove suspended matter before being released into infiltration basins. Pumped water is chlorinated before entering distributing mains. Recharge rates of only a few feet per day, similar to those found in the United States, are typical.

In the Netherlands, water supply systems for the cities of Amsterdam, Leiden, and The Hague include basins for recharging water into coastal sand dunes.[11,34,43] As most of the country is underlain by salt

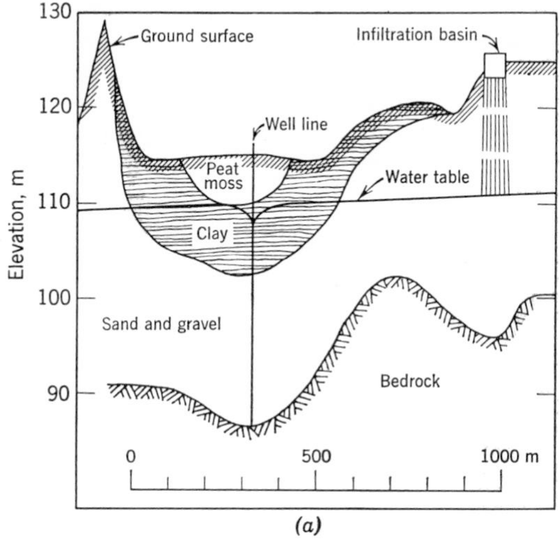

(a)

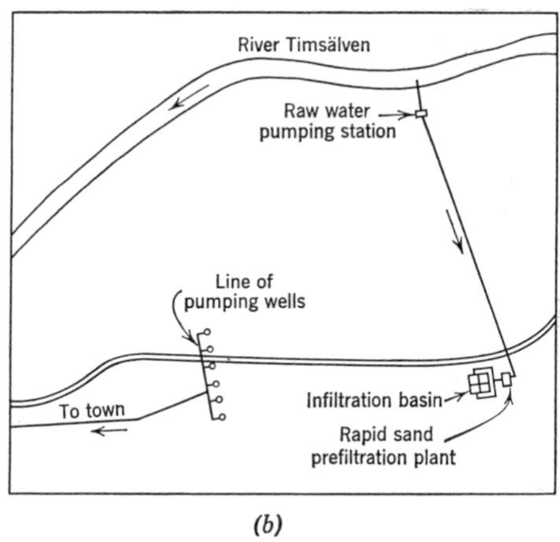

(b)

Fig. 11.11. Water supply system at Karlskoga, Sweden, featuring artificial recharge of filtered river water; (a) geologic section and (b) plan view (after Jansa [34]).

water, the dunes, with their fresh ground water from infiltration of rainfall, provide a unique ground water supply. However, overdevelopment of this source causes salt water under the dunes to rise (see Chapter 12). Therefore, recharging water into the dunes serves to stabilize the salt water, to provide natural filtration of polluted surface water, and to increase the volume of ground water storage.

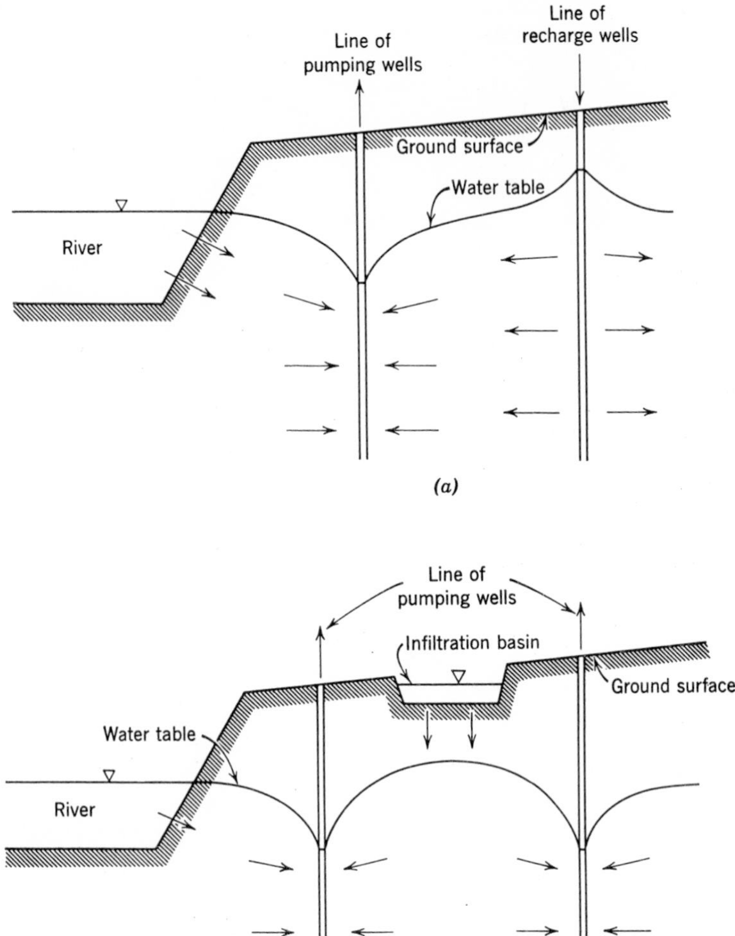

Fig. 11.12. Schematic cross-sections of two examples of German recharge installations bordering rivers: (*a*) induced recharge and recharge wells, and (*b*) induced recharge and infiltration basin.

References

1. Allison, L. E., Effect of microorganisms on permeability of soil under prolonged submergence, *Soil Sci.*, vol. 63, pp. 439–450, 1947.
2. Anon., Underground channels utilized for airport drainage, *Eng. News-Record*, vol. 130, no. 14, pp. 498–499, 1943.

3. Anon., Conservation of ground water in the Louisville area, Kentucky, *Jour. Amer. Water Works Assoc.*, vol. 37, pp. 543–562, 1945.
4. Anon., Artificial ground-water recharge—task group report, *Jour. Amer. Water Works Assoc.*, vol. 48, pp. 493–498, 1956.
5. Arnold, C. E., H. E. Hedger, and A. M. Rawn, *Report upon the reclamation of water from sewage and industrial wastes in Los Angeles County, California*, Los Angeles County Flood Control District, Los Angeles, 159 pp., 1949.
6. Babcock, H. M., and E. M. Cushing, Recharge to ground water from floods in a typical desert wash, Pinal County, Arizona, *Trans. Amer. Geophysical Union*, vol. 23, pp. 49–56, 1942.
7. Banks, H. O., R. C. Richter, J. J. Coe, J. W. McPartland, and R. Kretsinger, *Artificial recharge in California*, Calif. Div. Water Resources, Sacramento, 41 pp., 1954.
8. Barksdale, H. C., and G. D. Debuchananne, Artificial recharge of productive ground-water aquifers in New Jersey, *Econ. Geol.*, vol. 41, pp. 726–737, 1946.
9. Baumann, P., Ground-water movement controlled through spreading, *Trans. Amer. Soc. Civil Engrs.*, vol. 117, pp. 1024–1074, 1952.
10. Baumann, P., Ground water phenomena related to basin recharge, *Proc. Amer. Soc. Civil Engrs.*, vol. 81, sep. 806, 25 pp., 1955.
11. Biemond, C., Dune water flow and replenishment in the catchment area of the Amsterdam water supply, *Jour. Inst. Water Engrs.*, vol. 11, pp. 195–213, 1957.
12. Bliss, E. S., and C. E. Johnson, Some factors involved in ground-water replenishment, *Trans. Amer. Geophysical Union*, vol. 33, pp. 547–558, 1952.
13. Brashears, M. L., Jr., Ground-water temperature on Long Island, New York, as affected by recharge of warm water, *Econ. Geol.*, vol. 36, pp. 811–828, 1941.
14. Brashears, M. L., Jr., Artificial recharge of ground water on Long Island, New York, *Econ. Geol.*, vol. 41, pp. 503–516, 1946.
15. Brashears, M. L., Jr., Recharging ground-water reservoirs with wells and basins, *Min. Eng.*, vol. 5, pp. 1029–1032, 1953.
16. Buchan, S., Artificial replenishment of aquifers, *Jour. Inst. Water Engrs.*, vol. 9, pp. 111-163, 1955.
17. Burdick, C. B., Des Moines infiltration system was developed methodically, *Water Works Eng.*, vol. 99, pp. 461–463, 534, 536, 1946.
18. Butler, R. G., G. T. Orlob, and P. H. McGauhey, Underground movement of bacterial and chemical pollutants, *Jour. Amer. Water Works Assoc.*, vol. 46, pp. 97–111, 1954.
19. Calif. State Water Pollution Control Board, Report on the investigation of travel of pollution, *Publ.* 11, Sacramento, 218 pp., 1954.
20. Cederstrom, D. J., Artificial recharge of a brackish water well, *The Commonwealth*, vol. 14, no. 12, Virginia State Chamber of Commerce, Richmond, pp. 31, 71–73, 1947.
21. Christiansen, J. E., and O. C. Magistad, *Report for 1944—laboratory phases of cooperative water-spreading study*, U. S. Regional Salinity Laboratory, Riverside, Calif., 74 pp., 1945.
22. Clyde, G. D., Utilization of natural underground water storage reservoirs, *Jour. Soil and Water Conserv.*, vol. 6, pp. 15–19, 1951.
23. Conkling, H., Utilization of ground-water storage in stream-system developments, *Trans. Amer. Soc. Civil Engrs.*, vol. 111, pp. 275–354, 1946.

24. Erickson, E. T., Using runoff for ground-water recharge, *Jour. Amer. Water Works Assoc.*, vol. 41, pp. 647–649, 1949.
25. Ferris, J. G., Water spreading and recharge wells, *Proc. Indiana Water Conserv. Conf.*, Ind. Dept. Conserv., Div. Water Resources, Indianapolis, pp. 52–59, 1950.
26. Freeman, V. M., Water-spreading as practiced by the Santa Clara Water-Conservation District, Ventura County, Calif., *Trans. Amer. Geophysical Union*, vol. 17, pp. 465–471, 1936.
27. Gorman, A. E., Water-supply practice in Germany—1945, *Jour. New England Water Works Assoc.*, vol. 60, pp. 132–152, 1946.
28. Goudey, R. F., Reclamation of treated sewage, *Jour. Amer. Water Works Assoc.*, vol. 23, pp. 230–240, 1931.
29. Greenberg, A. E., and H. B. Gotaas, Reclamation of sewage water, *Amer. Jour. Public Health*, vol. 42, pp. 401–410, 1952.
30. Guyton, W. F., Artificial recharge of glacial sand and gravel with filtered river water at Louisville, Kentucky, *Econ. Geol.*, vol. 41, pp. 644–658, 1946.
31. Hallsten, J., Wells for drains, *The Highway Magazine*, vol. 46, pp. 212–213, 1955.
32. Hunt, G. W., Description and results of operations of the Santa Clara Valley Water Conservation District's project, *Trans. Amer. Geophysical Union*, vol. 21, pp. 13–23, 1940.
33. Imhoff, K., Water supply and sewage disposal in the Ruhr Valley, *Eng. News-Record*, vol. 94, no. 3, pp. 104–106, 1925.
34. Jansa, V., *Artificial replenishment of underground water*, Intl. Water Supply Assoc., Second Cong., Paris, 105 pp., 1952.
35. Johnson, A. H., Ground-water recharge on Long Island, *Jour. Amer. Water* Works Assoc., vol. 40, pp. 1159–1166, 1948.
36. Kazmann, R. G., River infiltration as a source of ground-water supply, *Trans. Amer. Soc. Civil Engrs.*, vol. 113, pp. 404–424, 1948.
37. Klaer, F. H., Jr., Providing large industrial water supplies by induced infiltration, *Min. Eng.*, vol. 5, pp. 620–624, 1953.
38. Lane, D. A., Surface spreading-operations by the basin-method and tests on underground spreading by means of wells, *Trans. Amer. Geophysical Union*, vol. 15, pp. 523–527, 1934.
39. Laverty, F. B., Correlating flood control and water supply, Los Angeles coastal plain, *Trans. Amer. Soc. Civil Engrs.*, vol. 111, pp. 1127–1158, 1946.
40. Laverty, F. B., Ground-water recharge, *Jour. Amer. Water Works Assoc.*, vol. 44, pp. 677–681, 1952.
41. Laverty, F. B., Water-spreading operations in the San Gabriel Valley, *Jour. Amer. Water Works Assoc.*, vol. 46, pp. 112–122, 1954.
42. Leggette, R. M., and M. L. Brashears, Jr., Ground-water for air-conditioning on Long Island, New York, *Trans. Amer. Geophysical Union*, vol. 19, pp. 412–418, 1938.
43. Lindenbergh, P. C., Drawing water from a dune area, *Jour. Amer. Water Works Assoc.*, vol. 43, pp. 713–724, 1951.
44. MacKichan, K. A., Estimated use of water in the United States, 1955, *Jour. Amer. Water Works Assoc.*, vol. 49, pp. 369–391, 1957.
45. Mather, J. R., The disposal of industrial effluent by woods irrigation, *Trans. Amer. Geophysical Union*, vol. 34, pp. 227–239, 1953.

46. Meinzer, O. E., General principles of artificial ground-water recharge, *Econ. Geol.,* vol. 41, pp. 191–201, 1946.
47. Merritt, M., Jr., East Orange, N. J., conserves its well supply by water spreading, *Water Works Eng.,* vol. 106, pp. 286–289, 1953.
48. Mitchelson, A. T., and D. C. Muckel, Spreading water for storage underground, *U. S. Dept. Agric. Tech. Bull.* 578, Washington, D. C., 80 pp., 1937.
49. Muckel, D. C., Research in water spreading, *Trans. Amer. Soc. Civil Engrs.,* vol. 118, pp. 209–219, 1953.
50. Rafter, G. W., Sewage irrigation, *U. S. Geological Survey Water-Supply Papers* 3 and 22, Washington, D. C., 100 and 100 pp., 1897 and 1899.
51. Richert, J. G., *On artificial underground water,* C. E. Fritze's Royal Bookstore, Stockholm, 33 pp., 1900.
52. Riedel, C. M., River water used at Dresden to increase ground supply, *Eng. News-Record,* vol. 112, no. 18, pp. 569–570, 1934.
53. Roper, R. M., Ground-water replenishment by surface water diffusion, *Jour. Amer. Water Works Assoc.,* vol. 31, pp. 165–179, 1939.
54. Rorabaugh, M. I., Stream-bed percolation in development of water supplies, *Assemblée Générale de Bruxelles, Assoc. Intl. d'Hydrologie Scientifique,* vol. 2, pp. 165–174, 1951.
55. Sanford, J. H., Diffusing pits for recharging water into underground formations, *Jour. Amer. Water Works Assoc.,* vol. 30, pp. 1755–1766, 1938.
56. Sanitary Eng. Research Lab., An investigation of sewage spreading on five California soils, *Tech. Bull.* 12, Univ. Calif., Berkeley, 53 pp., 1955.
57. Sanitary Eng. Research Lab., Studies in water reclamation, *Tech. Bull.* 13, Univ. Calif., Berkeley, 65 pp., 1955.
58. Sayre, A. N., and V. T. Stringfield, Artificial recharge of ground-water reservoirs, *Jour. Amer. Water Works Assoc.,* vol. 40, pp. 1152–1158, 1948.
59. Schiff, L., The effect of surface head on infiltration rates based on the performance of ring infiltrometers and ponds, *Trans. Amer. Geophysical Union,* vol. 34, pp. 257–266, 1953.
60. Schiff, L., Water spreading for storage underground, *Agric. Eng.,* vol. 35, pp. 794–800, 1954.
61. Schiff, L., The status of water spreading for ground-water replenishment, *Trans. Amer. Geophysical Union,* vol. 36, pp. 1009–1020, 1955.
62. Schiff, L., The Darcy law in the selection of water-spreading systems for ground-water recharge, *Symposia Darcy,* Publ. 41, Assoc. Intl. d'Hydrologie Scientifique, pp. 99–110, 1956.
63. Sisson, W. H., Recharge operations at Kalamazoo, *Jour. Amer. Water Works Assoc.,* vol. 47, pp. 914–922, 1955.
64. Sonderegger, A. L., Hydraulic phenomena and the effect of spreading of flood water in the San Bernardino Basin, Southern California, *Trans. Amer. Soc. Civil Engrs.,* vol. 82, pp. 802–851, 1918.
65. Steinbruegge, G. W., L. R. Heiple, N. Rogers, and R. T. Sniegocki, *Ground-water recharge by means of wells,* Agric. Exp. Sta., Univ. Arkansas, Fayetteville, 119 pp., 1954.
66. Stone, R., and W. F. Garber, Sewage reclamation by spreading basin infiltration, *Trans. Amer. Soc. Civil Engrs.,* vol. 117, pp. 1189–1217, 1952.
67. Stone, R. V., H. B. Gotaas, and V. W. Bacon, Economic and technical status of water reclaimed from sewage and industrial wastes, *Jour. Amer. Water Works Assoc.,* vol. 44, pp. 503–517, 1952.

68. Sundstrom, R. V., and H. W. Hood, Results of artificial recharge of the ground-water reservoir at El Paso, Texas, *Texas Board Water Engrs. Bull.* 5206, Austin, 19 pp., 1952.
69. Suter, M., High-rate recharge of ground water by infiltration, *Jour. Amer. Water Works Assoc.,* vol. 48, pp. 355–360, 1956.
70. Suter, M., The Peoria recharge pit: its development and results, *Proc. Amer. Soc. Civil Engrs.,* vol. 82, no. IR3, 17 pp., 1956.
71. Tibbetts, F. H., Water-conservation project in Santa Clara County, *Trans. Amer. Geophysical Union,* vol. 17, pp. 458–465, 1936.
72. Todd, D. K., Annotated bibliography on artificial recharge of ground water through 1954, *U. S. Geological Survey Water-Supply Paper* 1477, Washington, D. C., 115 pp., 1959.
73. Unklesbay, A. G., and H. H. Cooper, Jr., Artificial recharge of artesian limestone at Orlando, Florida, *Econ. Geol.,* vol. 41, pp. 293–307, 1946.
74. Whetstone, G. A., Mechanism of ground-water recharge, *Agric. Eng.,* vol. 35 pp. 646–647, 650, 1954.
75. Wise, L. L., The Richland story, pt. 2—artificially recharged wells provide city water, *Eng. News-Record,* vol. 143, no. 11, pp. 42–44, 1949.

Sea Water Intrusion in Coastal Aquifers

CHAPTER 12

Coastal aquifers come in contact with the ocean at or seaward of the coastline and here, under natural conditions, fresh ground water is discharged into the ocean. With increased demands for ground water in many coastal areas, however, the seaward flow of ground water has been decreased or even reversed, causing sea water to enter and to penetrate inland in aquifers. This phenomenon is sea water intrusion. If the salt water travels inland to well fields, underground water supplies become useless; moreover, the aquifer becomes contaminated with salt which may take years to remove even with adequate fresh ground water available to flush out the saline water. The importance of protecting coastal aquifers against this continual threat has led to investigations pointing toward methods for prevention or control of sea water intrusion.

Occurrence of Sea Water Intrusion

Wherever overdraft conditions occur in coastal aquifers connecting with the ocean, sea water intrusion can result. By lowering the water table in unconfined aquifers, or the piezometric surface in confined aquifers, the natural gradient sloping downward toward the ocean is reduced or reversed. Because two fluids of different densities are involved, a boundary surface, or interface, is formed wherever the fluids are in contact. The shape and movement of the interface are governed by a hydrodynamic balance of the fresh and salt waters.

Sea water intrusion also can develop or be accentuated wherever a direct artificial access exists between sea water and ground water. Sea level canals provided a means of ingress in the Miami, Fla., area,[12,25,28] whereas abandoned wells were primarily responsible for intrusion into the Santa Clara Valley of California.[39]

The problem of sea water intrusion has increased as population centers and concomitant water demands in localized coastal areas have developed. One of the earliest reports of intrusion was published in 1855 by Braithwaite,[10] who described the increasing salinity of waters pumped from wells in London and Liverpool, England. Today numerous coasts have sections subject to sea water contamination, as evidenced by reports from such places as Germany,[16] the Netherlands [8,21,26] and Japan.[23,32,40] Many small oceanic islands are completely underlain with aquifers containing sea water, which present special problems in developing fresh-water supplies.[24,31,34] In the United States the coastal perimeter is dotted with intruded localities within, among others, the states of Connecticut,[11] New York,[20] New Jersey,[3] Florida,[12,25] Texas,[41] and California.[2,27] The extensive California coast line has been subjected to an unusual amount of intrusion resulting from water needs accompanying a large influx of population into coastal areas; investigations by the State of California [2] revealed that sea water had encroached into 13 coastal aquifers occupying a total area of 90,000 acres. Seven other areas are immediately threatened and 60 others are potentially threatened.

Ghyben-Herzberg Relation between Fresh and Saline Waters

More than 50 years ago two investigators,[1,16] working independently along the European coast, found that salt water occurred underground, not at sea level but, rather, at a depth below sea level of about forty times the height of the fresh water above sea level. This distribution was attributed to a hydrostatic equilibrium existing between the two fluids of different densities. The equation derived to explain the phenomenon is generally referred to as the Ghyben-Herzberg relation after its originators.

In the coastal cross-section of an unconfined aquifer depicted in Fig. 12.1, the total hydrostatic pressure at A is

$$p_A = \rho_s g h_s \tag{12.1}$$

where ρ_s is the salt water density, g is the acceleration of gravity, and h_s is as shown in Fig. 12.1. Similarly, at B, which is at the same depth as A but inland from it,

$$p_B = \rho_f g h_f + \rho_f g h_s \tag{12.2}$$

where ρ_f is the fresh water density and h_f is as shown in Fig. 12.1. Equating these yields the Ghyben-Herzberg relation

$$h_s = \frac{\rho_f}{\rho_s - \rho_f} h_f \tag{12.3}$$

Taking $\rho_s = 1.025 \text{ g/cm}^3$ and $\rho_f = 1.000 \text{ g/cm}^3$,

$$h_s = 40 h_f \tag{12.4}$$

Field measurements in several coastal areas have substantiated this result. Studies since the original investigations have pointed out the limitations and simplifications involved in the Ghyben-Herzberg relation.[17] The intrusion is of course limited by the extent of the aquifer and the elevation of the water table. Also, near the shoreline the relation must break down to form a seepage face for fresh-water outflow. Hydrostatic equilibrium implies no flow, yet ground water flow invariably takes place near coast lines. From density considerations alone, without flow, a horizontal interface would develop with fresh

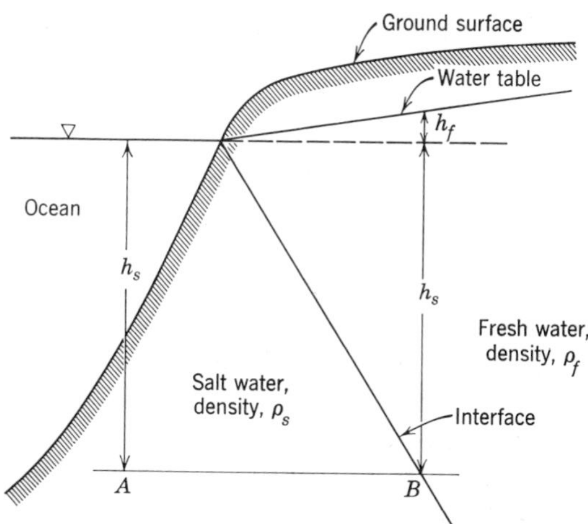

Fig. 12.1. Idealized sketch of fresh- and salt-water distributions in an unconfined coastal aquifer to illustrate the Ghyben-Herzberg relation.

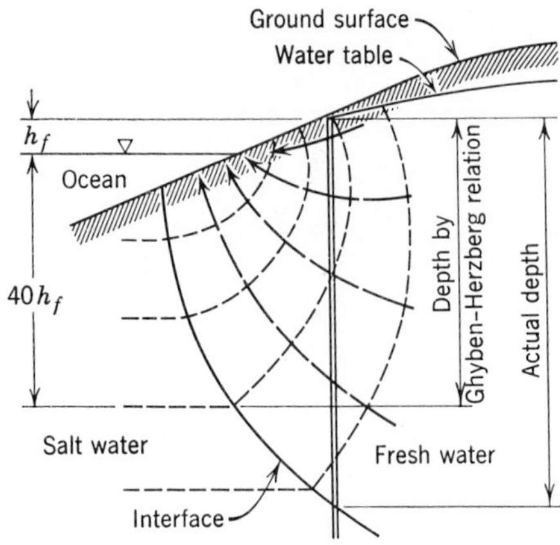

Fig. 12.2. Discrepancy between actual depth to salt water and depth calculated by the Ghyben-Herzberg relation (after Hubbert[17]).

water everywhere floating above salt water. A more realistic picture of intrusion is shown in Fig. 12.2 with a net of flow lines and equipotential lines. Because the total pressure along an equipotential line is constant and the flow lines are sloping upward, the depth to the interface given by the Ghyben-Herzberg relation is less than the actual depth. For flat gradients the difference remains small, but for steep gradients large errors may be incurred.

For confined aquifers the above derivation can also be applied by replacing the water table by the piezometric surface. It is important to note from the Ghyben-Herzberg relation that fresh-salt water equilibrium requires that the water table, or piezometric surface (*a*) lie above sea level, and (*b*) slope downward toward the ocean. Without these conditions, sea water will advance directly inland.

Shape of the Fresh-Salt Water Interface

In deriving the Ghyben-Herzberg relation, it was implicitly assumed that the fresh-salt water interface sloped downward from the coast. The interface shape and slope can be inferred for the case where flow occurs in the fresh-water zone only. Denoting the water table slope δ, as shown in Fig. 12.3, then from Darcy's law

$$\sin \delta = \frac{dh}{ds} = \frac{v}{K} \tag{12.5}$$

where v is velocity and K is permeability. Along this slope the water table elevation decreases in the direction of flow; consequently, according

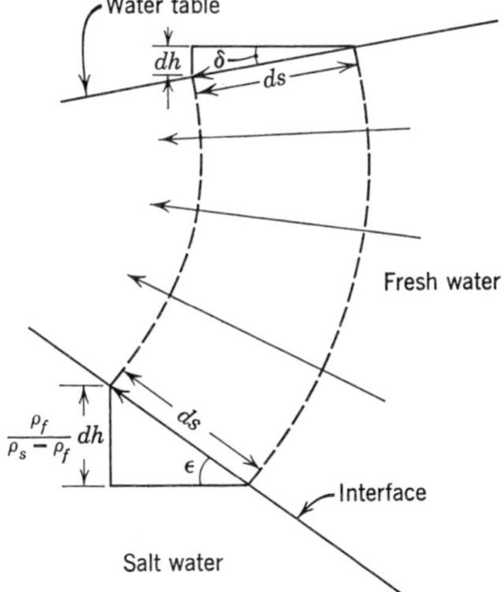

Fig. 12.3. Relation between slopes of the water table and the fresh-salt water interface

to Eq. 12.3, the fresh-salt water boundary must rise. Its slope ϵ (Fig. 12.3) is given by

$$\sin \epsilon = \frac{\rho_f}{\rho_s - \rho_f} \frac{v}{K} \tag{12.6}$$

Because of the converging boundaries, v must increase with distance. It follows, therefore, that the magnitudes of the slopes increase accordingly. This results in a concave interface with respect to the fresh water, as shown in Fig. 12.2.*

Length of the Intruded Sea Water Wedge

Reasoning from the Ghyben-Herzberg relation, a salt-water wedge must exist at the intersection of an aquifer with the ocean. Assuming that a seaward fresh-water flow q per foot of ocean front exists, then the approximate relation for a confined aquifer

$$q = \frac{1}{2}\left(\frac{\rho_s - \rho_f}{\rho_f}\right)\frac{Kb^2}{L} \tag{12.7}$$

can be derived starting from Darcy's law, where ρ_f and ρ_s are fresh- and salt-water densities, respectively, b and L are as defined in Fig. 12.4, and K is the coefficient of permeability. Equation 12.7 indicates for uniform aquifer and fluid conditions that the length of the intruded wedge is inversely proportional to the fresh-water flow. The equation

* A more rigorous derivation of the above reasoning was given by Hubbert.[17]

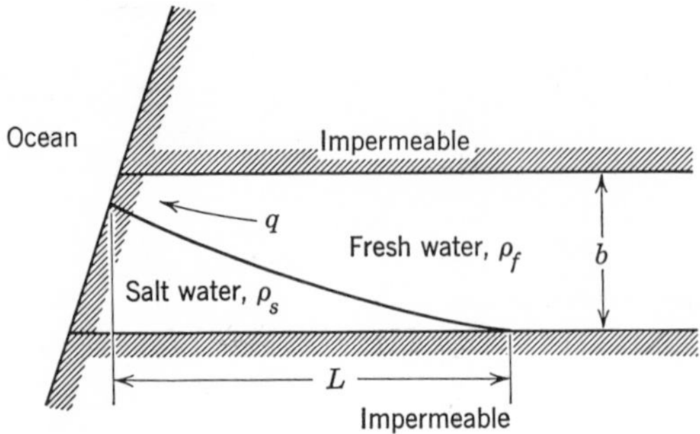

Fig. 12.4. Salt water wedge in a confined aquifer.

can also be applied to unconfined aquifers by replacing b by the saturated thickness, providing the flow does not deviate greatly from the horizontal. Sand model tests at the University of California [14] demonstrated the validity of the equation.

Structure of the Fresh-Salt Water Interface

Theoretically the interface between fresh- and salt-water bodies in an intruded aquifer represents a flow line, which implies no flow across the surface. However, observations [8, 11, 34] have shown that interfaces normally consist of narrow mixing zones a few feet or more in width. The zones result from dispersion occurring in porous media flow (see Chapter 3), from fluctuations in the interface produced by tides and seasonal water table fluctuations, and from molecular diffusion. The last effect is believed to be the least important because diffusion rates for concentration gradients occurring in interfacial zones are considerably less than usual ground water flow rates.

Prevention and Control of Sea Water Intrusion

Five methods have been suggested [2] for controlling intrusion: (*a*) reduction and/or rearrangement of pattern of pumping draft; (*b*) direct recharge; (*c*) development of a pumping trough adjacent to the coast; (*d*) maintenance of a fresh-water ridge above sea level along the coast; and (*e*) construction of artificial subsurface barriers. These methods, together with applications and limitations, are described in the following paragraphs.

Modification of Pumping. By reduction of the pumping draft on a coastal aquifer, the overdraft causing intrusion can be eliminated. This enables the ground water levels to rise above sea level and to maintain a seaward gradient. In terms of cost this may seem a direct solution to the problem, yet unless the reduction is made voluntarily by water users, which would be expected only if supplemental water from other sources is available at comparable cost, expensive and protracted legal action is required in many states. Water rights must be determined by an adjudication procedure with subsequent pumping controlled by a court or a watermaster.

Sometimes a like effect can be achieved by rearranging a basin pumping pattern. If pumping is concentrated near an inflow portion of a basin, steeper slopes would in some situations increase inflow into the basin, whereas reduced pumping near the coast might raise water levels to aid in repelling the entrance of sea water. The schematic diagram of a confined aquifer shown in Fig. 12.5 suggests the difference possible in piezometric surfaces when a heavy pumping area is shifted inland. Either reduction or rearrangement of pumping will not allow full development and utilization of the available ground water storage capacity; however, without other water supplies this limitation is justifiable in protecting the entire aquifer from contamination.

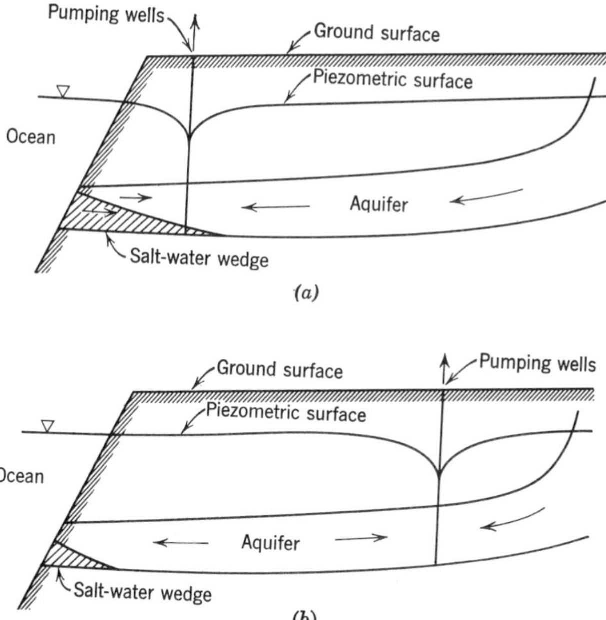

Fig. 12.5. Effect of pumping position on sea water intrusion into a coastal confined aquifer; (*a*) pumping near coast and (*b*) pumping inland.

Artificial Recharging. An obvious method for controlling sea water intrusion is that of artificially recharging an intruded aquifer from spreading areas or recharge wells. Overdraft would be eliminated and water levels and gradients would be properly maintained. The method is technically feasible, spreading areas being best suited for recharging unconfined aquifers, and recharge wells for confined aquifers. However, it may not be economically sound to construct, operate, and maintain a recharge system without reducing the basin pumpage. Importing high quality supplemental water, recharging it into the ground, and finally pumping it out in nearby areas forms an expensive cycle which, on a continuous basis, would lead to unduly high water costs. In California, consideration has been given to recharging waste waters (otherwise discharged directly into the ocean) for this purpose.

Pumping Trough. If a line of wells were constructed adjacent to and paralleling a coast, pumping would form a trough in the ground water level. Gradients created would limit sea water intrusion to a stationary wedge inland of the trough, as sketched in Fig. 12.6 for a confined aquifer. Such an installation would reduce the usable storage capacity of the basin, would be costly to install and operate, and would waste ground water in the mixture of sea and fresh waters pumped from the trough; hence, in general, it would not be economically feasible. The procedure might be temporarily applied to reduce salinity in intruded aquifers until another method could be operated; otherwise, on a permanent basis the method might be justified only in a basin where the ground water was sufficiently saline to require wasting substantial amounts for maintenance of salt balance.

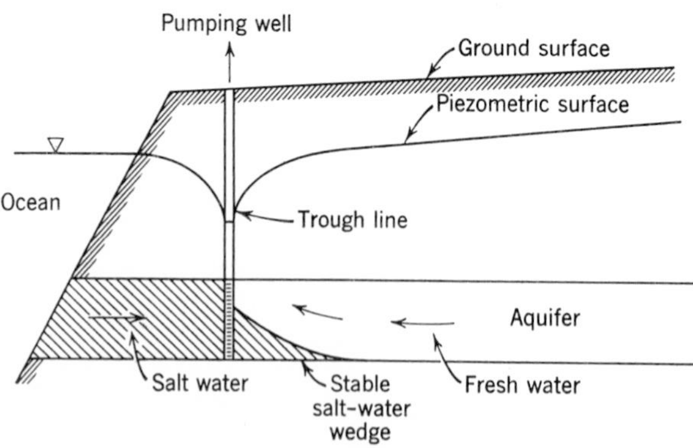

Fig. 12.6. Control of sea water intrusion by a pumping trough paralleling the coast.

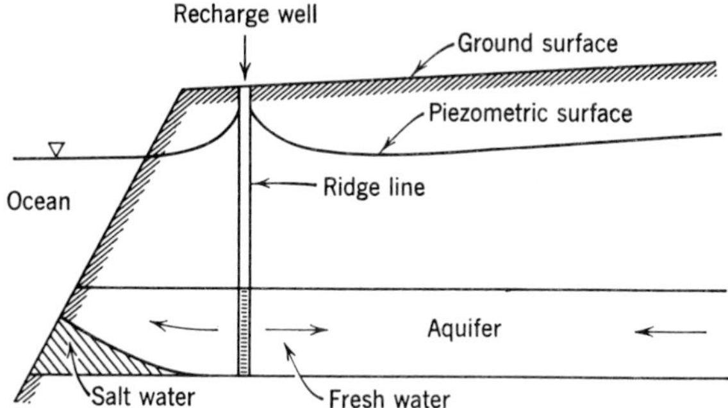

Fig. 12.7. Control of sea water intrusion by a pressure ridge paralleling the coast.

Pressure Ridge. Another method for control of intrusion is the exact opposite of the previous method, namely, formation and maintenance of a fresh-water pressure ridge adjacent to and paralleling the coast. In an unconfined aquifer surface spreading could create a water table ridge; in a confined aquifer, a line of recharge wells could form a ridge in the piezometric surface. A ridge must be of sufficient height above sea level to repel sea water, as indicated in Fig. 12.7. A small amount of recharged water would waste to the ocean, the remainder moving landward to supply part of the pumping draft. With recharge wells, the ridge would consist of a series of peaks at each well with saddles between. The necessary elevation of the saddles to displace ocean water would govern the well spacing and the recharge rates required. The ridge should be located inland from the saline front, otherwise sea water inland of the ridge will be driven further inland. To illustrate this, data from sand model studies [14] of recharge wells in a confined aquifer are shown in Fig. 12.8. The aquifer is represented by a rectangle with sea water to the left and fresh water right. In Fig. 12.8*a* the injection rate is not sufficient to halt intrusion, whereas in Fig. 12.8*b* the higher injection rate reverses the intrusion, and salt water landward of the well is flattened and moved further inland. The method of control has the advantage of not restricting the usable ground water storage capacity, but has the disadvantages of high initial and operating costs and the need for supplemental water. Reclaimed waste water of suitable quality might meet part of the need for the additional water required. Extensive field investigations of this method conducted in Los Angeles County, Calif., are described in the following section.

Subsurface Barrier. The final method of control involves the construction of a subsurface barrier which would reduce the permeability

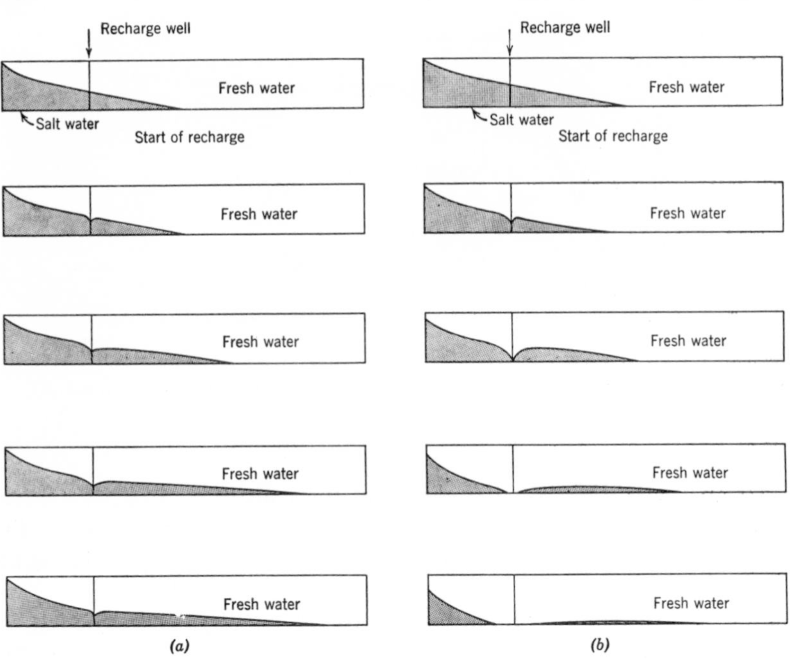

Fig. 12.8. Sand model results showing successive positions of a salt water wedge in a confined aquifer after recharging (*a*) at a small rate and (*b*) at a large rate through a well intersecting the wedge (after Harder and others[14]).

of an aquifer sufficiently to prevent inflow of sea water.[7,9] In relatively shallow aquifers a dike might be constructed of sheet piling, asphalt, concrete, or puddled clay.[30] To avoid trench construction an impermeable membrane might be formed by injecting one of the following through a line of holes: emulsified asphalt, cement grout, bentonite slurry, silical gel, or calcium acrylate. Laboratory studies[14] of bentonite slurries for this purpose led to the conclusion that a complete seal could not be provided for high differential heads in contact with salt water. In order to justify the initial outlay for a subsurface barrier, it must be permanent. Leakage caused by earthquake damage to a rigid-type barrier must be considered in some areas. A barrier would prove most feasible located in a narrow, shallow alluvial canyon connecting inland to a larger aquifer. The method has only limited applicability and initially is expensive, but operation and maintenance costs should be low. Full utilization of a basin's underground storage capacity could be made with a barrier.

Of the five methods described it should be noted that the pumping trough and the pressure ridge methods do not solve the basic problem of sea water intrusion—overdraft. Only when this deficiency is eliminated (or isolated as in the subsurface barrier method) is the problem solved. In areas where supplemental water is or will be available, it may be that it is not economically feasible to control intrusion. Looking ahead to the day of economically competitive methods for converting sea water to fresh water, pumping in coastal aquifers could be greatly reduced or abandoned and the need for controlling sea water intrusion eliminated.

Field Tests for Controlling Intrusion at Manhattan Beach, California

A comprehensive field test of the pressure ridge method has been conducted by the Los Angeles County Flood Control District at Manhattan Beach, Calif.[4,5,18,19] The confined aquifer selected for study was badly degraded by sea water. A line of recharge wells was located parallel to and about 2000 ft inland from the ocean, where the piezometric surface was 6 to 12 ft below sea level and the water contained 16,000 ppm chloride. Figure 12.9 shows a cross-section of the aquifer indicating the conditions existing prior to recharge. Twelve-inch re-

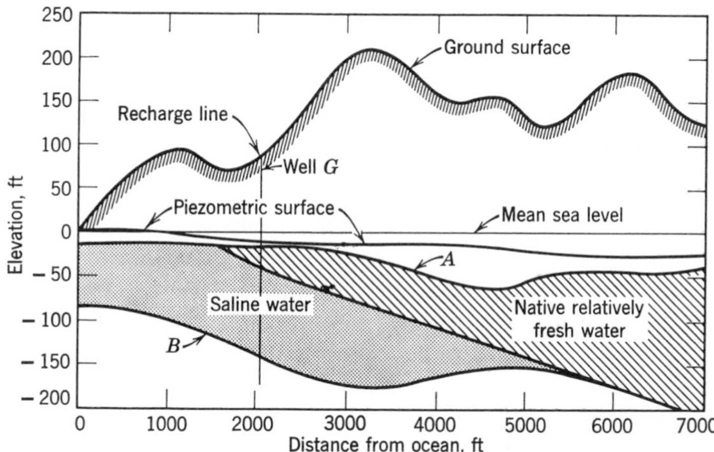

Fig. 12.9. Sea water intrusion at Manhattan Beach, Calif., prior to recharge *A*—upper boundary of aquifer; *B*—lower boundary of aquifer (after Laverty and van der Goot[19]).

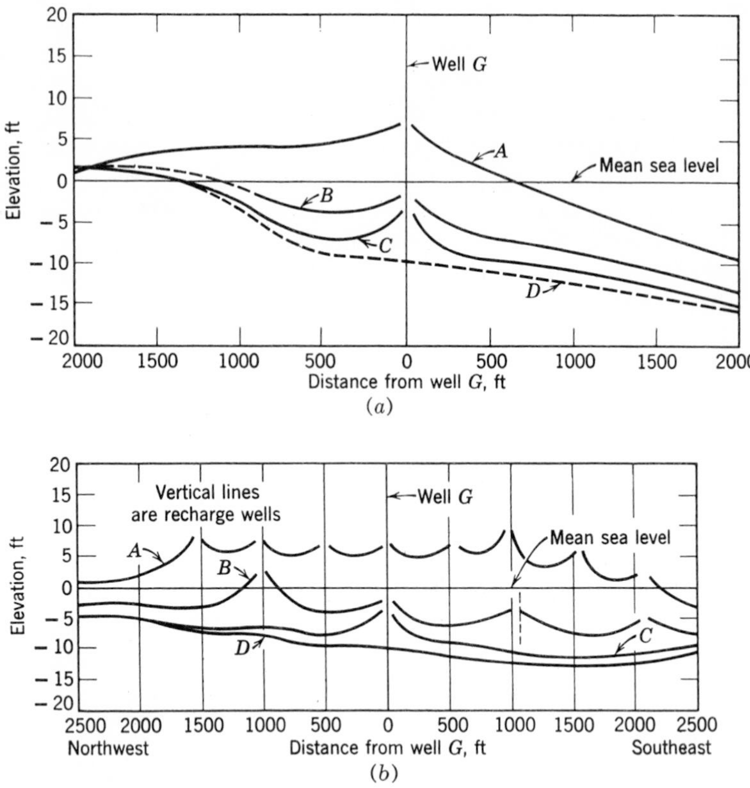

Fig. 12.10. Profiles of piezometric surfaces (*a*) normal to and (*b*) along the line of recharge wells, Manhattan Beach, Calif. *A*—Sept. 16, 1953; *B*—June 15, 1953; *C*—March 10, 1953; and *D*—static water level prior to beginning of recharge on Feb. 12, 1953 (after Laverty and van der Goot [19]).

charge wells surrounded by 3-in. gravel packs were spaced at 500-ft intervals to form a line 4000 ft long. Numerous small observation wells were drilled in the vicinity.

Injection was begun in one well early in 1953, later increased to four wells, and finally to eight wells. Profiles of pressure gradients normal to and along the recharge line, shown in Fig. 12.10, indicate that injection resulted in the successful maintenance of a fresh-water barrier. The combined total injection rate for the eight wells was about 5 cfs. Analysis of the relative landward and seaward gradients indicates that only 5 per cent of the recharge water will eventually be wasted to the ocean, and 95 per cent will flow landward to replenish the ground water basin. Chlorination of the recharge water at levels of 5 to 8 ppm was necessary to prevent clogging of wells by bacterial slimes.

The effect of the recharge program is illustrated by Fig. 12.11, showing the aquifer cross-section two years after recharge was begun. Comparing this with Fig. 12.9, the change of piezometric surface and the redistribution of fresh and salt waters are apparent. Because sea water had intruded landward of the recharge line, the recharge operation created a small saline wave of water moving inland. By taking chloride samples in observation wells, time variations of salinity during recharge were studied. Results from four wells located along a line normal to the recharge line and inland from it appear in Fig. 12.12. As the injected water moved inland it formed a wedge overlying the intruded saline water so that the entrapped saline water was gradually flattened, leading to an increased fraction of fresh water reaching inland wells with time.

The investigation demonstrated the technical feasibility of maintaining a recharge line parallel to the coast for control of sea water intrusion. Economic justification [19] of such a barrier to protect an entire ground water basin requires consideration of the value of assuring the protection of the safe yield of the basin, the cost of a supplemental water supply, the cost of distribution facilities for such a supply, and

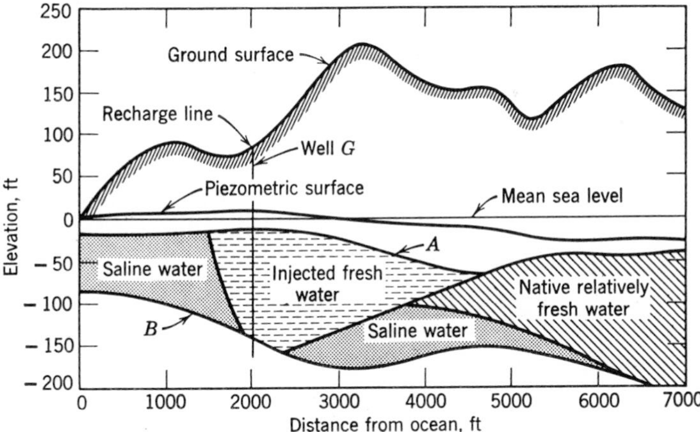

Fig. 12.11. Sea water intrusion at Manhattan Beach, Calif., two years after beginning of recharge. *A*—upper boundary of aquifer; *B*—lower boundary of aquifer (after Laverty and van der Goot [19]).

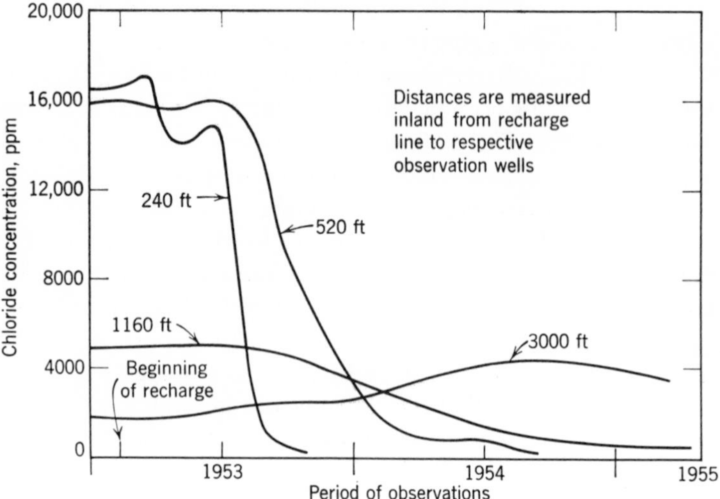

Fig. 12.12. Variation of chloride concentration with time in observation wells inland from line of recharge, Manhattan Beach, Calif. (after Laverty and van der Goot [19]).

the value of the basin for storage purposes in relation to providing adequate surface storage. Evidence in Los Angeles County led to the conclusion that the method is both technically and economically feasible.

Fresh-Salt Water Relations on Oceanic Islands

Most small oceanic islands are relatively permeable, consisting of sand, lava, coral, or limestone, so that sea water is in contact with ground water on all sides. Because fresh ground water is supplied entirely by rainfall, only a limited amount is available. A fresh-water lens, shown schematically in Fig. 12.13*a*, is formed by the radial movement of the fresh water toward the coast.*

From the Dupuit assumptions and the Ghyben-Herzberg relation an approximate fresh-water boundary can be determined. Assume a circular island of radius R, as shown in Fig. 12.13*a*, receiving an ef-

* A similar situation, except that it is in two dimensions, exists for ground water in sand dunes bordering the North Sea in the Netherlands. Infiltrated rainfall and artificially recharged water in the permeable dunes form a fresh-water lens parallel to the coast and underlain by salt water. As dune water is an important water supply source in the Netherlands, the ground water hydraulics of these areas has been intensively studied by Dutch engineers.[8]

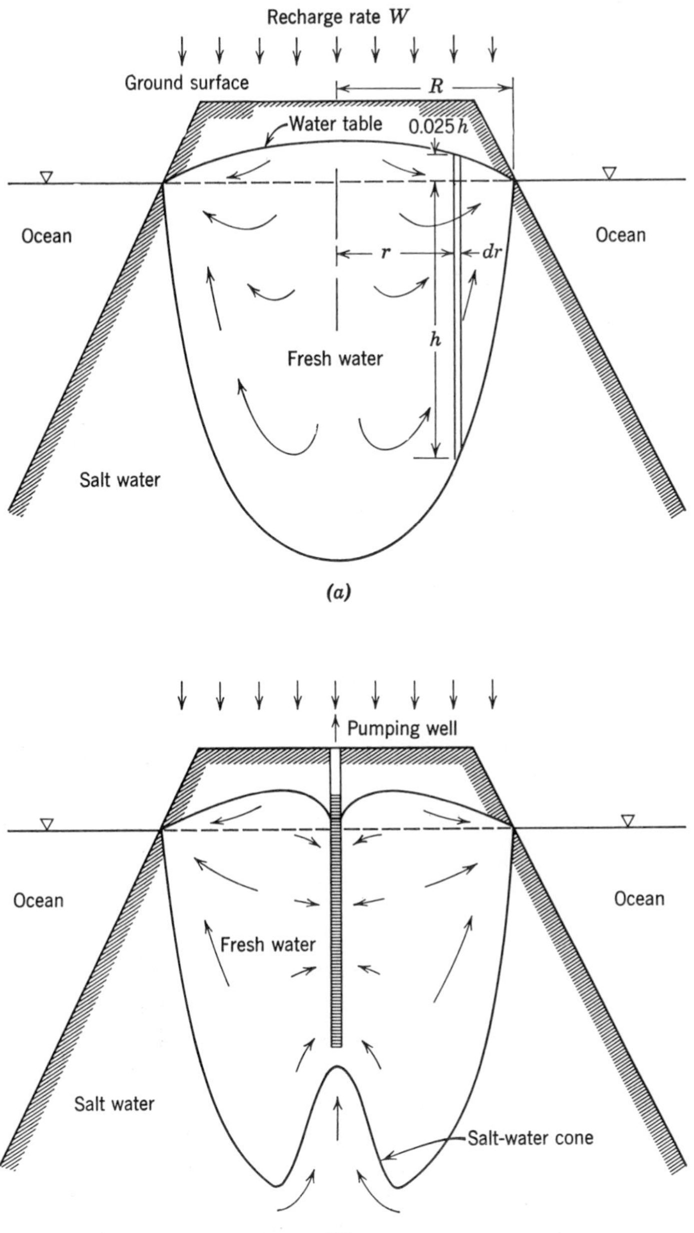

Fig. 12.13. Fresh-water lens in an oceanic island under (*a*) natural conditions and (*b*) with a pumping well.

fective recharge from rainfall at a rate W. The outward flow Q at radius r is

$$Q = 2\pi r K(1.025h) \frac{d(0.025h)}{dr} \tag{12.8}$$

where K is permeability and h is defined in Fig. 12.13*a*. The change in flow through a cylinder of radius r and thickness dr amounts to

$$dQ = 2\pi r W\, dr \tag{12.9}$$

Integrating, and noting that $Q = 0$ when $r = 0$, yields

$$Q = \pi r^2 W \tag{12.10}$$

Equating Eqs. 12.8 and 12.10 gives

$$\frac{Wr\, dr}{0.0512K} = h\, dh \tag{12.11}$$

Integrating and applying the boundary condition that $h = 0$ when $r = R$,

$$h^2 = \frac{W}{0.0512K}(R^2 - r^2) \tag{12.12}$$

Thus, the depth to salt water at any location is a function of the rainfall recharge, size of the island, and permeability. Tidal and seasonal fluctuations may form a transition zone between the fresh- and salt-water bodies; likewise, seepage surfaces at the coast line are subject to varying salinity concentrations.

The close proximity of sea water can introduce saline water into fresh ground water even without overdraft unless care is exercised in developing underground water supplies. An island well pumping water at a rate sufficient to lower the water table to or below sea level disturbs the fresh-salt water equilibrium. According to the Ghyben-Herzberg relation, salt water will rise as a cone, shown in Fig. 12.13*b*, to enter the well. In practice a brackish mixture of the two waters would cause abandonment of the well before salt concentrations approaching sea water were reached. To avoid this danger and to obtain the maximum ground water yield, island wells should be designed for minimum drawdown, just skimming fresh water from the top of the lens. The infiltration gallery (see Chapter 5), consisting of a horizontal collecting tunnel, is designed for this purpose.[38] Drawdowns of from a few inches to a few feet will in many instances furnish plentiful water supplies. Galleries, known locally as Maui-type wells, have been extensively installed for irrigation and municipal water supplies in the Hawaiian Islands.[34] The Marianas Islands [24] in the Pacific Ocean and the Bahama Islands [31] and Bermuda [38] in the Atlantic Ocean obtain water supplies from infiltration galleries.

Recognition of Sea Water in Ground Water

Analysis of ground water samples collected in zones of sea water intrusion may show a chemical composition differing from a simple

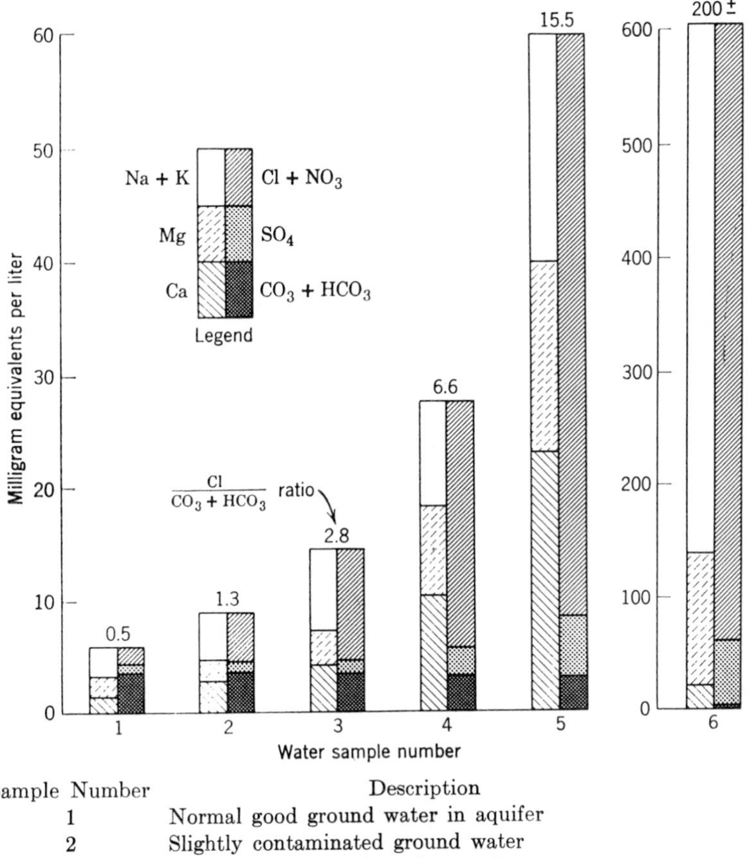

Sample Number	Description
1	Normal good ground water in aquifer
2	Slightly contaminated ground water
3	Moderately contaminated ground water
4	Injuriously contaminated ground water
5	Highly contaminated ground water (near seashore)
6	Sea water

Fig. 12.14. Chemical analyses of a line of well waters from Salinas Valley, Calif., extending from the center of the aquifer to the coast. Chloride-bicarbonate ratios are shown above each quality diagram (after Simpson [33]).

proportional mixing of sea water and ground water. Modifications in composition of sea water entering an aquifer can occur by three processes:[29] (*a*) base exchange between the water and the minerals of the aquifer,[22] (*b*) sulfate reduction and substitution of carbonic or other weak acid radicals, and (*c*) solution and precipitation. Only the last process can change the total salt concentration; however, the first two processes, which require maintenance of ionic balance, can alter the percentage by weight of different salt components and thereby the total dissolved solids in parts per million.

In order to avoid mistaken diagnoses of sea water intrusion as evidenced by temporary increases of total dissolved salts, Revelle[29] recommended the chloride-bicarbonate ratio as a criterion to evaluate intrusion.* Chloride is the dominant ion of ocean water, is unaffected by the above processes, and normally occurs in only small amounts in ground water. On the other hand, bicarbonate is usually the most abundant negative ion in ground water and occurs in only minor amounts in sea water. Although contaminants other than sea water can change a chloride-bicarbonate ratio, these would seldom be important in water collected from a well subject to intrusion.

An application of the ratio is shown by the series of chemical analyses in Fig. 12.14. Water samples were taken from wells in Salinas Valley, Calif., along a line extending from the aquifer, through the zone of sea water intrusion, and to the coast. The increase in the chloride-bicarbonate ratio, as well as the total salinity, can be seen as the coast is approached (from sample 1 to 6).

References

1. Badon Ghyben, W., Nota in verband met de voorgenomen putboring nabij Amsterdam, *Tijdschrift van het Koninklijk Instituut van Ingenieurs,* The Hague, p. 21, 1888–1889.
2. Banks, H. O., and R. C. Richter, Sea-water intrusion into ground-water basins bordering the California coast and inland bays, *Trans. Amer. Geophysical Union,* vol. 34, pp. 575–582, 1953.
3. Barksdale, H. C., The contamination of ground-water by salt water near Parlin, New Jersey, *Trans. Amer. Geophysical Union,* vol. 21, pp. 471–474, 1940.
4. Baumann, P., Ground-water movement controlled through spreading, *Trans. Amer. Soc. Civil Engrs.,* vol. 117, pp. 1024–1074, 1952.
5. Baumann, P., Experiments with fresh-water barrier to prevent sea water intrusion, *Jour. Amer. Water Works Assoc.,* vol. 45, pp. 521–534, 1953.

* Actually the $Cl/(CO_3 + HCO_3)$ ratio is employed for practical purposes.

6. Baumann, P., Ground-water phenomena related to basin recharge, *Proc. Amer. Soc. Civil Engrs.,* vol. 81, sep. 806, 25 pp., 1955.
7. Beardslee, C. G., Salt-water barrier at Cooke, *West. Const. News,* vol. 17, no. 2, pp. 53–55, 1942.
8. Biemond, C., Dune water flow and replenishment in the catchment area of the Amsterdam water supply, *Jour. Inst. Water Engrs.,* vol. 11, pp. 195–213, 1957.
9. Blakely, L. E., and V. A. Endersby, Prevention of underground leakage, *Jour. Amer. Water Works Assoc.,* vol. 40, pp. 873–882, 1948
10. Braithwaite, F., On the infiltration of salt water into the springs of wells under London and Liverpool, *Proc. Inst. Civil Engrs.,* vol. 14, pp. 507–523, 1855.
11. Brown, J. S., A study of coastal ground water with special reference to Connecticut, *U. S. Geological Survey Water-Supply Paper* 537, Washington, D. C., 101 pp., 1925.
12. Brown, R. H., and G. G. Parker, Salt-water encroachment in limestone of Silver Bluff, Miami, Florida, *Econ. Geol.,* vol. 40, pp. 235–262, 1945.
13. Childs, E. C., The equilibrium of rain-fed ground water resting on deeper saline water; the Ghyben-Herzberg lens, *Jour. Soil Sci.,* vol. 1, pp. 173–181, 1950.
14. Harder, J. A., T. R. Simpson, L.-K. Lau, F. L. Hotes, and P. H. McGauhey, *Laboratory research on sea water intrusion into fresh ground-water sources and methods of its prevention—final report,* Sanitary Eng. Research Lab., Univ. Calif., Berkeley, 68 pp., 1953.
15. Hayami, S., On the saline disaster and variation of coastal underground water caused by land subsidence accompanying the great earthquake of December 21, 1947, *Assemblée Générale de Bruxelles, Assoc. Intl. d'Hydrologie Scientifique,* vol. 2, pp. 249–251, 1951.
16. Herzberg, B., Die Wasserversorgung einiger Nordseebäder, *Jour. Gasbeleuchtung und Wasserversorgung,* vol. 44, pp. 815–819, 842–844, Munich, 1901.
17. Hubbert, M. K., The theory of ground-water motion, *Jour. Geol.,* vol. 48, pp. 785–944, 1940.
18. Laverty, F. B., Recharging wells expected to stem sea-water intrusion, *Civil Eng.,* vol. 22, pp. 313–315, 1952.
19. Laverty, F. B., and H. A. van der Goot, Development of a fresh-water barrier in southern California for the prevention of sea water intrusion, *Jour. Amer. Water Works Assoc.,* vol. 47, pp. 886–908, 1955.
20. Leggette, R. M., Salt water encroachment in the Lloyd sand on Long Island, N. Y., *Water Works Eng.,* vol. 100, pp. 1076–1079, 1107–1109, 1947.
21. Liefrinck, F. A., Water supply problems in Holland, *Public Works,* vol. 61, no. 9, pp. 19–20, 65–66, 69, 1930.
22. Love, S. K., Cation-exchange in ground water contaminated with sea water near Miami, Florida, *Trans. Amer. Geophysical Union,* vol. 25, pp. 951–955, 1944.
23. Nomitsu, T., Y. Toyohara, and R. Kamimoto, On the contact surface of fresh- and salt-water near a sandy sea-shore, *Mem. College Sci.,* Kyoto Imp. Univ., Ser. A, vol. 10, no. 7, pp. 279–302, 1927.
24. Ohrt, F., Water development and salt water intrusion on Pacific Islands, *Jour. Amer. Water Works Assoc.,* vol. 39, pp. 979–988, 1947.
25. Parker, G. G., Salt-water encroachment in Southern Florida, *Jour. Amer. Water Works Assoc.,* vol. 37, pp. 526–542, 1945.

26. Pennink, J. M. K., Investigations for ground-water supplies, *Trans. Amer. Soc. Civil Engrs.*, vol. 54-D, pp. 169–181, 1905.
27. Poland, J. F., Saline contamination of coastal ground water in Southern California, *Western City,* vol. 19, pp. 46, 48, 50, Oct. 1943.
28. Rader, E. M., Salt water encroachment into well water in the Miami area, *Proc. Amer. Soc. Civil Engrs.*, vol. 81, sep. 669, 11 pp., 1955.
29. Revelle, R., Criteria for recognition of sea water in ground-waters, *Trans. Amer. Geophysical Union,* vol. 22, pp. 593–597, 1941.
30. Rhodes, A. D., Puddled-clay cutoff walls stop sea-water infiltration, *Civil Eng.*, vol. 21, no. 2, pp. 21–23, 1951.
31. Riddel, J. O., Excluding salt water from island wells—a theory of the occurrence of ground water based on experience at Nassau, Bahama Islands, *Civil Eng.*, vol. 3, pp. 383–385, 1933.
32. Senio, K., On the ground water near the seashore, *Assemblée Générale de Bruxelles, Assoc. Intl. d'Hydrologie Scientifique,* vol. 2, pp. 175–177, 1951.
33. Simpson, T. R., Salinas Basin investigation, *Bull.* 52, Calif. Div. Water Resources, Sacramento, 230 pp., 1946.
34. Swartz, J. H., Resistivity-studies of some salt-water boundaries in the Hawaiian Islands, *Trans. Amer. Geophysical Union,* vol. 18, pp. 387–393, 1937.
35. Thompson, D. G., Some relations between ground-water hydrology and oceanography, *Trans. Amer. Geophysical Union,* vol. 14, pp. 30–33, 1933.
36. Todd, D. K., An abstract of literature pertaining to sea water intrusion and its control, *Tech. Bull.* 10, Sanitary Eng. Research Project, Univ. Calif., Berkeley, 74 pp., 1953.
37. Todd, D. K., Sea-water intrusion in coastal aquifers, *Trans. Amer. Geophysical Union,* vol. 34, pp. 749–754, 1953
38. Todd, D. K., Discussion of Infiltration galleries, *Proc. Amer. Soc. Civil Engrs.*, vol. 81, sep. 647, pp. 7–9, 1955.
39. Tolman, C. F., and J. F. Poland, Ground-water, salt-water infiltration, and ground-surface recession in Santa Clara Valley, Santa Clara County, California, *Trans. Amer. Geophysical Union,* vol. 21, pp. 23–35, 1940.
40. Toyohara, Y., A study on the coastal ground water at Yumigahama, Tottori, *Mem. College Sci.*, Kyoto Imp. Univ., Ser. A, vol. 18, no. 5, pp. 295–309, 1935.
41. Turner, S. F., and M. D. Foster, A study of salt-water encroachment in the Galveston area, Texas, *Trans. Amer. Geophysical Union,* vol. 15, pp. 432–435, 1934.
42. Wentworth, C. K., Storage consequences of the Ghyben-Herzberg theory, *Trans. Amer. Geophysical Union,* vol. 23, pp. 683–693, 1942.
43. Wentworth, C. K., Factors in the behavior of ground water in a Ghyben-Herzberg system, *Pacific Sci.*, vol. 1, pp. 172–184, 1947.
44. Wentworth, C. K., Growth of the Ghyben-Herzberg transition zone under a rinsing hypothesis, *Trans. Amer. Geophysical Union,* vol. 29, pp. 97–98, 1948.
45. Wentworth, C. K., The process and progress of salt-water encroachment, *Assemblée Générale de Bruxelles, Assoc. Intl. d'Hydrologie Scientifique,* vol. 2, pp. 238–248, 1951.

Legal Aspects of Ground Water

CHAPTER 13

With fuller development of water resources in the future, increased management of stream systems and ground water basins will be required to increase and maintain water yields of good quality. Such management depends not only on correct knowledge of natural water conditions, but also, and equally important, on legal control of water use that is both reasonable and practical. McGuinness[13] asked for "hydrologically sound statutes." Much needs to be done to clarify, simplify, and administer ground water laws in the United States. The Geological Survey, acting in an advisory capacity on the hydrologic feasibility of proposed water laws, has highlighted some of the existing legal problems, while many states are actively engaged in preparing new legislation leading to improved water codes.

Systems of Title to Ground Water

A water right is a right, granted by law, to take possession of water occurring in a natural source of water supply and to put it to a beneficial use. In the United States two major doctrines of water law for establishing water rights have been followed: the common-law doctrine of riparian rights and the doctrine of prior appropriation. A riparian right is based on ownership of land contiguous to a natural water supply; thus, for surface water this applies to lands bordering a stream.

For ground water, ownership of land overlying a water-bearing formation becomes the criterion, hence the term *land ownership right* [17] is more expressive. A prior appropriative right is based on appropriation and use of water belonging to the public, with earlier rights having preference over later ones. One doctrine is based on location; the other on time. The opposing natures of these doctrines have caused difficulties in interpreting water rights in states where both have been applied.

Doctrine of Land Ownership. The doctrine of land ownership rights originated in England in the first half of the nineteenth century, giving it the name English rule of unlimited use.* According to Hutchins,[8]

> . . . the practical arguments for acceptance of the English rule for "percolating waters" were: (*a*) the source and flow of these waters were so unknown that it is impossible to formulate any legal rules governing them; and (*b*) the recognition of correlative rights (of adjacent landowners) would substantially interfere with many important public projects, such as drainage of land, etc.

Competition for water in the United States, particularly in the West, made the English rule of unlimited use unsuitable. Evolving from a suit † in New Hampshire in 1862 came the principle that a man's right to use of percolating water on his own land is limited by the corresponding use of his neighbor, and "restricts each to a reasonable exercise of his own right, a reasonable use of his own property, in view of the similar rights of others." This became known as the American rule of reasonable use, which has been adopted in many states where the land ownership doctrine is applied.

In 1903 the California suit of Katz versus Walkinshaw ‡ led to a further modification of the land ownership rights doctrine. The California Supreme Court stated, "Disputes between overlying landowners concerning water for use on the land, to which they have an equal right, in cases where the supply is insufficient for all, are to be settled by giving to each a just and fair proportion." This became the so-called California rule, or doctrine of correlative rights. It holds that rights of landowners over a common ground water basin are coequal or correlative so that any one owner cannot take more than his share even for use on his own land if the rights of others are injured thereby.

* Conkling [2] preferred to describe it as "unreasonable use."

† Basset v. Salisbury Manufacturing Co., 43 N. H. 569, 82 Am. Dec. 179 (1862).

‡ Katz v. Walkinshaw, 141 Calif. 116, 70 Pac. 663 (1902), 74 Pac. 766 (1903).

Here "reasonable use" does not mean all water that is reasonably beneficial to an owner's lands regardless of others' needs, but only his reasonable share if there is insufficient supply for all needs. During times of short supply, use is restricted to lands overlying the ground water basin; however, when the supply is plentiful and no injury results, any amount may be reasonably taken for use on overlying or other lands.

Doctrine of Prior Appropriation. The basic concept of the second doctrine, that of prior appropriation, is that the landowner has no inherent right to use water from sources on, contiguous to, or underlying his land, but that rights to these sources are based on priority in time of beneficial use and may be lost after the use ceases.[17] Thus, an appropriator is one who uses water that had been regarded as common property or had been used by others. The appropriation doctrine in the United States can be traced to the early miners in California, who took water from streams for use in placer mining on public lands. The California Supreme Court recognized the doctrine in 1855, while acts of Congress in 1866 and 1870 recognized the right to appropriate water on public lands and protected even those lands that subsequently passed to private ownership.[17]

The Desert Land Act of 1877 contained the following:

> Provided however that the right to the use of water by the person so conducting the same, on or to any tract of desert land of six hundred and forty acres shall depend upon bona fide prior appropriation; and such right shall not exceed the amount of water actually appropriated, and necessarily used for the purpose of irrigation and reclamation; and all surplus water over and above such actual appropriation and use, together with the water of all lakes, rivers and other sources of water supply upon the public lands and not navigable, shall remain and be held free for the appropriation and use of the public for irrigation, mining and manufacturing purposes subject to existing rights.

Today all of the 17 Western states recognize the doctrine of prior appropriation to some extent. In essence the doctrine states that a man who is first in time to beneficially use water is the first in right, so that during shortages the later appropriators must cease their use in reverse order of priority. No rights are acquired for nonbeneficial use of water.

Because of the conflicting nature of the two major doctrines of water law, states have had to decide which doctrine to follow. Although both are in use, and some states even follow both rules to some extent, a recent tendency has been to weaken land ownership rights in favor of prior appropriation. Increased emphasis is being placed on reasonable and beneficial use where water shortages are developing. McGuinness[13] stated that members of the Geological Survey who have given thought to the subject believe that the doctrine of prior appropriation has fewer defects than the land ownership doctrine and can be made to lead to a greater degree of development and greater protection of vested rights. Wells A. Hutchins, leading authority on Western water law, and the National Resources Planning Board have both recommended[8,14] the doctrine of prior appropriation as the best available method for establishing water rights.

Prescriptive Rights. In certain states overlying landowners or prior appropriators can lose their water rights by adverse use, or prescription. A claimant to a prescriptive right must fulfill certain conditions specified by law. In California, for example, a prescriptive right can be acquired by taking and putting to beneficial use, for five consecutive years, ground water to which overlying landowners or prior appropriators have rights. If the rightful owner fails to interrupt the unlawful use before the end of the five-year prescription period, he loses his right to object to it and a prescriptive right is acquired by the claimant.

Legal Interpretation of Ground Water

Much of the confusion in legal interpretation of ground water dates from the past when ground water was only imperfectly understood.* Most water law of the past was based on an attempted distinction between "water courses"—defined as natural streams of surface or underground water flowing in definite channels from definite sources—and "percolating waters"—that is, waters moving slowly through the ground but not part of any definite underground stream. Various court decisions have even classified percolating water as diffused, tributary to springs, supplying surface wells, and seepage waters.[18] A workable ground water law must apply to all water in the zone of saturation and should recognize the interconnection between ground and surface waters.[13] In states where different rules of law apply to underground watercourses and percolating waters, perplexing problems of interpretation in court suits are created by these artificial distinctions.

* For example, the following statement appeared in a court decision of 1850 (Roath vs. Driscoll, 20 Conn. 533): "[Ground water] rises to great heights and moves collaterally, by influences beyond our apprehension. These influences are so secret, changeable and uncontrollable, we cannot subject them to the regulation of law, nor build upon them a system of rules, as has been done with streams upon the surface."

Ground Water Law in the United States

The consensus of authoritative opinion is that required legal control of ground water can and should be achieved at the state rather than at the federal level with as much control as may be practicable by local ground water users. It is desirable that laws of different states should be as consistent as possible, both in principle and in major provisions, so as to facilitate control of interstate waters.

Ground water laws in the various states differ widely in principle and degree of development. Many states have formulated rules based on court decisions rather than legislative actions. The diversity of state laws combined with continual modifications make it infeasible to summarize here ground water laws of the various states. Recent analyses of state ground water laws have been made by Hutchins,[8,9] McGuinness,[13] National Resources Planning Board,[14] the President's Water Resources Policy Commission,[15] and Thomas.[17]

Doctrines of water rights adopted by the various states generally follow a climatic pattern, as pointed out by Thomas.[17] Figure 13.1 shows areas of normal water surplus and deficiency * (based on whether or not the average annual precipitation exceeds the average annual potential evapotranspiration) together with water rights doctrines of the states. In the 31 Eastern states of water surplus, precipitation is ordinarily sufficient to provide adequate water on or adjacent to land of property owners, hence the prevalence of the land ownership doctrine. Recent water shortages in concentrated population areas of this region have led to importations of water from other sources, which in the future may lead to modifications incorporating the prior appropriation doctrine. The Rocky Mountain states are arid, except for the mountainous areas, and rainfall is insufficient even for dry farming. Crops depend upon imported irrigation water, hence the prior appropriation doctrine predominates. The Pacific Coast states and the Great Plains states from Montana to Texas tend to accept both the land ownership and prior appropriation doctrines. Climatically this follows because the Pacific Coast states contain both humid and arid regions, whereas the Great Plains states have a semiarid climate intermediate between those of the arid West and the humid East.

Water Rights in Overdraft Areas

Difficult problems of rights to ground water may develop in overdraft areas. Where annual withdrawal exceeds replenishment, the

* After Thornthwaite, C. W., "An Approach Toward a Rational Classification of Climate," *Geographical Review,* vol. 38, pp. 56–75, 1948.

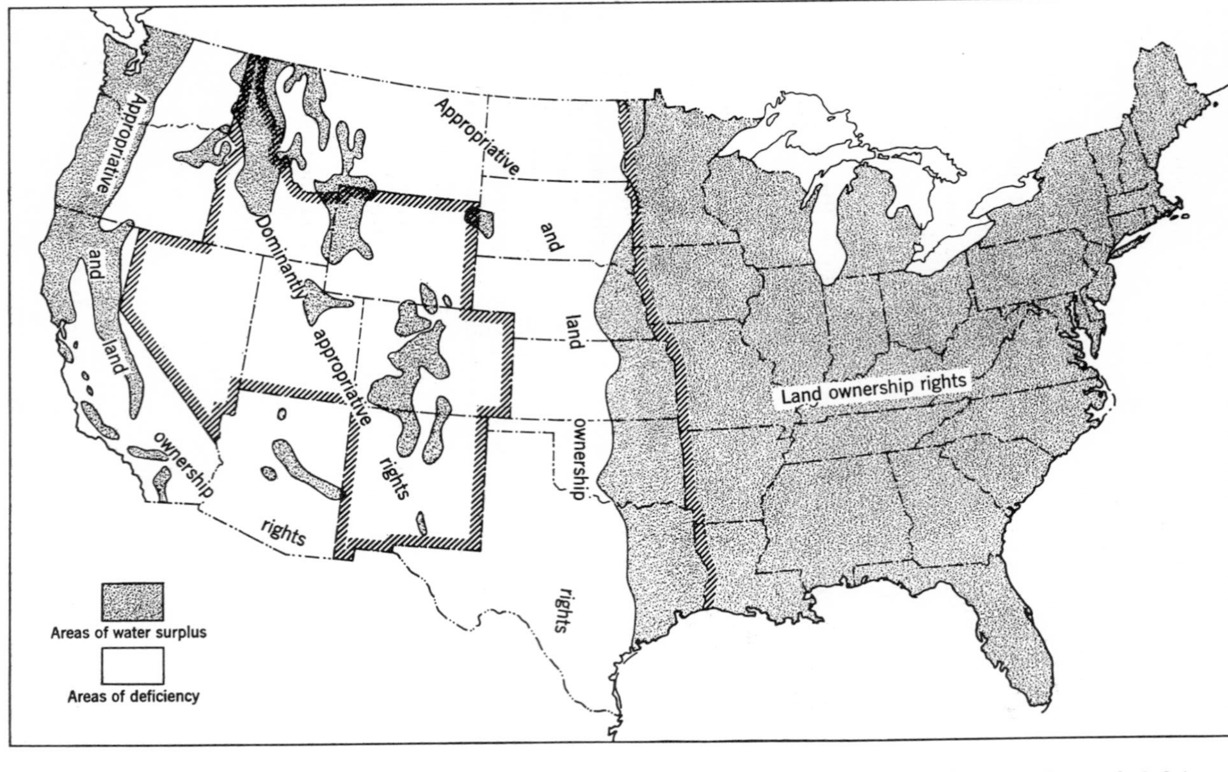

Fig. 13.1. Water rights doctrines by states of the United States, and areas of normal water surplus and deficiency (after Thomas[17]).

excess water comes from storage. Because water is regarded as a renewable natural resource, the mining of ground water is considered undesirable from a conservation standpoint (see Chapter 8).* However, if no alternate source of water is available, public opinion seems to favor the mining of water.[17] In other words, it is preferable to continue a water right until the water source is exhausted rather than limit the withdrawals to extend the availability of the water indefinitely. In such situations water rights, which by implication extend indefinitely in time, may continue although there may be no water to supply them.

The administration and control of ground water in overdraft areas poses many complex technical and legal problems. Controls can be exercised by an organization of overlying landowners, by enforcement of a court decree usually with the aid of a watermaster, or by a state administrative agency. Practical problems of control are the lengthy and costly court suits often involved. Ordinarily, an attempted regulation of pumpage from a ground water basin will enjoin all property owners as parties to the suit; the validity of all water rights must be reviewed and tested, and the hydrology of the basin must be determined. No one method exists for regulating ground water basins; individual situations involve varying hydraulic, economic, and legal conditions which produce many different solutions. It is apparent, however, that it is simpler to prevent than to cure overdrafts. In several Western states certain ground water reservoirs have been declared fully appropriated and new developments are not permitted.[17] Some Eastern states, by licensing new wells, are limiting pumping drafts and the number of years pumping may continue. Such police powers in the public benefit imply a doctrine of prior appropriation as water rights become a function of time rather than of land ownership.

An outstanding example of control initiated by action of water users occurred in Raymond Basin of San Gabriel Valley in Southern California. This action was only started because an auxiliary water supply, Metropolitan Water District water carried by conduit from the Colorado River, was available; otherwise the uncertainty of the outcome would have precluded such an action. The City of Pasadena, one of the water users, initiated an action in 1938 for adjudication of all underground water rights in the basin after its engineers had decided that recharge to Raymond Basin was considerably exceeded by draft.

* On the other hand, it is argued that depletion of a ground water supply can be justified on an economic basis. As has happened in several places in the Southwest, ground water was exploited to establish an economy that otherwise would not have been possible—and that then could finance the importation of distant water supplies.

Thirty-one parties were involved in the suit. In 1939 after a petition by many of the parties, the court referred the case to the State Division of Water Resources for a report on the physical facts. The Division reported in 1943 that recharge was about 70 per cent of draft. Final settlement came in 1949 with a ruling by the California Supreme Court * that pumping by all parties was to be proportionately reduced to make the total annual pumpage not exceed the safe yield. A watermaster was appointed to oversee pumpage. Fortunately, the reduction was accomplished without denying anyone his water supply because those parties which had other sources of water—such as the City of Pasadena, as a member of the Metropolitan Water District—were permitted to sell annually all or part of the water to which they had rights in the basin to those without access to another source. This purchased water could be pumped by the purchaser from his own wells.

A recent law enacted in California was designed to encourage development of substitute water supplies other than ground water.[16] Applying only to counties having substantial overdraft areas, it specified that the water right of a ground water user will not be impaired by ceasing or reducing his extraction of ground water if he uses instead water from an alternate source that is not tributary to the ground water supply.

Statutory Control of Recharged Ground Water

Most existing ground water law was developed to cover use of natural ground water supplies. Where surface water is placed underground to supplement ground water, title to the use of such recharged waters may rest on different principles from those applicable to natural ground water. As pointed out by Harding,[6] rights to recharged ground water may be vested in the overlying owner, in an organization of overlying landowners, in a non-landowning agency, or in the state.

The overlying owner may claim recharged water where no claims of ownership are made by the agency responsible for its occurrence. The artificial supply becomes abandoned ground water which mingles with the natural supply. Because physical works required to provide artificial ground water supplies usually involve costs exceeding the resources of individual owners, an organization of the benefited landowners may finance the recharging and retain title to the supplemental water. In states where recharging of ground water has been declared a beneficial use, organizations such as flood control, irrigation, and

* Pasadena v. Alhambra, 33 Calif. (2d) 908, 207 Pac. (2d) 17 (1949); certiorari denied, 339 U. S. 937 (1950).

water conservation districts have retained title to recharged waters for their members.

Water rights by an agency storing ground water under lands of others is illustrated by efforts of the U. S. Bureau of Reclamation to reserve rights to all return flows and waste from project water delivered to contracting areas. These claims present complicated legal and physical problems; the subject is under active study in the Central Valley Project of California.

Unappropriated ground water in most Western states belongs to the state. Hence if a state acquires surface water and places it underground on lands which it does not own, it is acting in the interest of the public as a non-landowning agency.

Common Regulations Applying to Ground Water

A variety of regulations have been established in most states to facilitate ground water development in the interest of the public. Some of the more common state requirements follow.

Any person drilling wells for others must be licensed. Installation, deepening, or reperforating of a well must be reported on prescribed forms; some states require well drilling permits instead. Drillers must submit geologic logs, including depth, color, character, size of material, and structure of the strata penetrated for all new and deepened wells. Wells furnishing domestic or municipal water must be properly constructed and finished to prevent contamination. Flowing artesian wells must be capped or regulated by suitable devices to prevent waste. Abandoned wells must be sealed to prevent waste, contamination, and accidents. Water pumped for cooling or air conditioning purposes must be returned to the ground through recharge wells; other states accomplish the same purpose by levying a sewer tax on ground water wasted into sewers. The disposal of any pollutants, such as brines or industrial wastes, which degrade the quality of public ground water supplies can be restricted.

References

1. Black, A. P., Basic concepts in ground water law, *Jour. Amer. Water Works Assoc.*, vol. 39, pp. 989–1002, 1947.
2. Conkling, H., Administrative control of underground water: physical and legal aspects, *Trans. Amer. Soc. Civil Engrs.*, vol. 102, pp. 753–837, 1937.
3. Critchlow, H. T., Policies and problems in controlling ground-water resources, *Jour. Amer. Water Works Assoc.*, vol. 40, pp. 775–783, 1948.

4. Harding, S. T., *Water rights for irrigation,* Stanford Univ. Press, Stanford, Calif., 176 pp., 1936.
5. Harding, S. T., United States water law, *Trans. Amer. Soc. Civil Engrs.,* vol. CT, pp. 343–356, 1953.
6. Harding, S. T., Statutory control of ground water in the western United States, *Trans. Amer. Soc. Civil Engrs.,* vol. 120, pp. 490–498, 1955.
7. Hughes, W. F., Proposed ground-water conservation measures in Texas, *Texas Jour. Sci.,* vol. 2, pp. 35–45, 1945.
8. Hutchins, W. A., Selected problems in the law of water rights in the West, *U. S. Dept. Agric. Misc. Publ.* 418, Washington, D. C., 513 pp., 1942.
9. Hutchins, W. A., Trends in the statutory law of ground water in the western states, *Texas Law Review,* vol. 34, pp. 157–191, 1955.
10. Hutchins, W. A., Irrigation water rights in California, *Agric. Exp. Sta. Circ.* 452, Univ. Calif., Berkeley, 56 pp., 1956.
11. Hutchins, W. A., *The California law of water rights,* State Calif., Sacramento, 571 pp., 1956.
12. McGuinness, C. L., Legal control of use of ground water, *Water Works Eng.,* vol. 98, pp. 475, 508, 510, 512, 1945.
13. McGuinness, C. L., Water law with special reference to ground water, *U. S. Geological Survey Circ.* 117, Washington, D. C., 30 pp., 1951.
14. National Resources Planning Board, *State water law in the development of the West,* Water Resources Committee, Subcommittee on State Water Law, Washington, D. C., 138 pp., 1943.
15. President's Water Resources Policy Commission, *Water resources law,* vol. 3, Washington, D. C., 777 pp., 1950.
16. State Calif., *Water code,* Sacramento, 756 pp., 1951.
17. Thomas, H. E., Water rights in areas of ground-water mining, *U. S. Geological Survey Circ.* 347, Washington, D. C., 16 pp., 1955.
18. Thompson, D. G., and A. G. Fiedler, Some problems relating to legal control of use of ground waters, *Jour. Amer. Water Works Assoc.,* vol. 30, pp. 1049–1091, 1938.
19. Tolman, C. F., and A. C. Stipp, Analysis of legal concepts of subflow and percolating waters, *Trans. Amer. Soc. Civil Engrs.,* vol. 106, pp. 882–933, 1941.

Model Studies and Numerical Analysis of Ground Water

CHAPTER 14

Ground water distribution and flow can be studied by means of analytic, field, and model techniques. Model studies and numerical analysis methods may have useful applications when direct analysis and adequate field investigation are not possible.

Ground water models can be grouped into four general types: sand, electrical, viscous fluid, and membrane. Of these, only the sand model represents a true model in that both aquifer and model involve flow through porous media. The other models are analogies of ground water flow, in that flow other than that through porous media occurs; however, kinematic and dynamic similarities exist on a macroscopic basis. Sizes and shapes of ground water models are determined by the particular purpose and type of model. Models of hydrologic interest are designed to represent aquifers and their boundaries.*

Sand Models

A sand model is a scale model of an aquifer with the boundaries scaled down and the permeability—absolute value and spatial distribution—modified. Sand models have been constructed in watertight boxes of various shapes, rectangular forms, columns, and sectors being

* The first ground water model is attributed to P. Forchheimer, who constructed a sand model for study of well flow at Graz, Austria, in 1898.

most common. Examples of two designs appear in Figs. 14.1 and 14.2. From the standpoint of aquifer type, unconfined aquifers can be modeled with the water table serving as the upper boundary; confined aquifers are reproduced by providing an impermeable cover so that pressure can be applied.

Visual identification of a water table is difficult; consequently, water table and piezometric levels can be obtained best from piezometers tapped into the model. Piezometer tubes should be small in order to minimize modifications of the flow pattern.

A coarse sand placed in small quantities under water and compacted consistently to remove air will yield a uniform permeability within the model. Anisotropic permeabilities can be achieved by layers of different sands.

Capillary rise in a sand model is disproportionately large compared to that occurring under field conditions. For studies of flow patterns, especially those involving confined aquifers, the effects are unimportant; however, in unconfined aquifer investigations of seepage, drawdown to wells, and similar phenomena, corrections for the large capillary rise are necessary.

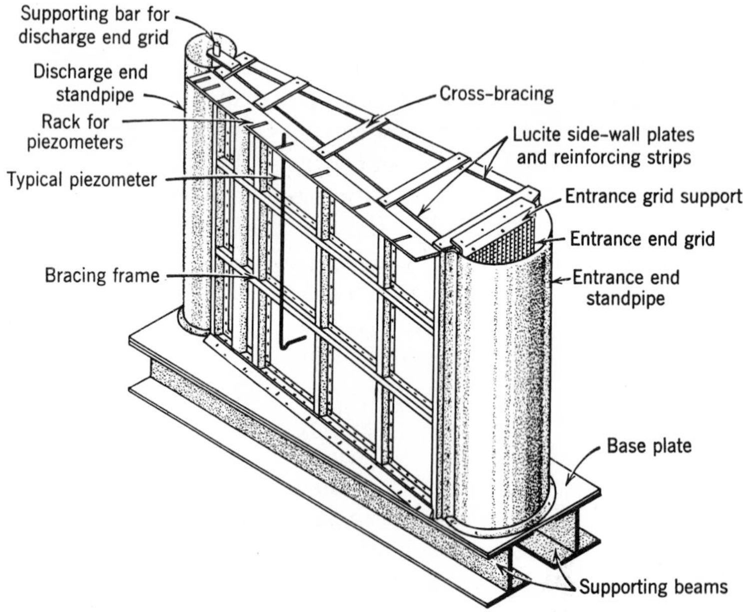

Fig. 14.1. Sand model of a well sector to study steady flow to a well penetrating an unconfined aquifer (after Hall [17]).

Fig. 14.2. Sand model to study sea water intrusion representing a vertical section through a confined aquifer. Reservoirs at each end contain waters of differcnt densities (after Harder and others [20]).

Because flows in both model and prototype are occurring in porous media, kinematic and dynamic similarities are obtained. Geometric similarity is defined by the model-prototype length ratio

$$L_r = \frac{L_m}{L_p} \tag{14.1}$$

where the subscripts r, m, and p refer to ratio, model, and prototype, respectively. Because Darcy's law applies to both model and prototype, the velocity ratio for the isotropic case can be expressed as

$$\frac{v_m}{v_p} = \frac{K_m i_m}{K_p i_p} \tag{14.2}$$

where K is coefficient of permeability and i is hydraulic gradient. With equal slopes, the prototype velocity is given by

$$v_p = \frac{v_m}{K_r} \tag{14.3}$$

and the flow rate by

$$Q_p = \frac{Q_m}{K_r L_r^2} \tag{14.4}$$

Sand models have been employed for investigating a variety of ground water flow problems. The literature furnishes examples of applications for studying seepage through earth dams and from canals,[36] ground water movement,[45] sea water intrusion in coastal aquifers,[20, 41] water spreading for ground water recharge,[3] and flow to and from wells.[2, 6, 17, 19, 62] By adding dyes at various points in the sand, the flow field can be revealed by dye streams.[10, 30, 31, 43, 54] Potassium dichromate is an effective and convenient dye substance for this purpose.

Electrical Models

The flow of an electric current can be expressed by Ohm's law

$$I = \sigma_0 \frac{dE}{dx} \tag{14.5}$$

where I is the electric current per unit area through a material of specific conductivity σ_0 and dE/dx is the voltage gradient. Equation 14.5 satisfies the Laplace equation and the analogy with Darcy's law is apparent.*

An electrical field produced by an applied voltage within a model reproducing ground water boundaries will be similar to ground water flow in the prototype. A correspondence exists between head and voltage, hydraulic gradient and voltage gradient, permeability and specific conductivity, equipotential lines of flow and equipotential lines of current, and flow lines and lines of current flow. Electrical models are restricted to steady flows, and the simpler types assume homogeneous isotropic aquifers. Solid, liquid, and gelatin conductors have been successfully employed. Alternating current minimizes polarization.

One limitation of electrical models is that there is no analogous force of gravity to produce a water table. Because lines of current flow are automatically distributed over an entire conducting surface, it is necessary to determine the free surface boundary on a trial-and-error basis. Atmospheric pressure exists everywhere along a free water surface, so that the decrease in head must be proportional to

* A sizable body of knowledge pertaining to electrical models has been contributed by the petroleum industry for analysis of secondary recovery operations. Much of this information is applicable to ground water hydrology, where it can be adapted to study a variety of well flow problems.

the electrical potential drop along this surface. This linear relation serves as a criterion for locating a water table.

Solid Conductors. Electrical conduction models with solid conductors have been constructed from thin metal sheets, carbon paper,[64] and graphite,[2] among others. A current applied at boundary electrodes produces a potential drop throughout the conductor. Sheet monel is a desirable conducting material for representing two-dimensional flow. Wells can be formed by drilling small holes and inserting electrodes; copper strips serve as outer boundaries. Equipotential lines are plotted by measuring the voltage drop with a galvanometer at various points on the monel sheet, and, in addition, potential gradients can be determined by two probes separated by a constant distance.

A graphite model to study unconfined radial flow into a well was constructed from a rectangular sheet of pressed carbon by Babbitt and Caldwell.[2] A narrow wedge, representing a small sector of a radial flow pattern, was formed as shown in Fig. 14.3. A 6-volt battery supplied current to conducting strips attached to the graphite. A potentiometer connecting the anode and a steel probe enabled equipotential lines to be located. The free surface was approximated by marking the point on each equipotential line having the same ratio to the total drawdown as the corresponding voltage of the equipotential line to the total voltage drop. By cutting along this line and repeating the process until no further change was warranted, the final free surface was located.

Liquid Conductors. Liquid models are useful for mapping flow fields of equipotential lines and flow lines.[59, 60] A simple model for

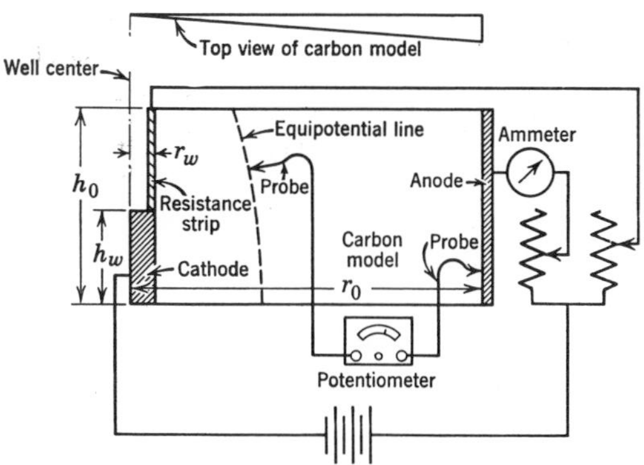

Fig. 14.3. Graphite model showing electrical circuit and connections to study unconfined radial flow to a well (after Babbitt and Caldwell [2]).

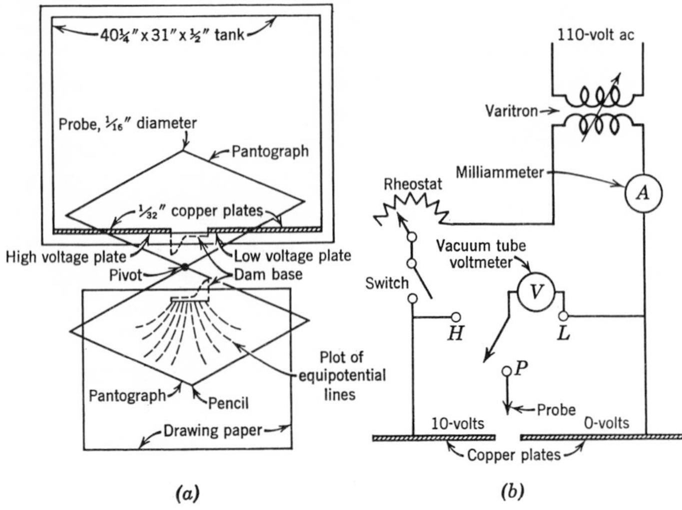

Fig. 14.4. Electrolytic model showing (*a*) apparatus and (*b*) wiring diagram for plotting equipotential lines of seepage beneath a masonry dam on a pervious foundation (after M. A. Selim, *Trans. Amer. Soc. Civil Engrs.*, 1947).

this purpose consists of a shallow wooden tank filled with an electrolyte of low conductivity. A dilute copper sulfate solution will prove satisfactory. Electrodes are attached at the boundaries for the situation under study and lines of constant potential drop are traced by a probe attached to a pantograph and connected in a voltmeter circuit (Fig. 14.4). By inserting a copper electrode into the electrolyte and connecting it as one of the boundaries, a well penetrating a uniform confined aquifer is represented with the equipotential lines analogous to contours of the piezometric surface. With several electrodes, a well field can be studied. In applications for the petroleum industry, injection and extraction wells are represented by electrodes attached to opposite sides of a transformer.[33] Currents in each electrode are adjusted by suitable resistance to correspond to well flow rates. In the same manner, effects of recharge wells on ground water can be studied.

Electrolytic models are adaptable also for analysis of seepage through porous media structures, such as earth dams, and under masonry dams on pervious foundations. In many situations both equipotential lines and flow lines can be mapped directly. For example, by attaching electrodes to the sides of a tank representing the streambed upstream and downstream from the impervious base of a dam (Fig. 14.5*a*), equipotential lines beneath the dam are located. Reversing the conducting and nonconducting surfaces, so that the base of the dam and the periphery of the tank other than the portion representing the streambed become the electrodes (Fig. 14.5*b*), flow lines beneath the dam are traced.

The above electrolytic models are restricted to two-dimensional representations; however, this limitation can be removed to study flow in aquifers of variable thickness.[40, 59] The bottom of the tank can be filled with paraffin and the configuration of the aquifer carved in the paraffin. When the tank is flooded with an electrolyte, the aquifer thickness is exactly modeled.

Gelatin Conductors. Gelatin models can be formed by adding small amounts of sodium chloride or copper sulfate to a hot gelatin and pouring it into a mold, representing aquifer boundaries, where it solidifies.[24] The ease with which the conducting gelatin can be shaped and formed in any desired manner is an important advantage. Zones of different permeabilities can be simulated by sheets or inserts of gelatin containing appropriate salt concentrations; moreover, variations in aquifer thickness can be reproduced by corresponding variations in gelatin thickness.

An example of the gelatin model and its application is furnished by Opsal.[42] Equal portions of gelatin and glycerin were added to water to form a gelatinous mass. Sodium chloride was added to in-

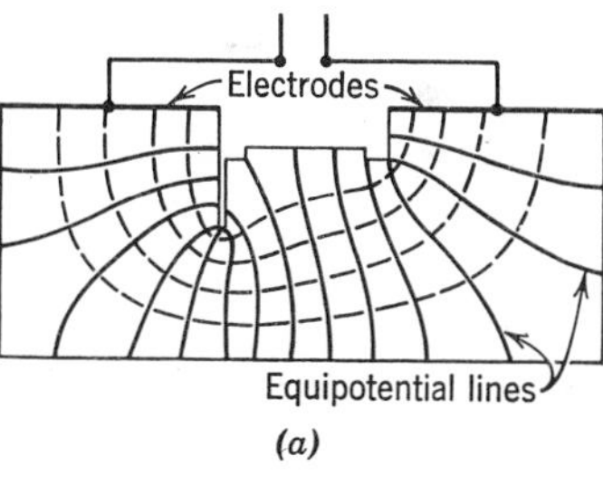

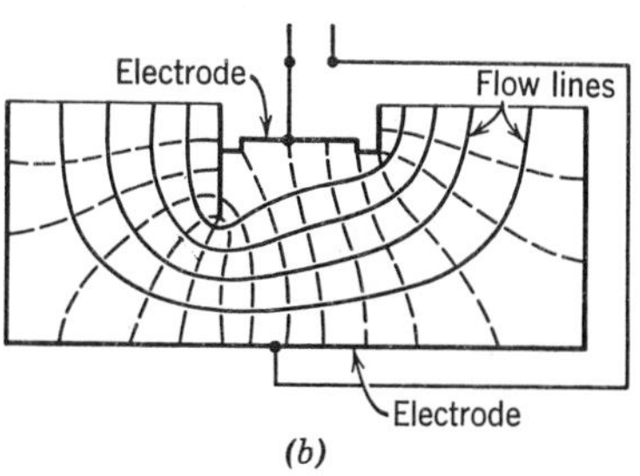

Fig. 14.5. Electrode arrangements in an electrolytic model for determining (*a*) equipotential lines and (*b*) flow lines of seepage beneath a masonry dam with a cutoff on a pervious foundation.

crease conductivity, and beta naphthol to prevent decay of the solution. The fluid was poured into a cylindrical tank having sides of stainless steel and a nonconductive bottom. An alternating current was applied between the sides and a center well-probe; a voltmeter measured the drop between the cylindrical boundary and an insulated probe making contact with the gelatin only at its end. The model represented a well penetrating a confined aquifer. The investigation consisted of measurements taken in a radial vertical section to establish equipotential lines for partially penetrating wells. Tests were also made on a well sector model in which the gelatin was cut by a hot wire to determine the free surface surrounding a well in an unconfined aquifer.

Color Tracers. Color tracer electrical models have facilitated study of the displacement of an injected fluid in a petroleum reservoir.[63] These are equally applicable for obtaining qualitative information regarding recharge wells. One type of model consisted of blotting paper saturated with phenolphthalein as an electrolyte.[61] Small cylindrical negative electrodes represented injection wells; positive electrodes were producing wells. The advance of hydroxyl ions from the negative to positive electrodes was indicated by a red color developing as the pH increased in the solution. The advancing color line corresponded to a two-dimensional fluid displacement and was recorded photographically. A similar apparatus utilized an agar gelatin containing zinc-ammonium chloride.[5] Electrodes representing injection wells contained copper-ammonium chloride so that when a voltage was applied, copper ions replaced zinc ions and thereby created an advancing green front.

Viscous Fluid Models *

If a viscous liquid flows between two closely spaced parallel plates forming a narrow channel, its movement is analogous to that of ground water flow in a two dimensional cross-section of an aquifer. The first models based on this principle were developed by Hele-Shaw[21,22,23] in England in 1897 to demonstrate flow patterns around variously shaped boundaries.

With laminar flow between two parallel plates, it can be shown that the flow lines form a two-dimensional potential flow field. The derivation follows from the generalized Navier-Stokes equations of motion

* Also known as Hele-Shaw and parallel plate models.

(see any elementary text on hydrodynamics). For steady flow with the Dupuit assumptions, the mean velocity of flow in the model is

$$v_m = \frac{b^2 \rho_m g}{3\mu_m} \frac{dh}{dx} \tag{14.6}$$

where b is the half-width of the channel; ρ_m and μ_m are the model fluid density and viscosity, respectively; g is the acceleration of gravity; and dh/dx is the surface slope. From the analogy to Darcy's law it follows that the plate spacing and fluid can be selected to correspond to a desired permeability. The velocity ratio

$$v_r = \frac{v_m}{v_p} = \frac{\rho_m b^2 \mu_p}{3\rho_p k \mu_m} = \frac{b^2 \rho_r}{3k\mu_r} \tag{14.7}$$

which, together with a given scale factor (length ratio) L_r of the model, enables the time ratio to be found from

$$T_r = \frac{L_r}{v_r} \tag{14.8}$$

Models of this type are constructed from two sheets of glass or plastic spaced a fixed distance apart.[56] Reservoirs to control fluid flow between the plates are attached at the sides or ends of the model. Oil or glycerin functions satisfactorily for the fluid; for small spacings even water flows in the laminar range. Dye added to the fluid defines the free surface for unconfined flows, and point sources of dye along inflow boundaries reveal flow lines.* Grid paper fastened to the back of the model facilitates measurements. Figure 14.6 shows one design of a viscous fluid model.

An important advantage of this model is that unsteady flows with irregular boundaries can be studied directly. By varying reservoir levels with time, the resulting free surface changes can be recorded by motion pictures. Also, because the plate spacing is related to permeability, any desired permeability variation can be introduced into the model by attaching thin laminated sheets at appropriate positions between the plates.

Flows in viscous fluid models have been studied as analogies of steady and unsteady flows in confined and unconfined aquifers.[1, 15, 16, 48, 55] Particular applications include studies of sea water intrusion,[47] bank storage adjacent to flooding streams,[57] seepage through earth dams,[38] subdrainage problems,[7, 29] and petroleum produc-

* A row of short pieces of indelible pencil leads is excellent for this purpose.

Fig. 14.6. A viscous fluid model. The free surface of the fluid under a steady flow condition can be seen in the glass channel (after Todd [56]).

tion.[26,44] Especially noteworthy are models of this type built in the Netherlands to study hydrologic conditions bordering the Dutch coast.[11,12,32,46,47] These models combined the effects of sea levels, rainfall, evaporation, fresh-water recharge into dune areas, polder drainage, and well pumpage.

Membrane Models

Another model analogy for ground water flow, pointed out by Hansen,[18] can be constructed with a rubber membrane. It was shown that for small slopes the surface of a membrane can be expressed in cylindrical coordinates as

$$\frac{d^2z}{dr^2} + \frac{1}{r}\frac{dz}{dr} = -\frac{W_m}{T_m} \tag{14.9}$$

where dz is the deflection at a radial distance dr from a central deflecting point, W_m is the weight of the membrane per unit area, and T_m is a uniform membrane tension. The Laplace equation in cylindrical coordinates can be expressed as

$$\frac{\partial^2 h}{\partial r^2} + \frac{1}{r}\frac{\partial h}{\partial r} + \frac{1}{r^2}\frac{\partial^2 h}{\partial \theta^2} + \frac{\partial^2 h}{\partial z^2} = 0 \tag{14.10}$$

where h is the hydraulic head, r is the radial distance, θ is the angular coordinate, and z is the vertical coordinate. For steady axially symmetrical flow of an incompressible fluid, it reduces to

$$\frac{d^2h}{dr^2} + \frac{1}{r}\frac{dh}{dr} = 0 \tag{14.11}$$

which is applicable to well flow in an ideal confined aquifer and a good approximation (for a small drawdown) in an unconfined aquifer. The membrane equation approximates Eq. 14.11 as the term $-W_m/T_m$ approaches zero.

To study the shape of a free surface around a well, a rubber membrane was clamped under uniform tension over a circular boundary in a horizontal position (see Fig. 14.7). A central probe, representing a pumping well, deflected the membrane. Measured deflections closely approximated the theoretical semilogarithmic drawdown relationship, although systematic deviations due to gravity were noted. The term $-W_m/T_m$ cannot be reduced to zero; however, placement of the membrane in a vertical plane should minimize this error. A combined membrane and electrical model, consisting of a cylindrical aluminum tank filled with an electrolyte and covered with a rubber membrane, was designed by Zee and others [66] to study unconfined well flow.

The membrane model is particularly adaptable to studies of multiple-

Fig. 14.7. Membrane model representing the piezometric surface around a multiple-well system with equal drawdowns in each well (courtesy V. E. Hansen).

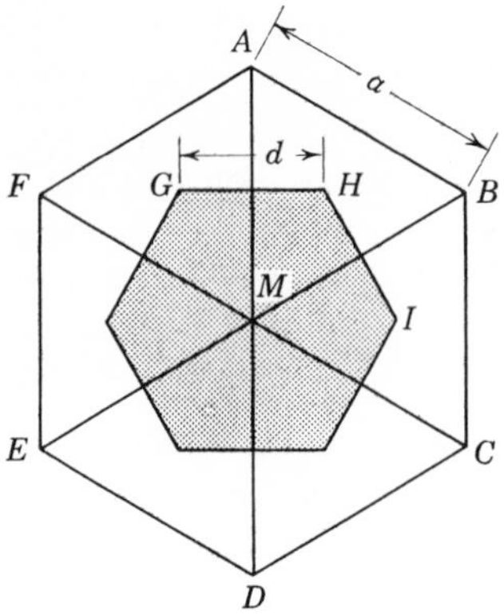

Fig. 14.8. Elemental hexagon for relaxation method.

well systems, simulated by a group of probes as shown in Fig. 14.7, and of complex boundary conditions, controlled by the membrane frame.

Numerical Analysis Methods

Nonlinear partial differential equations govern ground water flow where irregular boundaries or unsteady flows are involved. Except in special cases, these cannot be solved directly. Numerical analysis methods are based on the replacement of a partial differential equation by a finite difference equivalent which can then be solved by repeated arithmetic calculations. The procedure, known as the iteration or relaxation method, was developed by Southwell and his colleagues [49, 50, 51] and has been extensively applied to solve a variety of engineering and physics problems.

An introduction to the method can be given by an example for determining a piezometric surface for known boundary conditions. In Fig. 14.8 the small hexagon represents in plan view a very small portion of a confined aquifer assumed to have a saturated thickness equal to b. The component of flow from M toward A through section GH is given by Darcy's law,

$$Q_A = Kbd\frac{h_M - h_A}{a} \tag{14.12}$$

where K is the coefficient of permeability, a and d are distances shown in Fig. 14.8, and h_M and h_A are the piezometric heads at M and A, respectively. Similarly, the flow through HI is

$$Q_B = Kbd\frac{h_M - h_B}{a} \tag{14.13}$$

Summing the six component flows of the hexagon yields

$$\Sigma Q = Kbd \frac{6h_M - \Sigma h}{a} \tag{14.14}$$

where

$$\Sigma Q = Q_A + Q_B + Q_C + Q_D + Q_E + Q_F \tag{14.15}$$

and

$$\Sigma h = h_A + h_B + h_C + h_D + h_E + h_F \tag{14.16}$$

For horizontal flow $\Sigma Q = 0$ and Eq. 14.14 becomes

$$h_M = \frac{\Sigma h}{6} \tag{14.17}$$

Where a vertical water component occurs, such as from infiltrated water percolating through a semipervious confining layer, $\Sigma Q \neq 0$. The area of the interior hexagon equals $(\sqrt{3}/2)a^2$, and with an infiltration rate W,

$$\Sigma Q = \frac{\sqrt{3}}{2} a^2 W \tag{14.18}$$

Substituting this value in Eq. 14.14, the central head becomes

$$h_M = \frac{\Sigma h + C_A}{6} \tag{14.19}$$

where the constant

$$C_A = \frac{3a^2 W}{2Kb} \tag{14.20}$$

From Eqs. 14.17 and 14.19 it can be seen that an estimate of the piezometric head at the center of the hexagon is obtained from the heads of the perimeter points. Applying the method on a large scale for mapping a piezometric surface, a hexagonal grid is superimposed over an aquifer with known or assumed boundaries. Estimated heads based on known boundary heads are assigned to all grid points to start the computation. Central heads of all hexagons are computed in a systematic manner from the estimated perimeter heads of each. After obtaining a calculated head for each grid point, revised estimates of heads are adopted and the process is repeated over the entire grid. Each successive series of calculations reduces the difference between each estimated and computed head. Finally, when the differences become negligibly small, the resulting values represent the desired piezometric heads over the aquifer.

Figure 14.9 shows a portion of a solution for one situation. A flat agricultural area with high water tables has irregular boundaries, as

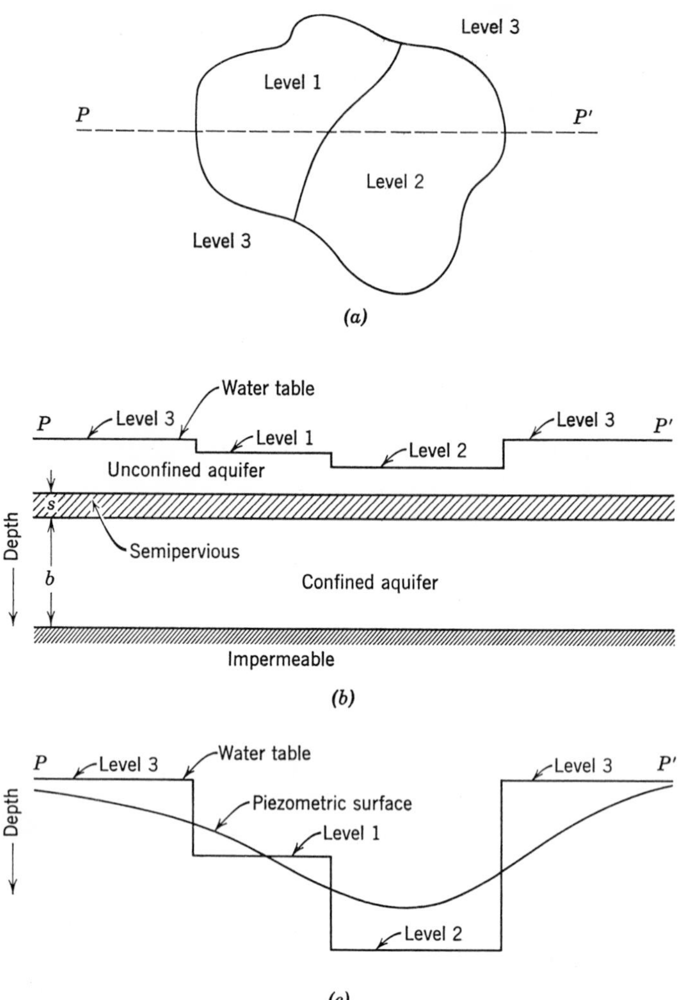

Fig. 14.9. Application of numerical analysis to compute the piezometric surface of a confined aquifer overlain by a semipervious stratum; (*a*) plan view, (*b*) vertical cross-section, and (*c*) ground water levels (after Edelman [13]).

shown in Fig. 14.9*a*. Surface drains control water tables in various parts of the area at levels indicated by the cross-section in Fig. 14.9*b*. A semipervious layer of thickness s and permeability K_1 overlies an aquifer of thickness b and permeability K_2. To find the piezometric surface of the lower aquifer, a hexagonal grid system is laid over the entire area and estimated piezometric heads are assigned to each intersection, assuming that water table and piezometric elevations coincide (at Level 3) outside of the area. From the above reasoning it can be shown that the central head for any hexagon is given by

$$h_M = \frac{\Sigma h + C_B H_M}{6 + C_B} \tag{14.21}$$

where H_M is the unconfined head and

$$C_B = \frac{3\,K_1 a^2}{2\,K_2 s b} \tag{14.22}$$

Heads are computed over the entire grid, differences adjusted, and the process repeated until no further adjustments are necessary. The result is the piezometric surface. A section through the area showing one solution appears in Fig. 14.9*c*.

Grid patterns other than the hexagonal form, described above, can be adopted for the relaxation method. Three patterns are shown in Fig. 14.10. An advantage of the square and clear hexagonal designs over the hexagonal is that fewer perimeter points are involved in each central point calculation.

Experience with the method leads to shortcuts in estimating intersection values, thereby reducing the number of approximations required. Except in the simplest cases, computations are lengthy and tedious. For large problems electronic computers can be of material assistance.

Numerical analysis has been applied to a variety of ground water problems. Included are seepage,[49] drainage,[34] and well flow[4, 28, 35, 65] studies. Regional analyses of ground water levels have been carried out by Edelman[13] in the Netherlands and by Stallman[52, 53] in the United States.

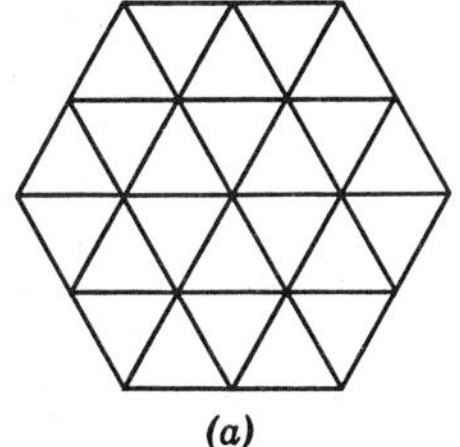

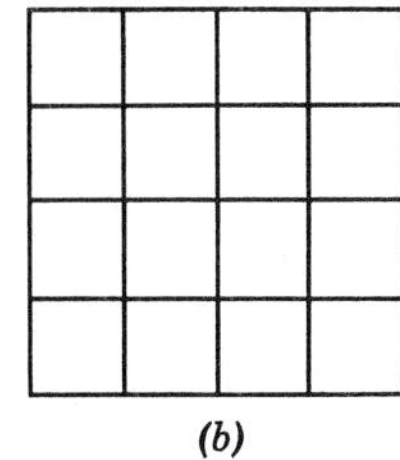

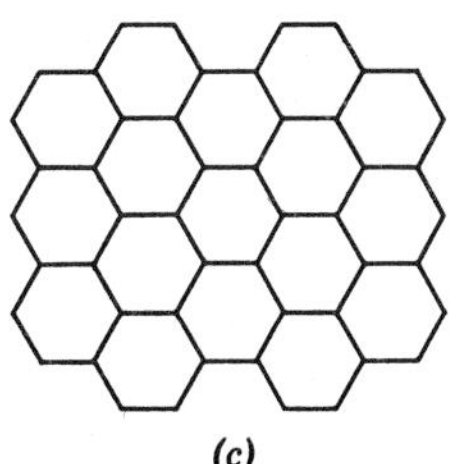

Fig. 14.10. Grid systems for the relaxation method: (*a*) hexagonal, (*b*) square, and (*c*) clear hexagonal.

References

1. Aravin, V. I., Experimental investigation of unsteady flow of ground water (in Russian), *Trans. Sci. Research Inst. Hydrotechnics,* USSR, vol. 30, pp. 79–88, 1941.
2. Babbitt, H. E., and D. H. Caldwell, The free surface around, and the interference between, gravity wells, *Univ. Illinois Eng. Exp. Sta. Bull.* 374, Urbana, 60 pp., 1948.
3. Baumann, P., Ground-water movement controlled through spreading, *Trans. Amer. Soc. Civil Engrs.,* vol. 117, pp. 1024–1074, 1952.
4. Boreli, M., Free-surface flow toward partially penetrating wells, *Trans. Amer. Geophysical Union,* vol. 36, pp. 664–672, 1955.
5. Botset, H. G., The electrolytic model and its application to the study of recovery problems, *Trans. Amer. Inst. Min. and Metal. Engrs.,* vol. 165, pp. 15–25, 1946.
6. Boulton, N. S., The flow pattern near a gravity well in a uniform water-bearing medium, *Jour. Inst. Civil Engrs.,* vol. 36, pp. 534–550, 1951.
7. Casagrande, A., and W. L. Shannon, Base course drainage for airport pavements, *Trans. Amer. Soc. Civil Engrs.,* vol. 117, pp. 792–820, 1952.
8. Dachler, R., *Grundwasserströmung,* J. Springer, Vienna, 141 pp., 1936.
9. d'Andrimont, R., Note préliminaire sur une nouvelle méthode pour étudier expérimentalement l'allure des nappes aquifères dans les terrains permeables en petit, *Annales Soc. Geol. Belgique,* vol. 32, Liége, pp. M115–M120, 1905.
10. d'Andrimont, R., Sur la circulation de l'eau des nappes aquifères contenues dans des terrains permeables en petit, *Annales, Soc. Geol. Belgique,* vol. 33, Liége, pp. M21–M33, 1906.
11. Dietz, D. N., Een modelproef ter bestudeering van niet-stationnaire bewegingen van het grondwater, *Water,* vol. 25, The Hague, pp. 185–188, 1941.
12. Dietz, D. N., Ervaringen met modelonderzoek in de hydrologie, *Water,* vol. 28, The Hague, pp. 17–20, 1944.
13. Edelman, J. H., *Over de berekening van grondwaterstroomingen,* Doctorate thesis, Delft Tech. Univ., Netherlands, 77 pp., 1947.
14. Felius, G. P., Recherches hydrologiques par des modèles électriques, *Assemblée Générale de Rome, Assoc. Intl. d'Hydrologie Scientifique,* vol. 2, pp. 162–169, 1954.
15. Gunther, E., Lösung von Grundwasseraufgaben mit Hilfe der Strömung in dünnen Schichten, *Wasserkraft und Wasserwirtschaft,* vol. 35, no. 3, pp. 49–55, 1940.
16. Gunther, E., Untersuchung von Grundwasserströmungen durch analoge Strömungen zäher Flüssigkeiten, *Forschung auf dem Gebiete des Ingenieurwesens,* vol. 11, pp. 76–88, 1940.
17. Hall, H. P., An investigation of steady flow toward a gravity well, *La Houille Blanche,* vol. 10, pp. 8–35, 1955.
18. Hansen, V. E., Complicated well problems solved by the membrane analogy, *Trans. Amer. Geophysical Union,* vol. 33, pp. 912–916, 1952.
19. Hansen, V. E., Unconfined ground-water flow to multiple wells, *Trans. Amer. Soc. Civil Engrs.,* vol. 118, pp. 1098–1130, 1953.

20. Harder, J. A., T. R. Simpson, L.-K. Lau, F. L. Hotes, and P. H. McGauhey, *Laboratory research on sea water intrusion into fresh ground-water sources and methods of its prevention—final report,* Sanitary Eng. Research Lab., Univ. Calif., Berkeley, 68 pp., 1953.
21. Hele-Shaw, H. S., Experiments on the nature of the surface resistance in pipes and on ships, *Trans. Inst. Naval Architects,* vol. 39, pp. 145–156, 1897.
22. Hele-Shaw, H. S., Investigation of the nature of surface resistance of water and of stream-line motion under certain experimental conditions, *Trans. Inst. Naval Architects,* vol. 40, pp. 21–46, 1898.
23. Hele-Shaw, H. S., Stream-line motion of a viscous film, *Rep. 68th Meeting British Assoc. for the Advancement Sci.,* pp. 136–142, 1899.
24. Horner, W. L., and W. A. Bruce, Electrical-model studies of secondary recovery, in *Secondary recovery of oil in the United States,* 2nd ed., Amer. Petroleum Inst., New York, pp. 195–203, 1950.
25. Hubbert, M. K., Theory of scale models as applied to the study of geologic structures, *Bull. Geol. Soc. Amer.,* vol. 48, pp. 1456–1520, 1937.
26. Hubbert, M. K., Entrapment of petroleum under hydrodynamic conditions, *Bull. Amer. Assoc. Pet. Geol.,* vol. 37, pp. 1954–2026, 1953.
27. Hurst, W., Electrical models as an aid in visualizing flow in condensate reservoirs, *The Pet. Engr.,* vol. 12, no. 10, pp. 123–124, 127, 129, 1941.
28. Kashef, A. I., Y. S. Touloukian, and R. E. Fadum, Numerical solutions of steady-state and transient flow problems—artesian and water-table wells, *Purdue Univ. Eng. Exp. Sta. Bull.* 117, Lafayette, Ind., 116 pp., 1952.
29. Kellogg, F. H., Investigation of drainage rates affecting the stability of earth dams, *Trans. Amer. Soc. Civil Engrs.,* vol. 113, pp. 1261–1309, 1948.
30. Kirkham, D., Artificial drainage of land: streamline experiments, the artesian basin—I, *Trans. Amer. Geophysical Union,* vol. 20, pp. 677–680, 1939.
31. Kirkham, D., Pressure and streamline distribution in waterlogged land overlying an impervious layer, *Proc. Soil Sci. Soc. Amer.,* vol. 5, pp. 65–68, 1940.
32. Krul, W. F. J. M., and F. A. Liefrinck, *Recent ground-water investigations in the Netherlands,* Elsevier Publishing Co., New York, 78 pp., 1946.
33. Lee, B. D., Potentiometric-model studies of fluid flow in petroleum reservoirs, *Trans. Amer. Inst. Min. and Metal. Engrs.,* vol. 174, pp. 41–66, 1948.
34. Luthin, J. N., and R. A. Gaskell, Numerical solution for tile drainage of layered soils, *Trans. Amer. Geophysical Union,* vol. 31, pp. 595–602, 1950.
35. Luthin, J. N., and V. H. Scott, Numerical analysis of flow through aquifers toward wells, *Agric. Eng.,* vol. 33, pp. 279–282, 1952.
36. Mavis, F. T., and T. P. Tsui, Percolation and capillary movement of water through sand prisms, *Bull.* 18, Univ. Iowa Studies in Eng., Iowa City, 25 pp., 1939.
37. McNown, J. S., E.-Y. Hsu, and C.-S. Yih, Applications of the relaxation technique in fluid mechanics, *Trans. Amer. Soc. Civil Engrs.,* vol. 120, pp. 650–686, 1955.
38. Mikhailov, G. K., On maximum gradients near drainage of earth dams (in Russian), *Trans. Acad. Sci.,* Div. Tech. Sci., USSR, no. 2, pp. 109–112, 1956.
39. Muskat, M., *The flow of homogeneous fluids through porous media,* McGraw-Hill, New York, 763 pp., 1937.
40. Muskat, M., The theory of potentiometric models, *Trans. Amer. Inst. Min. and Metal. Engrs.,* vol. 179, pp. 216–221, 1949.
41. Nomitsu, T., Y. Toyohara, and R. Kamimoto, On the contact surface of fresh-

and salt-water under the ground near a sandy sea-shore, *Mem. College Sci.*, Kyoto Imperial Univ., Ser. A, vol. 10, no. 7, pp. 279–302, 1927.

42. Opsal, F. W., Analysis of two- and three-dimensional ground-water flow by electrical analogy, *The Trend in Eng. at the Univ. Washington,* vol. 7, no. 2. Seattle, pp. 15–20, 32, 1955.
43. Pennink, J. M. K., *Grondwater stroombanen,* Stadsdrukkery, Amsterdam, 151 pp., 1915.
44. Polubarinova-Kochina, P. Y., and A. R. Shkrich, On the problem of displacement of the oil-contour front (in Russian), *Trans. Acad. Sci.,* Div. Tech. Sci., USSR, no. 11, pp. 105–107, 1954.
45. Potter, W. D., and M. V. Baker, Some of the factors influencing the behavior of perched water-tables at the North Appalachian Experimental Watershed near Coshocton, Ohio, *Trans. Amer. Geophysical Union,* vol. 19, pp. 393–402, 1938.
46. Santing, G., Infiltratie en modelonderzoek, *Water,* vol. 35, no. 21, pp. 234–238; no. 22, pp. 243–246, The Hague, 1951.
47. Santing, G., Modèle pour l'étude des problèmes de l'écoulement simultane des eaux souterraines douces et saluées, *Assemblée Générale de Bruxelles, Assoc. Intl. d'Hydrologie Scientifique,* vol. 2, pp. 184–193, 1951.
48. Semchinova, M. M., Comparison of experimental data with theory for the case of unsteady flow located on a horizontal water table (in Russian), *Inghenerny Sbornik,* Inst. Mech., Acad. Sci., USSR, vol. 15, pp. 195–200, 1953.
49. Shaw, F. S., and R. V. Southwell, Relaxation methods applied to engineering problems, VII, Problems relating to the percolation of fluids through porous materials, *Proc. Royal Soc.,* Ser. A, vol. 178, pp. 1–17, 1941.
50. Southwell, R. V., *Relaxation methods in engineering science,* Oxford Univ. Press, London, 252 pp., 1940.
51. Southwell, R. V., *Relaxation methods in theoretical physics,* Oxford Univ. Press, London, 248 pp., 1946.
52. Stallman, R. W., Numerical analysis of regional water levels to define aquifer hydrology, *Trans. Amer. Geophysical Union,* vol. 37, pp. 451–460, 1956.
53. Stallman, R. W., Use of numerical methods for analyzing data on ground water levels, *Symposia Darcy,* Publ. 41, Assoc. Intl. d'Hydrologie Scientifique, pp. 227–231, 1956.
54. Stallworth, T. W., Quickly constructed model facilitates seepage studies, *Civil Eng.,* vol. 20, no. 7, pp. 45–46, 1950.
55. Todd, D. K., Unsteady flow in porous media by means of a Hele-Shaw viscous fluid model, *Trans. Amer. Geophysical Union,* vol. 35, pp. 905–916, 1954.
56. Todd, D. K., Flow in porous media studied in Hele-Shaw channel, *Civil Eng.,* vol. 25, no. 2, p. 85, 1955.
57. Todd, D. K., Ground-water flow in relation to a flooding stream, *Proc. Amer. Soc. Civil Engrs.,* vol. 81, sep. 628, 20 pp., 1955.
58. Todd, D. K., Laboratory research with ground-water models, *Symposia Darcy,* Publ. 41, Assoc. Intl. d'Hydrologie Scientifique, pp. 199–206, 1956.
59. Vreedenburgh, C. G. J., and O. Stevens, Electric investigation of underground water flow nets, *Proc. Intl. Conf. Soil Mech. and Foundation Eng.,* vol. 1, Harvard Univ., Cambridge, Mass., pp. 219–222, 1936.
60. Wolf, A., Use of electrical models in study of secondary recovery projects, *The Oil and Gas Jour.,* vol. 46, no. 50, pp. 94–98, 1948.
61. Wyckoff, R. D., and H. G. Botset, An experimental study of the motion of

particles in systems of complex potential distribution, *Physics,* vol. 5, pp. 265–275, 1934.

62. Wyckoff, R. D., H. G. Botset, and M. Muskat, Flow of liquids through porous media under the action of gravity, *Physics,* vol. 3, pp. 90–113, 1932.
63. Wyckoff, R. D., H. G. Botset, and M. Muskat, The mechanics of porous flow applied to water-flooding problems, *Trans. Amer. Inst. Min. and Metal. Engrs.,* vol. 103, pp. 219–249, 1933.
64. Wyckoff, R. D., and D. W. Reed, Electrical conduction models for the solution of water seepage problems, *Physics,* vol. 6, pp. 395–401, 1935.
65. Yang, S., *Seepage toward a well analyzed by the relaxation method,* Ph. D. thesis, Harvard Univ., Cambridge, Mass., 1949.
66. Zee, C. H., D. F. Peterson, and R. O. Bock, Flow into a well by electric and membrane analogy, *Proc. Amer. Soc. Civil Engrs.,* vol. 81, sep. 817, 21 pp., 1955.

Conversion Factors and Constants

APPENDIX

Length

1 in. = 2.540 cm
1 ft = 12 in.
= 30.48 cm
1 yd = 3 ft
1 mile = 5280 ft
= 1.609 km

Volume

1 cm^3 = 0.264×10^{-3} U. S. gal
1 ft^3 = 7.48 U. S. gal
1 U. S. gal = 3.785 liters
= 231 $in.^3$
= 0.134 ft^3
= 3.07×10^{-6} acre-ft
1 acre-ft = 43,560 ft^3
= 3.26×10^5 gal
1 cfs-day = 1.98 acre-ft

Specific Weight

Water: 1 ft^3 = 62.37 lb at 60° F
= 62.31 lb at 20° C
1 gal = 8.338 lb at 60° F

Area

1 sq in. = 6.452 cm^2
1 sq ft = 929.03 cm^2
1 acre = 43,560 ft^2
= 4.047×10^3 m^2
1 sq mile = 640 acres
= 2.590 km^2

Weight

1 lb = 453.59 g
= 16 oz
= 7000 grains

Discharge

1 cfs = 449 gal/min
= 6.46×10^5 gal/day
= 1.98 acre-ft/day
= 28.3 liters/sec

Density

Water: 1 cm^3 = 0.999 g at 60° F
= 0.998 g at 20° C
1 ft^3 = 1.938 slugs at 60° F
= 1.936 slugs at 20° C
Air: 1 cm^3 = 1.226×10^{-3} g at 1 atm and 15° C
Soil: 1 cm^3 = 1.1 to 1.8 g (bulk density in place)
= 2.65 g (average particle density for soils and rocks)

Viscosity

Water: 1.124 centipoises at 60° F
1.005 centipoises at 20° C
1 centipoise = 0.01 poise = 0.01 dyne-sec/cm^2
1 lb-sec/ft^2 = 478.8 poises

Pressure

1 atmosphere = 1.0132×10^6 dynes/cm^2
= 1013.2 millibars
= 14.696 lb/in.^{2}
= 76 cm Hg at 0° C
= 1033.2 cm water at 4° C
= 33.90 ft water at 4° C
1 ft water at 4° C = 2.242 cm Hg
= 0.4335 lb/in.^{2}

Permeability

(K_s = lab. coef. of permeability)
1 K_s = 4.72×10^{-5} cm/sec
1 darcy = 0.987×10^{-8} cm^2
1 darcy = 1.062×10^{-11} ft^2
1 darcy = 18.2 K_s (for water at 60° F)
1 darcy = 0.966×10^{-3} cm/sec (for water at 20° C)
1 cm/sec = 1.02×10^{-5} cm^2 (for water at 20° C)

Water Quality

1 ppm = 1 mg/l
1 grain/U. S. gal = 17.1 ppm
1 taf = 735 ppm
Equivalent wt of ion = atomic wt of ion/valence of ion
meq/l of ion = ppm of ion/equivalent wt of ion
1 meq/l = 1 me/l
= 1 epm

1 meq/l of cations = 100 EC $\times 10^6$
1 ppm = 1.56 EC $\times 10^6$
} Approximations for most natural waters in the range of 100 to 5000 μmho/cm at 25° C

Index